# BIOLOGY
## The Dynamics of Life

# Content Mastery
## Teacher Edition

## Glencoe
## McGraw-Hill

New York, New York    Columbus, Ohio    Woodland Hills, California    Peoria, Illinois

## A GLENCOE PROGRAM
# BIOLOGY: THE DYNAMICS OF LIFE

*Student Edition*

*Teacher Wraparound Edition*

*Laboratory Manual, SE and TE*

*Reinforcement and Study Guide, SE and TE*

*Content Mastery, SE and TE*

*Section Focus Transparencies and Masters*

*Reteaching Skills Transparencies and Masters*

*Basic Concepts Transparencies and Masters*

*BioLab and MiniLab Worksheets*

*Concept Mapping*

*Chapter Assessment*

*Critical Thinking/Problem Solving*

*Spanish Resources*

*Tech Prep Applications*

*Biology Projects*

*Computer Test Bank Software and Manual*
  *WINDOWS/MACINTOSH*

*Lesson Plans*

*Block Scheduling*

*Inside Story Poster Package*

*English/Spanish Audiocassettes*

*MindJogger Videoquizzes*

*Interactive CD-ROM*

*Videodisc Program*

*Glencoe Science Professional Series:*
  *Exploring Environmental Issues*
  *Performance Assessment in the Biology Classroom*
  *Alternate Assessment in the Science Classroom*
  *Cooperative Learning in the Science Classroom*
  *Using the Internet in the Science Classroom*

## Glencoe/McGraw-Hill

*A Division of The **McGraw-Hill** Companies*

Send all inquiries to:
Glencoe/McGraw-Hill
936 Eastwind Drive
Westerville, OH 43081

ISBN 0-02-828250-7
Printed in the United States of America.
1 2 3 4 5 6 7 8 9 10   047   08 07 06 05 04 03 02 01 00 99

# Contents

# To the Teacher

*Content Mastery* was developed to help poor readers, English language learners, and other students requiring extra help. This booklet helps students master the basic concepts presented in ***Biology: The Dynamics of Life***, and reinforces their reading and study skills. The four-page content mastery module for each chapter and each BioDigest supplies activities that help students master the "big picture" of the chapter, assimilate concepts presented in the individual teaching sections, and understand key vocabulary words.

The first page of each content mastery module for a chapter is called *Get the Big Picture*. This activity allows students to master the main idea of the chapter through summaries or idea-map outlines. The second and third pages include activities that present topics from each of the chapter sections. Topics are presented in a straightforward manner to facilitate students' comprehension. The fourth page is called *Review the Vocabulary*. This activity provides students with a review of vocabulary words in a variety of formats. Whenever appropriate, activities use visuals to enhance students' understanding.

A study skills section precedes the content mastery activities. This section gives students ideas on how to improve their reading and vocabulary, learn from visuals, and make and interpret idea maps. Answer pages for each *Content Mastery* worksheet are included at the end of this booklet.

# Study Skills

## A. Improve Your Reading Skills

Active readers are good readers.

**Active readers**

- get ready before they read.
- use skills that help them when they read.
- review to remember after they read.

Here's what you can do to become an active reader!

### Before You Read

**Get Ready to Read**

- Find a quiet time and place to read—library, study hall, home.
- Don't read when you're tired.
- Don't read when you're hungry.
- Wait until you have finished a section before you take a break.

**Scan**

- Quickly scan the material so you will know what it is about.
- Look at pictures and read the captions, titles, headings, and words in bold print.

**Write**

- Write notes about what you see when you scan.
- Write questions about what you see.
- Write topics you want to find out about when you read.
- Write a preview outline from the section topics.

### As You Read

- Find the main idea of each section or paragraph—this is usually in the first sentence.
- Study the pictures, maps, graphs, and tables, and think about the information in them.
- Write down the main ideas and other notes about what you read.
- After you read the whole section, reread the parts you didn't understand.

# Study Skills

### *After You Read*

- Review your outline or the notes you wrote while you were reading.
- If you still have questions, ask a classmate or your teacher for help.
- Write important facts or ideas on flash cards.
- Review your flash cards to help you remember what you've read.

## B. Improve Your Vocabulary Skills

Active readers learn the meanings of new words.

### Active readers

- recognize clues to help find the meaning.
- look for familiar words and word parts in new words.
- use a dictionary often.
- practice new words so they can remember new meanings.

Here's how you can improve your vocabulary!

### *When You See a New Word*

#### Scan

- Read the sentence and look for clues about the meaning of the word. These are called context clues.
- Look for pictures or visuals that contain the word.

In the following table, you can find different kinds of context clues that you can use to help you figure out the meanings of new words.

## Search for Context Clues

| | | |
|---|---|---|
| **Comparison and contrast** | The runner started the race with energy and excitement, but as she crossed the finish line, the *fatigue* and strain showed on her face. | This sentence contrasts the word *fatigue* with energy and compares it to strain. This tells you that someone who is fatigued is strained and has no energy. |
| **Definition and description** | Elena is a *biologist*, a scientist who studies living things. | The sentence describes a *biologist* as someone who studies living things. |
| **Synonyms** | Carl is very *dependable*. His teachers and his parents know that he is reliable and can be trusted. | The word *dependable* is described by the synonyms reliable and trusted. |
| **Tone and setting** | An air of *jubilation* surrounded the members of the science team as they received their medals for first place in the national competition. | The setting of the sentence and the action describe a situation that is positive and full of celebration. |
| **A series of clues** | The ocelot, jaguar, and mountain lion are all *endangered* species. | The animals that are mentioned are all rare. This tells you something about the word *endangered*. |
| **Cause and effect** | The student group was known for its *boisterous* meetings, so the principal asked extra teachers to monitor the meeting and keep order. | *Boisterous* describes the meetings and tells you that something needs extra supervision. |

# Study Skills

### Break It Down

- Find the root word.
- Write it and ask questions about its meaning.
- Find the affix—the part in front of or after the root word.
- Write it down and use a dictionary to look up its meaning.

# public•ize

In this table, you can see how to break words into their roots and affixes.

| Word | Root | Affix and Meaning | Meaning |
|------|------|-------------------|---------|
| imperfect | perfect | im- (not) | not perfect |
| semicircle | circle | semi- (half) | half of a circle |
| teacher | teach | -er (one who) | one who teaches |
| backward | back | -ward (in the direction of) | to the back |
| publicize | public | -ize (make) | make public |

### Remember New Words

- Say the word aloud.
- Write another sentence using the word.
- Make flash cards that include the word and its meaning.
- Review your flash cards to help you remember the meanings of the new words.

# Study Skills

## C.  Learn From Visuals

 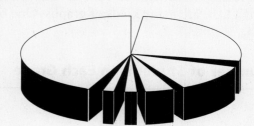

Tables, graphs, photographs, diagrams, and maps are called visuals. Good readers use all kinds of visuals to help them learn.

### Active readers

- find the purpose for the visual they see.
- find information in the visual.
- connect the information they find to what they are studying.

Here's how you can improve your skill in learning from visuals.

### *When You First Look at a Visual*

#### Scan

- Look at the visual.
- Decide its purpose. Why is it there?
- Find the title.
- Read the caption.

#### Write

- Write the purpose of the visual. Why is it there?
- Write the key information.
- Write the title of the visual.
- Write the main idea or message.

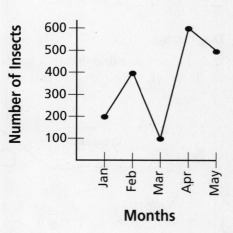

## *As You Study the Visual*

### Graphs

Graphs are pictures of related information. A graph tells you something about a specific situation. There are many kinds of graphs. One of the most common is the bar graph.

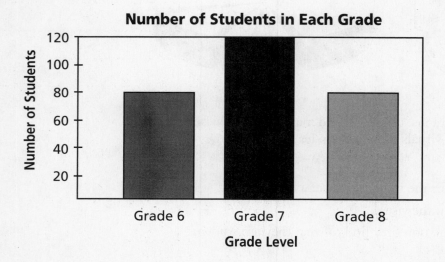

**Number of Students in Each Grade**

A bar graph helps you compare similar information about different items. The separate items being measured are shown as rectangles side by side on the graph.

### Diagrams

A diagram is a drawing that has labels on it. It can show how something works or what the parts are called.

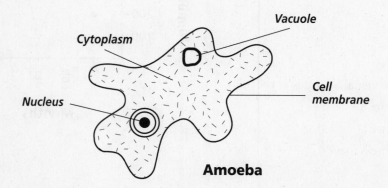

**Amoeba**

A diagram often gives the names of the parts of something, like this diagram of an amoeba. Science books often have many diagrams.

# Study Skills

## Tables

Tables organize words and numbers for easier reading. They have a title, columns (up and down), and rows (side to side). In this table, the columns show the innings, and the rows show the points each team scored.

| Points Earned in the Baseball Game | | | | | | | | | | |
|---|---|---|---|---|---|---|---|---|---|---|
| **Inning** | **1** | **2** | **3** | **4** | **5** | **6** | **7** | **8** | **9** | **Total Points** |
| **Green Team** | 0 | 0 | 1 | 1 | 0 | 0 | 0 | 3 | 0 | 5 |
| **Blue Team** | 1 | 0 | 1 | 0 | 2 | 0 | 1 | 0 | 1 | 6 |

## Maps

Maps give all kinds of different information. Some examples are location, direction, and land features. They can have words, symbols, numbers, lines, and colors.

### Coal Fields of the United States

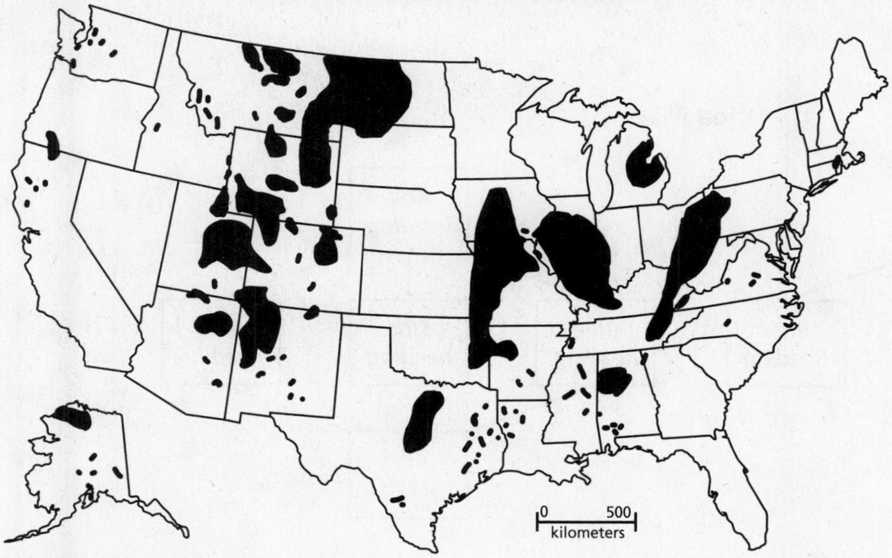

**Figure 6.11**

Coal is the most abundant fossil fuel on Earth. The coal deposits of the United States are mainly bituminous coal, which is preferred for electric power generation.

# Study Skills

## D. Make Chapter and Section Idea Maps

Active readers organize the information they read.

### Active readers

- divide the information into smaller units.
- put the information in a logical order.

### *Starting Out*

### Scan and Write

- Scan the chapter for main topics and subheadings—in your biology text-book, red headings are main topics and blue headings are subtopics.
- Scan for **boldface** key terms.
- Scan for any visuals.
- Write the information in some kind of graphic map.

Here's an example of one kind of idea map.

**Idea Map**

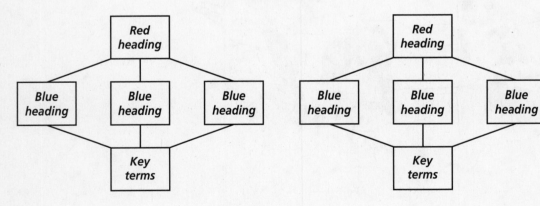

**Biology: The Study of Life**

## Get the Big Picture

Find the section titles and the red and blue headings in Chapter 1 of your textbook. Use the section titles to fill in the rectangles in the idea map below. Use the red headings to fill in the ovals. Some of the rectangles and ovals have been filled in for you.

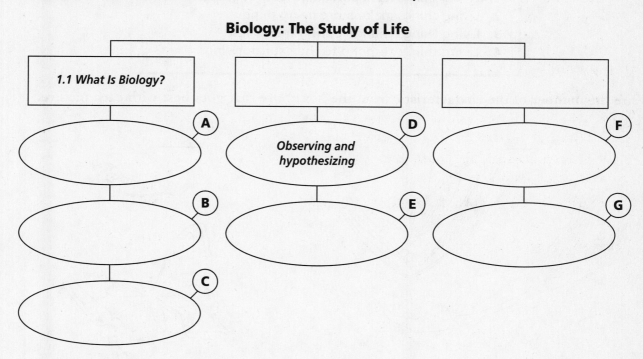

**Biology: The Study of Life**

1.1 What Is Biology?

A

B

C

D
Observing and hypothesizing

E

F

G

**Each statement below goes with one of the headings in the ovals above. Write the letter of each heading on the line in front of the statement it goes with.**

_____ All living things, even humans, need one another for survival.

_____ All organisms have structure and share traits with other organisms.

_____ All organisms respond to stimuli and make adjustments to environmental conditions.

_____ The microscope and the gas chromatograph are some of the tools biologists use in their studies.

_____ Scientists always report measurements in SI.

_____ Society as a whole must take responsibility for the ethical use of scientific discoveries.

**Chapter 1**

## Biology: The Study of Life, *continued*

## Study the Pictures

---

**Characteristics of Living Things**
1. Living things have parts that work together.
2. Living things make more living things.
3. Living things change during their lives.
4. Living things respond to their surroundings.

---

**Write the number of the characteristic from the box above that goes best with each picture.**

A _____

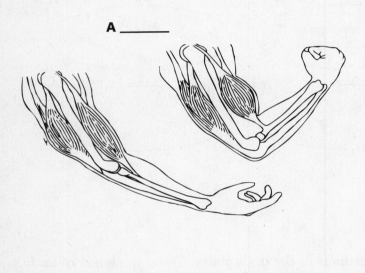

C _____

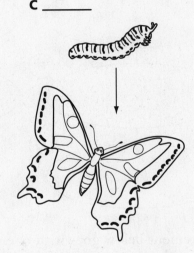

B _____

D _____

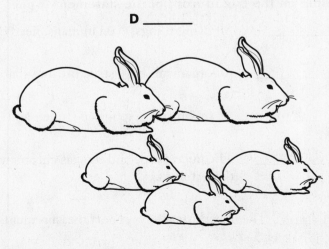

**Chapter 1** **Biology: The Study of Life,** continued

*Section 1.2  The Methods of Biology*
*Section 1.3  The Nature of Biology*

## Study the Reading

**Read the paragraphs in the box and answer the question that follows.**

> A biologist named Katharine Payne visited the elephants at a zoo. She felt the air around her throbbing like the rumbling of thunder. When she felt the air throb, she noticed that the skin on the foreheads of the elephants moved.
>
> Also, the elephants seemed to communicate without making any noise. They did not make a sound, but they would start and stop moving at the same time. Payne knew that some animals, such as whales, made sounds too low for humans to hear. She thought, "Maybe elephants, like whales, use low sounds to communicate with each other."

An **observation** is something you see or notice. A **fact** is something you know.

**Fill in the first box with something Payne observed the elephants doing. Fill in the second box with something she observed about the air around her. Fill in the last box with a fact she knew.**

| *Observation:* |
| --- |

↓

| *Observation:* |
| --- |

↓

| *Fact:* |
| --- |

↓

| *Hypothesis:*  Maybe elephants use low-pitched sounds to communicate with each other. |
| --- |

In **descriptive research,** scientists report observations in the form of observational data such as written descriptions.

In **quantitative research,** scientists report observations in the form of numerical data such as counts and measurements.

**1.** The observations made by Payne would be classified as what type of research?

_____

**Chapter 1** **Biology: The Study of Life,** *continued*

## Review the Vocabulary

adaptation (ad ap TAY shun)
data
energy
evolution (ev uh LEW shun)
homeostasis (hoh me o STAY sus)
organism
response
species (SPEE sheez)

theory
biology
dependent variable
environment
experiment
hypothesis (hi PAHTH us sus)
organization
safety symbol
stimulus

control
development
ethics
growth
independent variable
reproduction
scientific methods
technology (tek NAHL uh jee)

**The Chapter 1 vocabulary words are listed above. Review the definitions of these words. Then draw a line to match each word in the box with its definition.**

**a.** biology
**b.** ethics
**c.** reproduction
**d.** homeostasis
**e.** experiment

**1.** What you do to test a hypothesis
**2.** Making of offspring
**3.** Moral principles and values held by humans
**4.** Study of living things
**5.** Living things maintaining body functions

**Use the words in the box to fill in the blanks in the sentences that follow. You will not use all the words.**

response     organism     organization     control
stimulus     adaptation     technology     evolution

**6.** A(n) _____ has all four traits of life.

**7.** A(n) _____ causes living things to respond.

**8.** Scientific research for society's needs or problems is called _____ .

**9.** A(n) _____ in an experiment is used as a standard for comparison.

**10.** _____ is the change in a species over time.

**BioDigest**
**1**     **What Is Biology?**

## Get the Big Picture

Find the red and blue headings in BioDigest 1. Use the blue headings to fill in the rectangles in the idea map below. Use the red headings to fill in the ovals. One rectangle and one oval have been filled in for you.

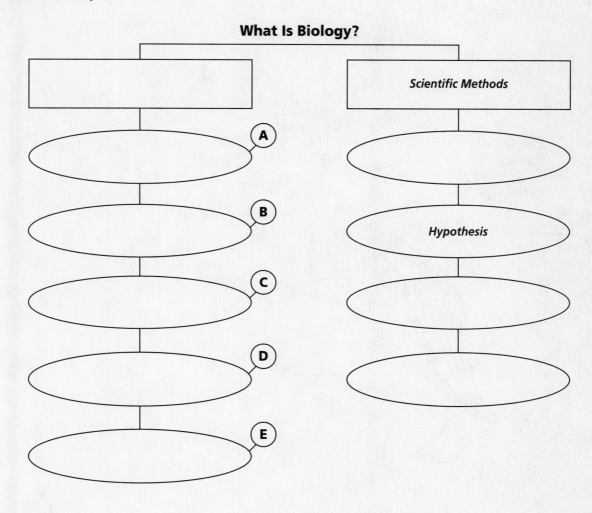

**What Is Biology?**

*Scientific Methods*

*Hypothesis*

Write the letter of the oval that matches the characteristics of life shown below.

_____

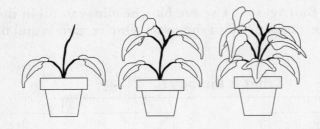

_____

_____

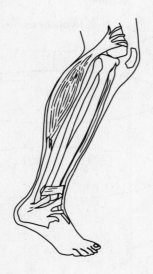

**What Is Biology?,** *continued*

## Study the Graph

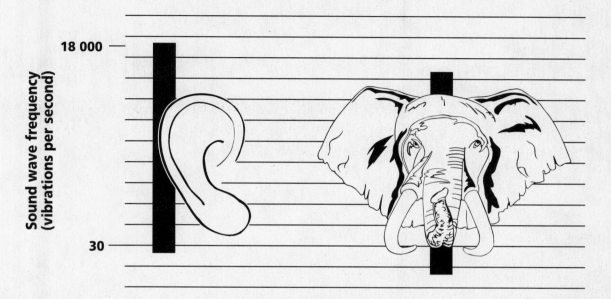

**Hearing Range of Humans and Range of Sounds Elephants Make**

Use the graph to answer the questions.

**1.** What is being measured on the graph?

_____

**2.** According to the graph, what is the normal hearing range of humans?

_____

**3.** Explain whether or not a human can hear all the sounds an elephant makes.

_____

_____

**4.** Is the collection of the data for the graph an example of descriptive research or quantitative research? Explain.

_____

_____

## Chapter 2 Principles of Ecology

**Content Mastery**

### Get the Big Picture

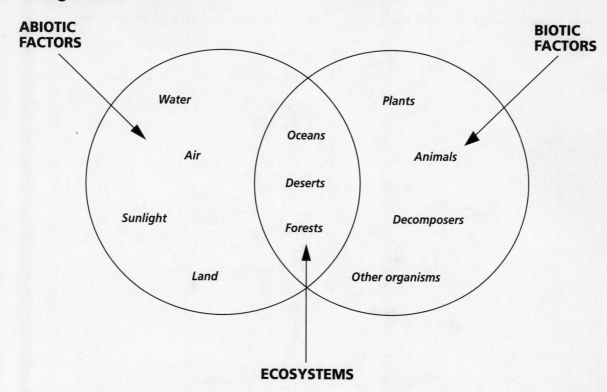

ABIOTIC FACTORS

BIOTIC FACTORS

Water

Plants

Oceans

Air

Animals

Deserts

Sunlight

Forests

Decomposers

Land

Other organisms

**ECOSYSTEMS**

Ecology is the study of interactions between the biotic factors and abiotic factors on Earth. Biotic factors are all living things. Abiotic factors are all nonliving things. An ecosystem is all the interactions between the biotic factors and abiotic factors in a certain place.

**Use the diagram to answer the following questions.**

**1.** What things make up the biotic factors on Earth? Give examples.

_____

**2.** What things make up the abiotic factors on Earth? Give examples.

_____

**3.** What is an ecosystem? Give examples.

_____

_____

**4.** During the carbon cycle, plants take in carbon dioxide gas from the air and use it to make food. So the carbon cycle involves the air and plants. Where on the diagram does the carbon cycle belong?

_____

_____

**Content Mastery**

*Section 2.1  Organisms and Their Environment*

## Study the Pictures

Label each drawing with one of these words: community, ecosystem, organism, population.

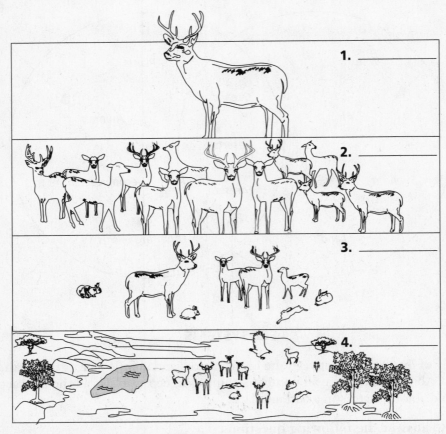

1. _____

2. _____

3. _____

4. _____

**1.** Define a **population**. Give an example of a population of animals from the drawings above.

_____

_____

**2.** Define a **community**. Give an example of a community from the drawings above.

_____

_____

**3.** Define an **ecosystem**. Give an example of an ecosystem from the drawings above.

_____

_____

_____

**CONTENT MASTERY**

**Chapter 2** **Principles of Ecology,** *continued*

*Section 2.2 Nutrition and Energy Flow*

## Complete the Diagrams

The diagram below shows the organisms in a food chain. Draw arrows between the organisms to complete the food chain.

The diagram below shows the organisms in a food web. Draw arrows between the organisms to complete the food web.

**Chapter 2** **Principles of Ecology,** *continued*

## Review the Vocabulary

| | |
|---|---|
| abiotic factors (ahy bi YAH tihk) | autotroph |
| biosphere (BI o sfeer) | biotic factors (bi YAH tihk) |
| commensalism (kuh MEN suh liz um) | community |
| decomposer | ecology (ih KAH luh jee) |
| ecosystem (EE khy sihs tum) | food chain |
| food web | habitat |
| heterotroph (HET uh ruh trohfs) | mutualism (MYEW chuh lih zum) |
| niche (NIHCH) | parasitism (PAYR uh sih tih zum) |
| population | scavengers |
| symbiosis (sihm bee OH sus) | trophic level (TROH fihk) |

**Fill in the blank in each sentence below with the correct word from the list above. You will not use all the words.**

1. An organism's _____ is the place where it lives out its life.

2. Vultures are _____ because they eat animals that are already dead.

3. The role a species has in its environment is called its _____ .

4. The study of interactions among organisms and their environments is called _____ .

5. A _____ is a group of organisms of one species that mate with one another and live in the same place at the same time.

6. An _____ uses the energy from the sun or energy stored in chemical compounds to make its own food.

7. The portion of Earth that supports life is called the _____ .

8. A _____ is a group of populations that interact with one another.

9. An organism that feeds on other organisms is called a _____ .

10. A relationship between two organisms in which one organism benefits while the other organism is harmed is called _____ .

11. A _____ breaks down and absorbs nutrients from dead organisms.

12. The nonliving parts of an organism's environment are _____ .

## Get the Big Picture

Use the picture below to answer the questions that follow.

**Succession in a Plant Community**

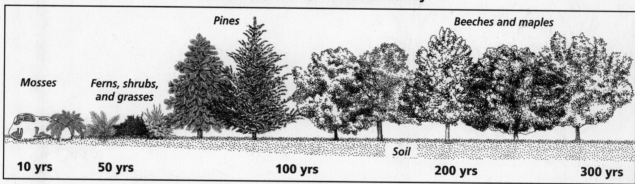

Pines

Beeches and maples

Mosses

Ferns, shrubs, and grasses

Soil

| 10 yrs | 50 yrs | 100 yrs | 200 yrs | 300 yrs |

**1.** What type of plants were the first to grow in this community?

_____

**2.** What types of plants were the first to grow in soil?

_____

**3.** What types of plants were the last to grow in this community?

_____

**4.** Why did it take many years for trees to grow in this community?

_____

_____

**Chapter 3**   **Communities and Biomes,** continued

## Study the Pictures

**A. Burned Forest**                 **B. New Island**

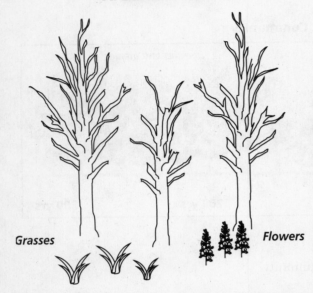

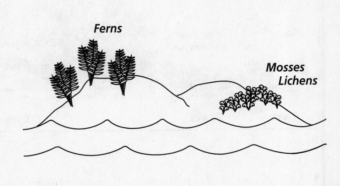

Look at the pictures and read what is in the boxes. Then use the pictures and definitions to answer the questions.

| **Primary Succession** |
| --- |
| This happens when organisms start to live in a new place. |

| **Secondary Succession** |
| --- |
| This happens when organisms start to live again in a place that had been destroyed by a flood, fire, or other natural disaster. |

**1.** Which picture shows **primary succession?** Explain your answer.

_____

_____

**2.** Which picture shows **secondary succession?** Explain your answer.

_____

_____

**3. True or false?** Primary succession happens after a grassland is destroyed by a flood.

_____

**Chapter 3** **Communities and Biomes,** *continued*

## Study the Picture

Use the picture below to answer the questions that follow.

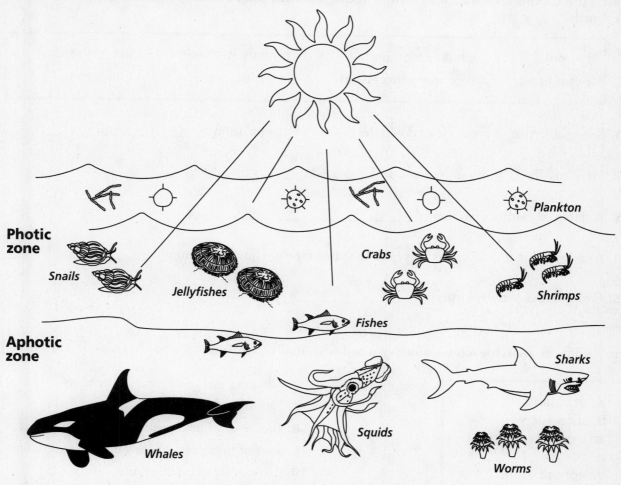

**4.** What are four kinds of organisms that live in the **photic** zone?

_____

_____

**5.** What are three kinds of organisms that live in the **aphotic** zone?

_____

_____

**6.** Suppose that the photic zone becomes polluted, and many organisms living there die. What might happen to the organisms in the aphotic zone? Explain your answer.

_____

_____

## Review the Vocabulary

Match the Chapter 3 vocabulary words in the box with the definitions below. You will not use all the words.

| | | | |
|---|---|---|---|
| biome | climax community | primary succession | limiting factor |
| permafrost | secondary succession | intertidal zone | plankton |

**1.** Something that stops or slows down the growth of a population _____

**2.** Happens after a community has been destroyed _____

**3.** A stable or mature community _____

**4.** A large group of ecosystems that have the same type of climax community _____

**5.** Ground that is always frozen _____

Draw a line to match each vocabulary word with its description.

| | |
|---|---|
| **a.** grassland | **6.** Changes in a community over time |
| **b.** succession | **7.** Driest biome |
| **c.** tropical rain forest | **8.** Biome in which cereal grains are grown |
| **d.** tundra | **9.** Part of the ocean where sunlight penetrates |
| **e.** aphotic zone | **10.** Most of its trees are conifers |
| **f.** desert | **11.** Body of water in which salt water and fresh water mix |
| **g.** estuary | **12.** Has warm weather and plenty of rainfall |
| **h.** taiga | **13.** Has no trees |
| **i.** temperate forest | **14.** Part of the ocean where sunlight does not penetrate |
| **j.** photic zone | **15.** Most of its trees lose their leaves every year |

## Chapter 4 — Population Biology

### Get the Big Picture

Find the red and blue headings in Chapter 4 of your textbook. Use the red headings to fill in the rectangles in the idea map below. Use the blue headings to fill in the ovals. Some of the rectangles and ovals have been filled in for you.

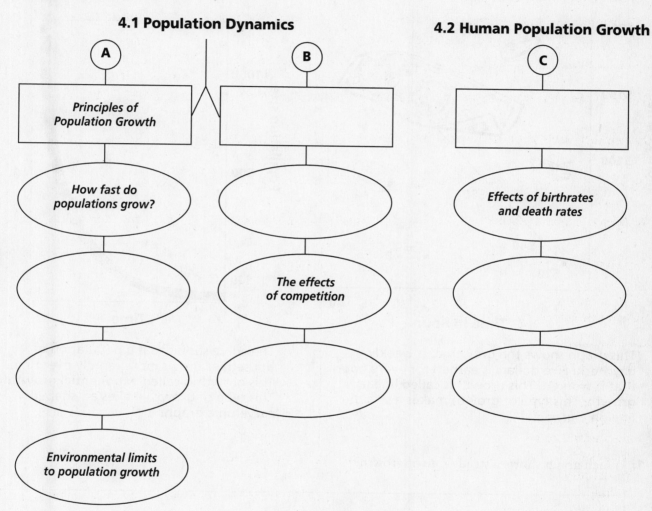

**4.1 Population Dynamics**

A — *Principles of Population Growth*
- *How fast do populations grow?*
- 
- *Environmental limits to population growth*

B —
- 
- *The effects of competition*
- 

**4.2 Human Population Growth**

C —
- *Effects of birthrates and death rates*
- 
- 

**Each statement below goes with one of the headings in the rectangles above. Write the letter of each heading on the line in front of the statement that goes with it.**

_____ Scientists, called demographers, study the growth trends of populations.

_____ A limited food supply can slow down population growth.

_____ Many populations are controlled by prey-predator relationships.

**Chapter 4** **Population Biology,** *continued*

## Study the Graphs

Use the graphs to answer the questions.

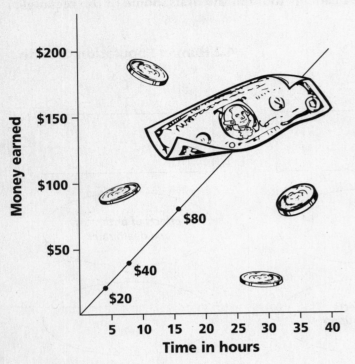

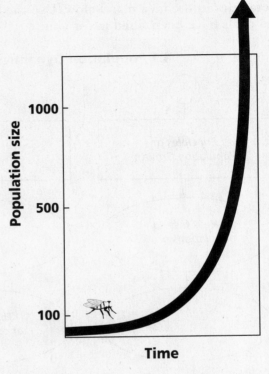

This graph shows the growth of a weekly paycheck. Five dollars is earned for every hour that is worked. This growth is called **linear growth**. This type of growth makes a straight line on a graph.

The curve shows that a population of house flies grows more rapidly over time. This growth is called **exponential growth**. This type of growth makes a J-shaped curve on a graph.

**1.** Which graph shows a steady rate of growth?

_____

_____

**2.** Which graph shows growth at an increasing rate?

_____

_____

**3.** If you graphed the population growth of household cockroaches, would the graph show a straight line or J-shaped curve? Explain your answer.

_____

_____

*Section 4.2 Human Population Growth*

## Study the Table

Use the table to answer the questions that follow.

| **Birthrates and Death Rates Around the World (mid-1996)** | | | |
|---|---|---|---|
| | **Birthrates (per 1000 people)** | **Death Rates (per 1000 people)** | **Growth Rate (per 1000 people)** |
| **Rapidly Growing Countries** | | | |
| Jordan | 39 | 4 | 33 |
| Iraq | 43 | 7 | 36 |
| Uganda | 46 | 21 | 25 |
| **Slowly Growing Countries** | | | |
| Poland | 12 | 10 | 2 |
| Italy | 10 | 10 | 0 |
| Ireland | 13 | 9 | 4 |

**The numbers in this table are based on numbers of births and deaths for every 1000 people in each country. The death rate is subtracted from the birthrate to find the growth rate.**

**1.** What was the birthrate of Uganda?

_____

**2.** What was the death rate of Iraq?

_____

**3.** What was the population growth rate of Ireland?

_____

**4.** Which country had the fastest growing population?

_____

**5.** Why did Italy have a growth rate of zero?

_____

_____

**Chapter 4** **Population Biology,** *continued*

## Review the Vocabulary

Use the Chapter 4 vocabulary words in the box to fill in the puzzle.

| emigration | age structure |
|---|---|
| demography | carrying capacity |

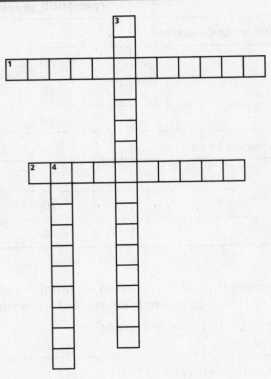

### Across

**1.** proportions of a population that are at different age levels

**2.** study of population growth characteristics

### Down

**3.** number of organisms of one species that an environment can support

**4.** movement of individuals out of a population

Use the vocabulary words in the box to complete the sentences.

| density-dependent factors | density-independent factors |
|---|---|
| exponential growth | immigration |

**5.** Limiting factors that affect populations more as the populations grow are

called _____ .

**6.** A growth rate that increases with time results in _____ .

**7.** Limiting factors that affect populations the same way regardless of their size are

called _____ .

**8.** _____ is the movement of individuals into a population.

CONTENT MASTERY

**Biological Diversity and Conservation**

### Get the Big Picture

Read the paragraphs about biodiversity. Then answer the questions that follow.

> Biodiversity is the variety of life in a certain area. The greater the number of species in an area, the greater is the area's biodiversity.

> Biodiversity provides people with a variety of foods, medicines, and useful products such as clothing and furniture.

> People threaten biodiversity when they destroy the habitats of plants and animals. Building houses and roads, burning forests for farmland, and polluting the environment can destroy habitats.

> People can preserve biodiversity by creating national parks where plants and animals are protected and by keeping endangered animals in zoos.

**1.** What is biodiversity?

**2.** Is there greater biodiversity in a desert or in a tropical rain forest? Explain your answer.

**3.** How do national parks help preserve biodiversity?

**4.** Why is biodiversity important to people?

**5.** How might building houses and roads threaten biodiversity?

**Chapter 5** Biological Diversity and Conservation, *continued*

## Study the Picture

In the picture below, draw a circle around the air pollution. Draw a square around the water pollution. Draw a triangle around the land pollution.

In the table below, list some of the problems caused by air, water, and land pollution.

| Air Pollution | Water Pollution | Land Pollution |
|---|---|---|
|  |  |  |

### Answer the following question.

How can pollution cause a species to disappear?

_____

_____

_____

**Chapter 5**   **Biological Diversity and Conservation,** *continued*

*Section 5.2 Conservation of Biodiversity*

**Study the diagram. Then answer the questions that follow.**

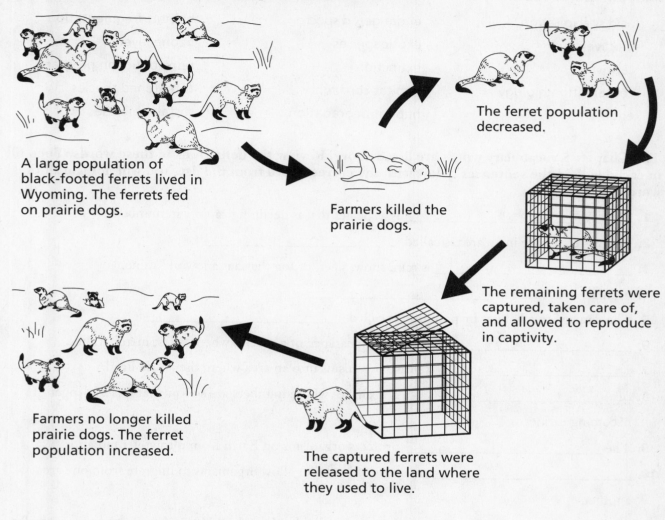

A large population of black-footed ferrets lived in Wyoming. The ferrets fed on prairie dogs.

Farmers killed the prairie dogs.

The ferret population decreased.

The remaining ferrets were captured, taken care of, and allowed to reproduce in captivity.

The captured ferrets were released to the land where they used to live.

Farmers no longer killed prairie dogs. The ferret population increased.

**1.** What caused the ferret population to decrease?

_____

_____

**2.** Why were the remaining ferrets captured?

_____

_____

**3.** After the captured ferrets were released, why did the ferret population increase?

_____

_____

## Review the Vocabulary

| | | |
|---|---|---|
| acid precipitation | endangered species | habitat fragmentation |
| biodiversity | exotic species | ozone layer |
| captivity | extinction | reintroduction programs |
| conservation biology | habitat corridors | threatened species |
| edge effect | habitat degradation | sustainable use |

**The Chapter 5 vocabulary words are listed above. Review the definitions of these words. Then fill in each blank in the sentences below with the correct word from the list. You will not use all the words.**

1. A(n) _____ is a species that is declining rapidly in number.

2. The variety of life in an area is called _____ .

3. _____ is rain, snow, sleet, or fog that has a low pH value.

4. Animals in zoos are in _____ .

5. The damage to a habitat by pollution is called _____ .

6. _____ is the disappearance of a species when its last member dies.

7. _____ release organisms into an area where they once lived.

8. A(n) _____ is a species whose numbers are so low that it is in danger of becoming extinct.

9. The _____ protects organisms on Earth from ultraviolet radiation.

10. _____ are strips of land that allow organisms to migrate from one area to another.

11. A(n) _____ is a species that has been brought to an area where it normally does not live.

12. _____ is the separation of a wilderness area from other wilderness areas.

## BioDigest 2 Ecology

### Get the Big Picture

**Read the paragraphs in the box. Then answer the questions.**

> The plants in a forest are autotrophs. They use sunlight to make their own food. The animals in the forest are heterotrophs. They eat plants and other animals for food. For example, the squirrels eat nuts and seeds. The birds eat seeds and insects. The rabbits and insects eat leaves. The raccoons eat fish, frogs, insects, nuts, and fruit. The foxes eat insects, squirrels, rabbits, young raccoons, and birds.
>
> A heterotroph can be a herbivore, a carnivore, or an omnivore. A herbivore eats only plants. A carnivore eats only animals. An omnivore eats plants and animals. A forest has all three kinds of heterotrophs.

**1.** Describe one kind of food chain in a forest. _____

_____

**2.** What is the autotroph in the food chain you described? _____

**3.** What is a heterotroph in the food chain you described? _____

_____

**4.** What is the difference between an omnivore and a carnivore? _____

_____

**5.** What kind of heterotroph is a fox? _____

**6.** What kind of heterotroph is a raccoon? _____

**7.** What kind of heterotroph is a rabbit? _____

**8.** What are some nonliving things that the plants and animals in the forest need to survive?

_____

**9.** What might happen to the rabbit population if all the foxes were removed from the forest? Explain your answer. _____

_____

_____

**10.** If a fire destroyed the forest, what would happen to the area where the forest used to be?

_____

Copyright © Glencoe/McGraw-Hill, a division of the McGraw-Hill Companies, Inc.

## Label the Cycle

**Read the paragraph in the box. Then look at the water cycle in the picture. On the lines provided, write where condensation and evaporation are shown in the cycle.**

> Water cycles through an ecosystem by the processes of evaporation and condensation. Evaporation of water occurs when liquid water changes into water vapor. Condensation of water occurs when water vapor changes into liquid water.

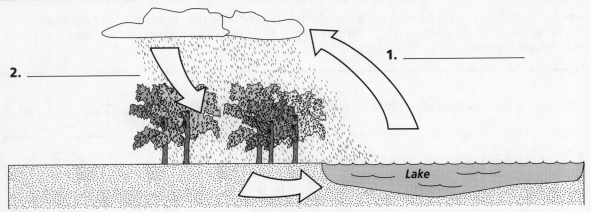

1. _____

2. _____

*Lake*

## Study the Cycle

**Study the carbon cycle below. Then answer the questions.**

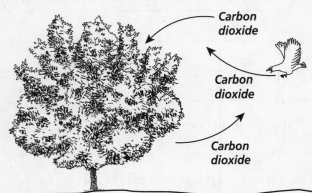

*Carbon dioxide*

*Carbon dioxide*

*Carbon dioxide*

Plants take in carbon dioxide gas. They use the carbon to make food.

Plants and animals release carbon dioxide gas. They produce carbon dioxide when their cells break down food for energy.

**1.** Why do plants and animals release carbon dioxide?

_____

**2.** What happens to the carbon dioxide that is released by plants and animals?

_____

**3.** Why do plants need carbon dioxide?

_____

**Content Mastery**

## Study the Diagram

The diagram shows three groups of organisms found in a community — producers, herbivores, and carnivores. The rectangles compare the biomasses of the three groups. Biomass is the total weight of all the organisms that belong to one of the groups of organisms in a community. The larger the rectangle in the diagram, the larger is the biomass of that group of organisms. Study the diagram. Then answer the questions.

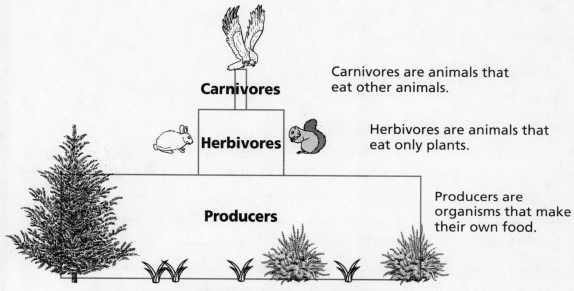

**Carnivores**

Carnivores are animals that eat other animals.

**Herbivores**

Herbivores are animals that eat only plants.

**Producers**

Producers are organisms that make their own food.

**Biomasses of Different Types of Organisms**

**1.** Why is a rabbit considered to be a herbivore?

_____

**2.** What is a producer?

_____

**3.** To which group of organisms does a hawk belong?

_____

**4.** Which group of organisms in a community has the smallest biomass?

_____

**5.** Which group of organisms in a community has the largest biomass?

_____

**6.** Why do you think the biomass of the herbivores is greater than the biomass of the carnivores?

_____

## Study the Graph

**Look at the graph. Then answer the questions.**

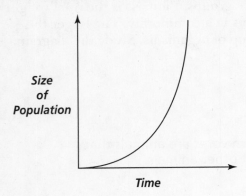

*Size of Population*

*Time*

1. What kind of population growth is shown in the graph? _____

2. What kinds of conditions would be necessary for a population to exhibit the kind of growth shown in the graph? _____

_____

3. Why aren't populations able to grow indefinitely? _____

_____

## Number the Steps

**Farmland that is not planted for many years may eventually change into a forest. The sequence of changes that occurs in a community over time is called succession. Number the steps below from 1 to 5 to show how an abandoned farm changes into a forest.**

_____  **4.**  Tree saplings block out more of the sun, causing the flowers, grasses, and bushes to die.

_____  **5.**  Weeds grow on the barren land.

_____  **6.**  Tree saplings grow into a forest of trees.

_____  **7.**  Flowers, grasses, and small bushes grow and produce shade.

_____  **8.**  Tree seeds are protected by the shade and grow into saplings.

## Chapter 6 The Chemistry of Life

### Get the Big Picture

Read what is in the boxes and study the pictures. Then fill in the blanks in the statements below.

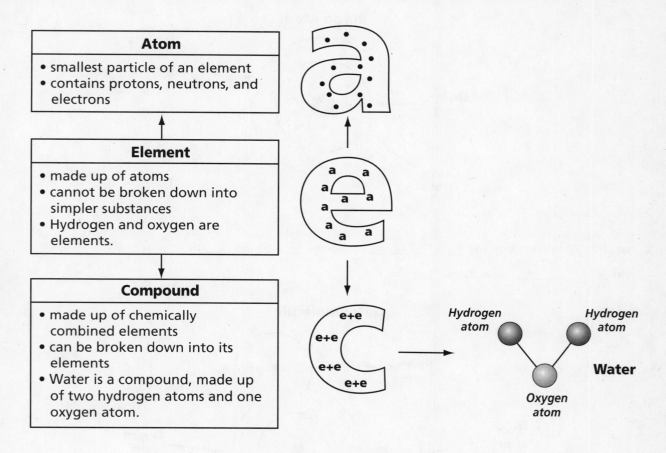

**Atom**
- smallest particle of an element
- contains protons, neutrons, and electrons

**Element**
- made up of atoms
- cannot be broken down into simpler substances
- Hydrogen and oxygen are elements.

**Compound**
- made up of chemically combined elements
- can be broken down into its elements
- Water is a compound, made up of two hydrogen atoms and one oxygen atom.

*Hydrogen atom*      *Hydrogen atom*

**Water**

*Oxygen atom*

1. Elements are made up of _____ .

2. Inside the atoms are _____ , _____ , and
   _____ .

3. Elements combine to form _____ .

4. Water can be broken down into _____ and _____ .

**Chapter 6** The Chemistry of Life, *continued*

## Study the Diagram

Use the diagrams to complete the sentences and answer the questions.

### Boron Atom

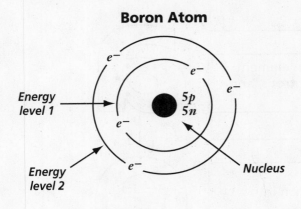

**1.** An atom of boron contains _____ protons, _____ neutrons, and _____ electrons.

### Water Molecule

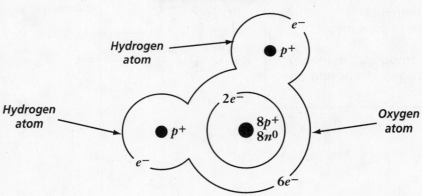

**2.** In a water molecule, each hydrogen atom shares _____ electron(s) with the oxygen atom.

**3.** What kind of bond is formed between the atoms of a water molecule?

_____

**4.** How does this bond affect the stability of the atoms?

_____

## Study the Diagram

Order each step from 1 to 3 to show how diffusion occurs. Then complete the sentences.

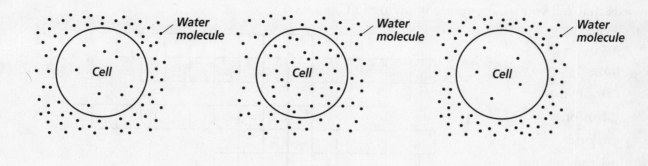

_____          _____          _____

**5.** During diffusion, particles move from an area of _____ concentration to an

area of _____ concentration.

**6.** Diffusion occurs because particles are always _____ randomly.

Use the diagram to answer the questions below.

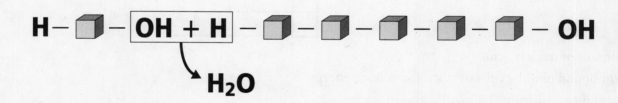

**7.** Does the above reaction show condensation or hydrolysis?

_____

**8.** Is the reaction used to make a polymer or to break apart a polymer?

_____

**Chapter 6** The Chemistry of Life, *continued*

Content Mastery

## Review the Vocabulary

Some of the Chapter 6 vocabulary words are listed below. Review the definitions of these words. Then use the clues to complete the puzzle. The letters in the dark boxes will make up three words that tell you what you are studying in Chapter 6.

atom

base

carbohydrate

diffusion

enzyme

hydrogen bond

metabolism

nucleic acid

nucleotide

polar molecule

polymer

protein

solution

**1.** subunit of nucleic acids

**2.** compound used by cells to store and release energy

**3.** substance that forms hydroxide ions in water

**4.** all the chemical reactions that occur in an organism

**5.** mixture in which a substance dissolves into another substance

**6.** movement of particles from an area of higher concentration to an area of lower concentration

**7.** smallest particle of an element that has the characteristics of that element

**8.** molecule with a positive end and a negative end

**9.** weak bond formed between water molecules, due to their polarity

**10.** polymer made of amino acids that is essential to all life

**11.** large molecule made of many smaller molecules bonded together

**12.** large molecule that stores information in cells

**13.** protein that changes the rate of a chemical reaction

CONTENT MASTERY

**A View of the Cell**

## Get the Big Picture

**Read the paragraphs in the box and study the pictures. Then answer the questions that follow.**

> Cells are the smallest units of life. They come in many sizes and shapes. Cells can be found as single cells or joined together in groups as in skin cells. Prokaryotic cells were the first cells to evolve. They had very simple internal parts. Later, more complex cells, called eukaryotic cells, evolved. Eukaryotic cells have more internal parts, called organelles. Prokaryotic cells do not have organelles.
>
> Organelles are surrounded by membranes. These organelles do different jobs for the cell such as digest food or make energy. The nucleus is a major organelle that acts like a brain. It has all the information necessary to run the cell and to make new cells. Plants and animals are made up of many kinds of eukaryotic cells that live and work together. These different kind of cells help adapt the plants and animals to living in a wide variety of environments.

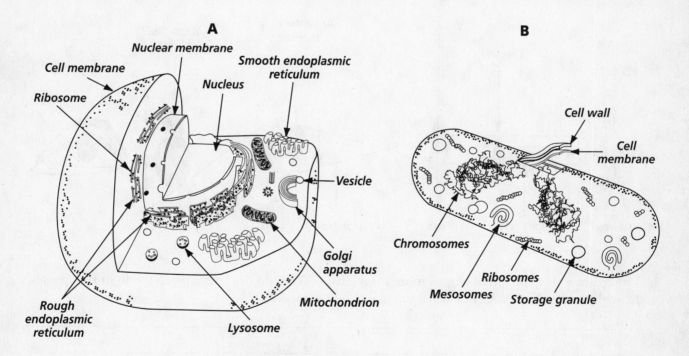

A

Cell membrane
Nuclear membrane
Smooth endoplasmic reticulum
Nucleus
Ribosome
Vesicle
Golgi apparatus
Mitochondrion
Rough endoplasmic reticulum
Lysosome

B

Cell wall
Cell membrane
Chromosomes
Ribosomes
Mesosomes
Storage granule

**1.** Which cell in the picture is a prokaryotic cell? Explain your answer.

_____

**2.** Which of the two types of cells do scientists think was the first to evolve? Why do they think this?

_____

*Section 7.1 The Discovery of Cells*
*Section 7.2 The Plasma Membrane*
*Section 7.3 Eukaryotic Cell Structure*

## Study the Reading

Read the paragraph in the box and study the figure. Then answer the questions that follow.

> The first microscope was made about 300 years ago. When light rays pass through certain shapes of glass, the rays bend and change direction. Pairs of convex lenses—round pieces of glass shaped like ovals—are used in microscopes. These lenses make very tiny objects such as cells appear larger. As light passes through the first lens, the light rays bend and then cross, as you can see in the diagram. By the time the crossed light rays reach the second lens, the object is magnified—it appears bigger. If you could see the object after the light passed through the first lens, the object would seem to be upside down. When the light reaches the second lens, it bends again so that you perceive the object as right side up.

**Light Microscope**

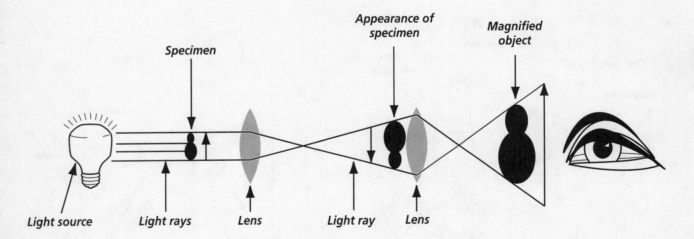

**1.** A microscope is made up of two or more glass lenses. What do the lenses do to the light that passes through them? What does this do to the object being looked at?

_____

_____

_____

**2.** Why is it important to have the second lens in the microscope?

_____

_____

_____

## Study the Diagram

When scientists examined the eukaryotic cell under the microscope, they discovered a small, self-contained package filled with individual parts called organelles. Some organelles make proteins; others store food. Still other organelles make and store energy. The cell is surrounded by a plasma membrane, which allows materials to enter and leave the cell, maintaining homeostasis.

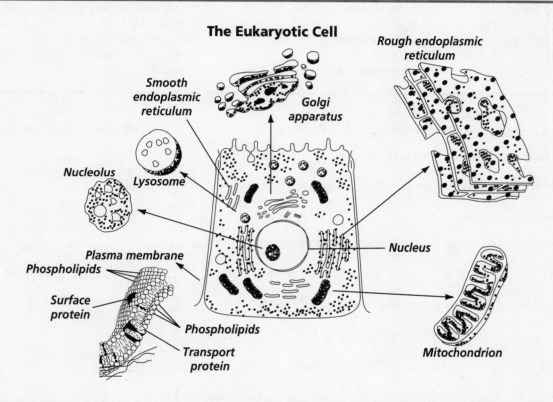

**The Eukaryotic Cell**

Smooth endoplasmic reticulum

Golgi apparatus

Rough endoplasmic reticulum

Nucleolus

Lysosome

Plasma membrane

Phospholipids

Surface protein

Phospholipids

Transport protein

Nucleus

Mitochondrion

**3.** The Golgi apparatus receives and distributes proteins for the cell. Describe what the Golgi apparatus looks like.

_____

_____

**4.** How many nuclei do you see in the cell?

_____

**5.** Look at the close-up of the plasma membrane. What is it made of?

_____

_____

## Review the Vocabulary

| | | |
|---|---|---|
| cell | electron microscope | nucleolus |
| cell theory | endoplasmic reticulum | nucleus |
| cell wall | eukaryote (yew KER ee oht) | organelle |
| chlorophyll | flagella | phospholipid |
| chloroplast | fluid mosaic model | plasma membrane |
| chromatin | Golgi apparatus (GALW jee) | plastid |
| cilia | homeostasis | prokaryote (pro KER ee oht) |
| compound light | lysome | ribosome |
| microscope | microfilament | selective permeability |
| cytoplasm | microtubule | transport protein |
| cytoskeleton | mitochondria | vacuole |

**Review the Chapter 7 vocabulary words listed above. Match the words with the definitions below.**

1. Cell having a nucleus and other membrane-bound organelles _____

2. Short, hairlike projections on a cell's surface that are composed of microtubules

   _____

3. Fluid-filled space within the cytoplasm; temporarily stores food _____

4. Building block of both unicellular and multicellular organisms _____

5. Contains the cell's DNA and manages cell functions _____

6. Green pigment that traps light energy from the sun _____

7. The process of maintaining the cell's environment _____

8. Organelles in which food molecules are broken down to produce ATP _____

9. Creates selective permeability of plasma membrane _____

10. Rigid structure outside the plasma membrane of plant cell _____

11. Membrane sacs that receive and package proteins _____

12. Serves as a boundary between the cell and its external environment _____

13. Cell lacking a nucleus or other membrane-bound organelles _____

## Chapter 8  Cellular Transport and the Cell Cycle

### Get the Big Picture

Study the picture and answer the questions that follow.

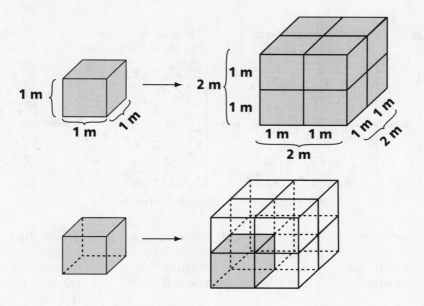

When a cube is doubled in size, the outside area, called the surface area, grows by four times the size. The inside area, called the volume, grows by eight times.

1. Suppose you double the length, height, and width of a cube. By how many times does the surface area of the cube increase?

_____

2. Suppose you double the length, height, and width of a cube. By how many times does the volume of the cube increase? Hint: count the number of little cubes inside the big cube.

_____

3. Think about what you have just learned about what happens to the surface area and volume of a cube when it doubles in size. What will happen to the surface area and volume of a cell if it doubles in size?

_____

4. How would this increase in cell size affect the cell's ability to get nutrients and get rid of wastes?

_____

_____

5. What does a cell do to make sure that it does not grow too big?

_____

**Chapter 8** **Cellular Transport and the Cell Cycle,** *continued*

## Study the Diagrams

Study the diagrams of the cells. Then circle the word that best completes each sentence.

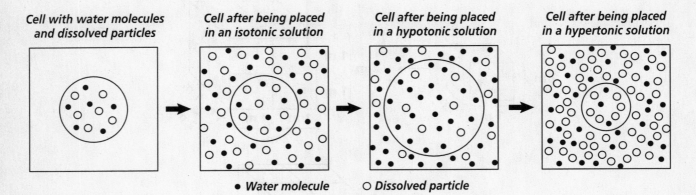

Cell with water molecules and dissolved particles | Cell after being placed in an isotonic solution | Cell after being placed in a hypotonic solution | Cell after being placed in a hypertonic solution

• *Water molecule*    ○ *Dissolved particle*

When the cell is placed in an isotonic solution, water molecules  move into and out of the cell at the same rate.

When the cell is placed in a hypotonic solution, more water molecules enter the cell than leave the cell.

When the cell is placed in a hypertonic solution, more water molecules leave the cell than enter the cell.

**1.** Placing a cell in a hypertonic solution causes the cell to (swell, shrink, stay the same).

**2.** Placing a cell in an isotonic solution causes the cell to (swell, shrink, stay the same).

**3.** Placing a cell in a hypotonic solution causes the cell to (swell, shrink, stay the same).

**Chapter 8   Cellular Transport and the Cell Cycle,** *continued*

**Content Mastery**

## Review the Vocabulary

Use the Chapter 8 vocabulary words in the box below to fill in the puzzle. You will not use all of the words.

| centromere |
| cancer |
| gene |
| centrioles |
| spindle |
| chromosomes |
| mitosis |

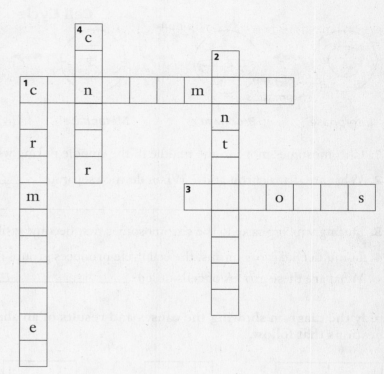

### ACROSS

**1.** joins two sister chromatids

**3.** process of nuclear division

### DOWN

**1.** structures that contain DNA

**2.** small, dark, cylindrical structures made of microtubules

**4.** result of uncontrolled cell division

Use the vocabulary words in the box below to fill in the blanks in the statements. You will not use all of the words.

| isotonic solution | hypotonic solution | endocytosis | active transport |
| hypertonic solution | osmosis | exocytosis | passive transport |

**5.** In a _____ , the concentration of dissolved substances is lower than the concentration inside a cell.

**6.** _____ is the diffusion of water through a selectively permeable membrane.

**7.** _____ is the expulsion of materials from a vacuole of a cell.

Section 8.2  **Cell Growth and Reproduction**
Section 8.3  **Control of the Cell Cycle**

## Study the Diagrams

Study the diagrams of the cell cycle and answer the questions that follow.

### Cell Cycle

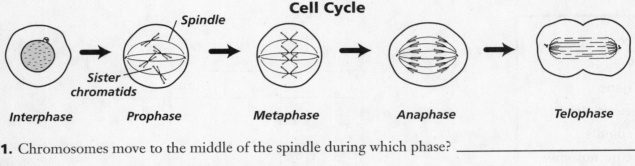

Interphase  Prophase  Metaphase  Anaphase  Telophase

**1.** Chromosomes move to the middle of the spindle during which phase? _____

**2.** What are sister chromatids? When do they separate? _____

_____

**3.** During which phase do the chromosomes first become visible? _____

**4.** In multicellular organisms, the cell cycle produces groups of cells that perform the same function. What are these groups of cells called? _____

Study the diagram showing the causes and results of an abnormal cell cycle. Then answer the questions that follow.

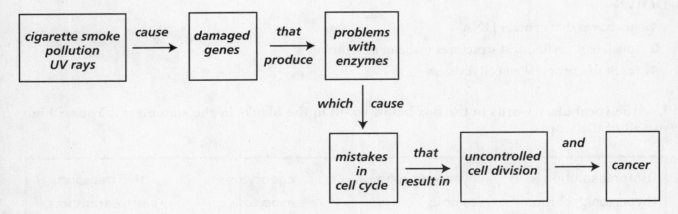

**5.** What happens when there are problems with the enzymes that control the cell cycle?

_____

**6.** Name three environmental factors that can damage the genes that produce those enzymes.

_____

**7.** What can result from an abnormal cell cycle? _____

## Chapter 9 Energy in a Cell

**Content Mastery**

### Get the Big Picture

**Study the picture. Then answer the questions that follow.**

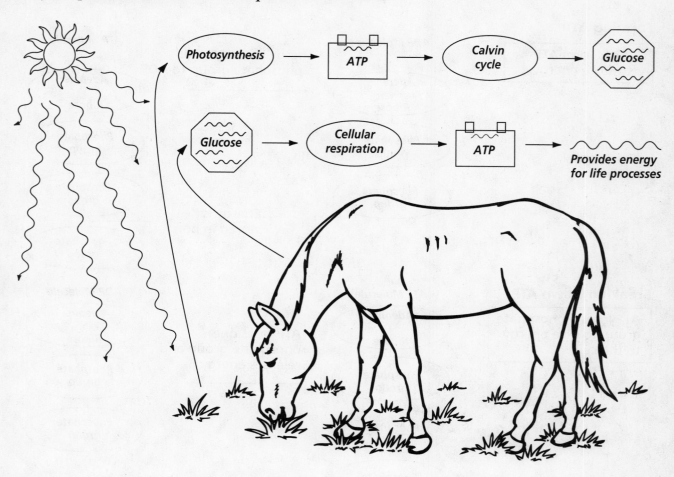

**1.** How do plants store energy from the sun? Write the steps below.

**(a)** _____

**(b)** _____

**2.** How do animals use the sun's energy that is stored in plants? Write the steps below.

**(a)** _____

**(b)** _____

**3.** Which molecules store energy in both plants and animals? _____

**Chapter 9** **Energy in a Cell,** *continued*

**Content Mastery**

*Section 9.1  ATP in a Molecule*
*Section 9.2  Photosynthesis: Trapping the Sun's Energy*
*Section 9.3  Getting Energy to Make ATP*

## Study the Energy Map

Use the energy map to answer the questions.

### Forming ATP

| Cells form ATP to store energy. |

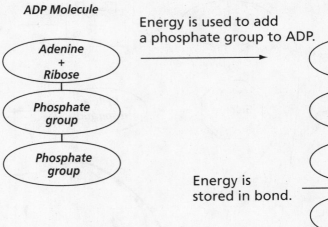

ADP Molecule

Adenine + Ribose

Phosphate group

Phosphate group

Energy is used to add a phosphate group to ADP.

ATP Molecule

Adenine + Ribose

Phosphate group

Phosphate group

Energy is stored in bond.

Phosphate group

### Breaking Down ATP

| ATP loses a phosphate group to give energy to the cell. |

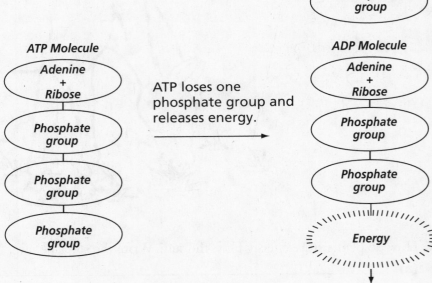

ATP Molecule

Adenine + Ribose

Phosphate group

Phosphate group

Phosphate group

ATP loses one phosphate group and releases energy.

ADP Molecule

Adenine + Ribose

Phosphate group

Phosphate group

Energy

**1.** How is ATP formed? _____

**2.** Where is the energy stored in an ATP molecule? _____

_____

**3.** How does ATP give energy to the cell? _____

_____

**4.** What is left after an ATP molecule loses a phosphate group? _____

**Chapter**
**9** **Energy in a Cell,** *continued*

## Study the Diagram

Use the diagram to answer the question.

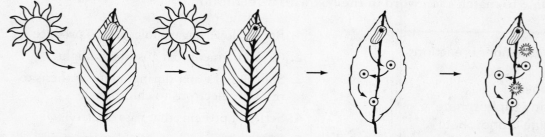

Sunlight hits green chlorophyll molecules.

The chlorophylls' electrons absorb the sun's energy.

The electrons move to other molecules.

As the electrons move, they release energy to form ATP molecules.

**5.** Describe the steps that plants use to store the sun's energy. Remember to number the steps.

_____

_____

_____

## Study the Energy Map

Use the energy map to answer the questions.

**Energy Processes**

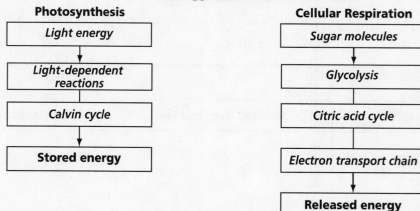

**Photosynthesis**

| Light energy |
| Light-dependent reactions |
| Calvin cycle |
| **Stored energy** |

**Cellular Respiration**

| Sugar molecules |
| Glycolysis |
| Citric acid cycle |
| Electron transport chain |
| **Released energy** |

**6. a.** What happens to energy during photosynthesis? _____

   **b.** What happens to energy during cellular respiration? _____

**7.** What process does your body use to get the energy it needs for running or for riding a bike?

_____

Copyright © Glencoe/McGraw-Hill, a division of the McGraw-Hill Companies, Inc.

## Review the Vocabulary

Use the Chapter 9 Vocabulary words in the box below. Review the definitions of these words. Then draw a line to match each word in the box with its definition.

| |
|---|
| **a.** light-independent reactions |
| **b.** photolysis |
| **c.** chlorophyll |
| **d.** adenosine triphosphate |
| **e** adenosine diphosphate |
| **f.** electron transport chain |
| **g.** photosynthesis |
| **h.** cellular respiration |

**1.** Breaks down sugar molecules to produce ATP

**2.** Green pigment that absorbs sunlight

**3.** Splitting of water during photosynthesis to resupply electrons to chlorophyll

**4.** Series of proteins that pass electrons

**5.** Energy-storing molecule that has two phosphate groups

**6.** Part of photosynthesis that does not require sunlight and takes place in the stroma

**7.** Biological process that traps energy from the sun to make carbohydrates

**8.** Energy-storing molecule that has three phosphate groups

Look at each Chapter 9 vocabulary word in the box below. If the word goes with photosynthesis, write it in the table under *Photosynthesis*. If the word goes with aerobic respiration, write it under *Aerobic Respiration*. If the word goes with anaerobic processes, write it under *Anaerobic Processes*. A word may go under more than one heading.

| | | | |
|---|---|---|---|
| citric acid cycle | light-dependent reactions | glycolysis | electron transport chain |
| lactic acid fermentation | alcoholic fermentation | Calvin cycle | |

| **Photosynthesis** | **Aerobic Respiration** | **Anaerobic Processes** |
|---|---|---|
| | | |
| | | |
| | | |
| | | |

## BioDigest 3  The Life of a Cell

### Get the Big Picture

Find the red and blue headings in BioDigest 3. Use the blue headings to fill in the rectangles in the idea map below. Use the red headings to fill in the ovals. One rectangle and one oval have been filled in for you.

**The Life of a Cell**

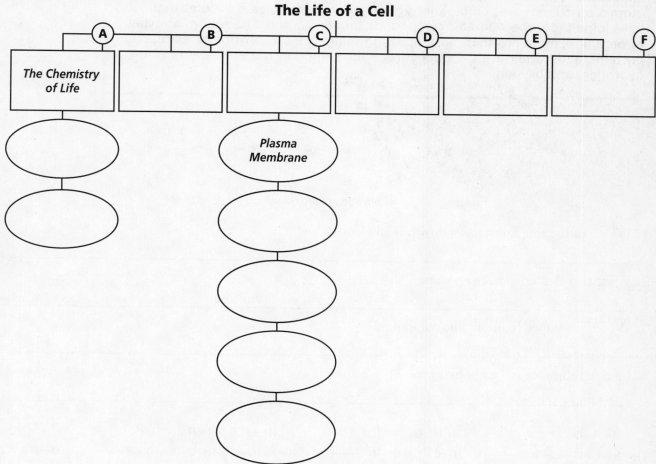

Each statement below goes with one of the headings in the rectangles above. Write the letter of each heading on the line in front of the statement it goes with.

_____ The presence or lack of membrane-bound structures within cells is used to classify cells.

_____ The functions of a cell are controlled by the nucleus.

_____ Cells use ATP as the most common source of energy.

_____ The smallest component of an element is an atom.

_____ A cell divides when it reaches a size that its plasma membrane cannot transport enough nutrients and wastes to maintain cell growth.

## The Life of a Cell, *continued*

## Study the Reading

Every substance is an element or a combination of elements. Elements include oxygen, which has the atomic symbol O; carbon, C; hydrogen, H; aluminum, Al; and nitrogen, N. The smallest component of an element is an atom. Compounds are combinations of elements. Molecules are atoms that have joined together. Organic compounds contain carbon. The four main types of organic compounds that make up living things are carbohydrates, lipids, proteins, and nucleic acids. Carbohydrates are compounds that contain carbon, hydrogen, and oxygen.

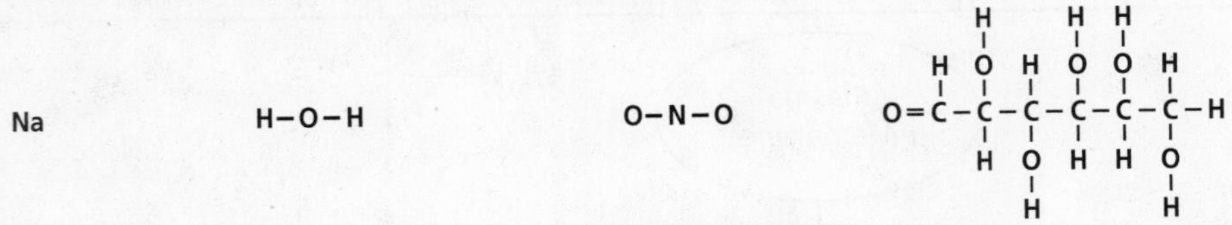

| Na | H–O–H | O–N–O | *glucose structure* |
|---|---|---|---|
| sodium | water | nitrogen monoxide | glucose |

**1.** Which of the four substances shown is an element?

_____

**2.** What two elements make up water?

_____

**3.** Which substance is an organic compound?

_____

**4.** Which substance is a carbohydrate?

_____

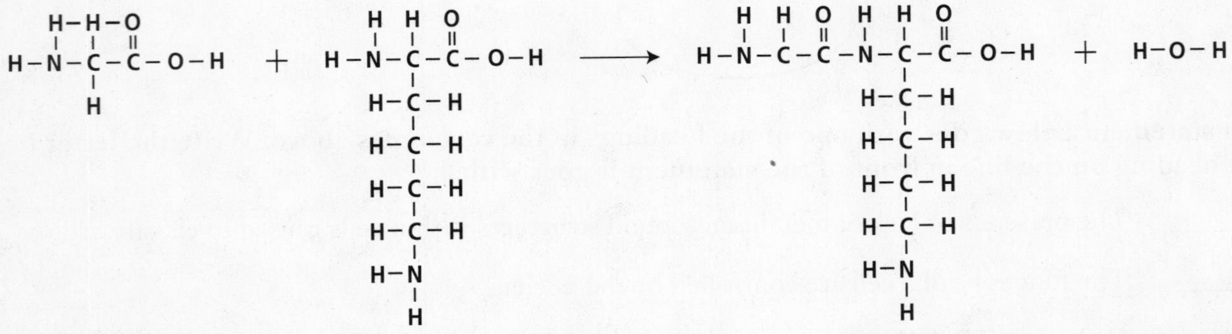

glycine    +    lysine    ⟶    a dipeptide    +    water

**5.** The diagram above shows the formation of an organic compound called a dipeptide. In the reaction, two amino acids, glycine and lysine, are joined together by a peptide bond forming the dipeptide and water. Circle the atoms in glycine and lysine that form water when the peptide bond is formed.

## Study the Pictures

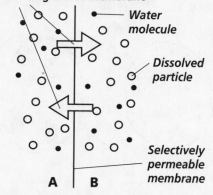

I **Rate of water molecules moving across membrane**

— **Water molecule**

— **Dissolved particle**

— **Selectively permeable membrane**

A   B

II

A   B

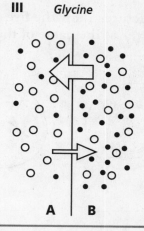

III   *Glycine*

A   B

| The concentration of dissolved particles on each side of the membrane is equal. | The concentration of dissolved particles on side A is less than the concentration on side B. | The concentration of dissolved particles on side A is more than the concentration on side B. |
|---|---|---|

Characteristics of isotonic, hypotonic, and hypertonic solutions

- The concentration of a dissolved material in an **isotonic** solution is the same as the concentration of the dissolved material in a cell.

- The concentration of a dissolved material in a **hypotonic** solution is less than the concentration of the dissolved material within a cell.

- The concentration of a dissolved material in a **hypertonic** solution is more than the concentration of the dissolved material within a cell.

**1.** In which picture is the rate of water molecules moving from side A to B greater than the rate of water moving from side B to A?

_____

**2.** If picture II represents a cell placed in a hypertonic solution, does side A or side B represent the interior of the cell?

_____

**3.** Describe what will happen to animal cells placed in a hypotonic solution. Explain why this will happen.

_____

_____

**4.** Describe what will happen to animal cells placed in a hypertonic solution.

_____

_____

**BioDigest 3**

## The Life of a Cell, *continued*

## Study the Pictures

The pictures show the five stages of mitosis in sequence. Write the letter of the description and the letter of the name of the stage below each picture.

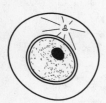   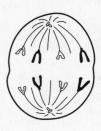 

1. _____  2. _____  3. _____  4. _____  5. _____

### Description

**a.** Chromosomes move to equator of the cell.

**b.** Chromosomes separate and move to opposite poles of the cell.

**c.** Duplicated chromosomes condense and mitotic spindle forms on the opposite poles of the cell.

**d.** Intense metabolic activity takes place prior to mitosis.

**e.** Two daughter cells each with a complete set of chromosomes form as cytoplasm divides.

### Stage

**A.** anaphase

**B.** interphase

**C.** metaphase

**D.** prophase

**E.** telophase

## Study the Reading

> Cells store energy in molecules of adenosine triphosphate (ATP). As plant cells produce sucrose from glucose and fructose, energy is released from the breakdown of ATP to adenosine diphosphate (ADP) and inorganic phosphate ($P_i$).

Use the word list to complete the diagram on the right.

ATP

energy

fructose

sucrose

_____ ⟶ _____ + ADP + $P_i$

glucose + _____ ⟶ _____ + water

# Chapter 10   Mendel and Meiosis

## Get the Big Picture

**Study the diagram and read the explanations. Then answer the questions below.**

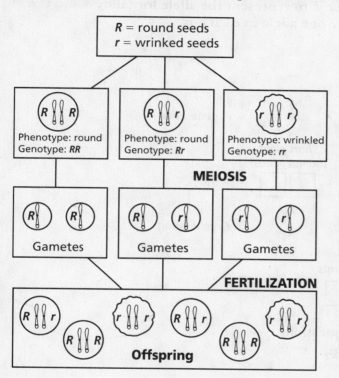

R = round seeds
r = wrinked seeds

Phenotype: round
Genotype: RR

Phenotype: round
Genotype: Rr

Phenotype: wrinkled
Genotype: rr

**MEIOSIS**

Gametes    Gametes    Gametes

**FERTILIZATION**

**Offspring**

Garden pea plants have two alleles of the gene that controls seed shape. The allele for round seeds, *R*, is dominant. The allele for wrinkled seeds, *r*, is recessive.

A pea plant inherits one allele for seed shape from its female parent and one allele from its male parent. Each allele is on a different chromosome of a homologous pair.

During meiosis, the homologous chromosomes separate. As a result, each gamete that is formed has only one allele for seed shape.

During fertilization, gametes fuse to form offspring. The phenotype and genotype of an offspring depend on which alleles were in the gametes that produced the offspring.

**1.** How is the phenotype of a pea plant different from its genotype?

_____

_____

**2.** Why does a pea plant with the genotype *Rr* have round seeds, not wrinkled seeds?

_____

_____

**3.** Why does a pea plant with the genotype *Rr* produce some gametes that have the allele for round seeds, *R*, and other gametes that have the allele for wrinkled seeds, *r*?

_____

_____

**4.** Two gametes fused and formed an offspring that had wrinkled seeds. What kind of allele for seed shape did each gamete have?

_____

_____

**Chapter 10** **Mendel and Meiosis,** *continued*

*Section 10.1 Mendel's Laws of Heredity*

## Study the Diagram

The diagram below shows one of the crosses Mendel made while studying garden pea plants. Identify the genotypes of the plants. Use the letter *T* to represent the allele for tallness and the letter *t* to represent the allele for shortness. Write one allele in each box.

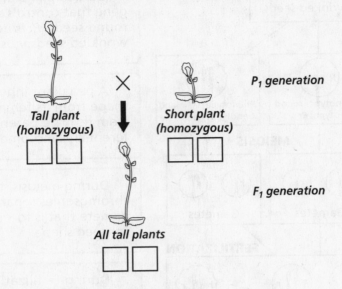

Tall plant
(homozygous)

Short plant
(homozygous)

$P_1$ generation

$F_1$ generation

All tall plants

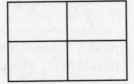

**Use the diagram above to answer the following questions.**

**1.** Why were all the plants in the $F_1$ generation tall?

_____

_____

**2.** Mendel continued his experiment by allowing the $F_1$ plants to self-pollinate. Make a Punnett square to find the expected genotypes of the offspring.

**3.** What fraction of the offspring of the $F_1$ generation would you expect to be tall? What fraction would you expect to be short?

_____

_____

CONTENT MASTERY

### Chapter 10  Mendel and Meiosis, *continued*

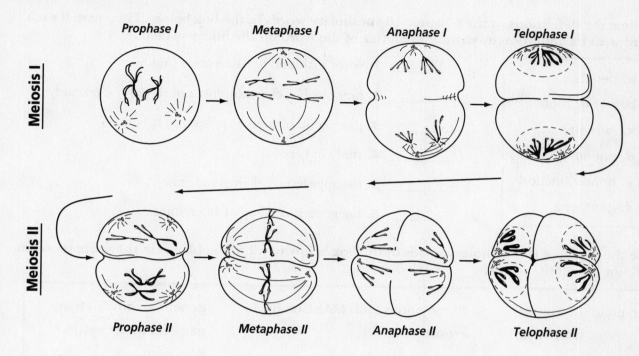

## Study the Diagram

Meiosis I

Prophase I    Metaphase I    Anaphase I    Telophase I

Meiosis II

Prophase II    Metaphase II    Anaphase II    Telophase II

**Use the diagram to answer the questions.**

**1.** Meiosis I begins with one cell. By the end of meiosis II, how many cells are formed?

_____

**2.** During which phase(s) does crossing over occur? Why is crossing over important?

_____

_____

_____

**3.** Compare how homologous chromosomes line up during metaphase I and metaphase II.

_____

_____

_____

**4.** Why is it important that meiosis produces gametes that have only half the number of chromosomes of the parent cell?

_____

_____

_____

**Content Mastery**

## Review the Vocabulary

Review the definitions of the Chapter 10 vocabulary words in the box below. Then match each word with its definition by writing the letter of the word on the line provided.

| | |
|---|---|
| **a.** genetics | _____ **1.** when male and female gametes unite |
| **b.** fertilization | _____ **2.** homologous chromosomes not separating properly |
| **c.** heredity | _____ **3.** passing on of traits to offspring |
| **d.** phenotype | _____ **4.** study of heredity |
| **e.** nondisjunction | _____ **5.** the appearance of an organism |
| **f.** genotype | _____ **6.** the genetic makeup of an organism |

Use the Chapter 10 vocabulary words in the box below to fill in the blanks in the sentences. You will not use all the words.

| | | |
|---|---|---|
| diploid (DIH plo“d) | homologous (huh MAHL uh gus) | genetic recombination |
| haploid (HAP loyd) | crossing over | gametes (GAM eets) |
| heterozygous | meiosis (mi OH sus) | dominant |
| sexual reproduction | zygote (ZI goht) | pollination |

**7.** A cell with two of each kind of chromosome is called _____ .

**8.** Sperm or egg cells are _____ .

**9.** A cell with one of each kind of chromosome is a(n) _____ cell.

**10.** _____ chromosomes have genes for the same traits in the same order on both chromosomes.

**11.** Specialized body cells make gametes in a process that involves _____ .

**12.** A(n) _____ is the cell created when a sperm fertilizes an egg.

**13.** _____ _____ involves the production and subsequent fusion of gametes.

**14.** When nonsister chromatids exchange genes, the process is called _____ _____ .

**15.** The reassortment of genetic information, which results in variation among organisms, is called _____ _____ .

**CONTENT MASTERY**

## Chapter 11 DNA and Genes

### Get the Big Picture

Study the picture. Then answer the questions.

The phosphate group and the sugar, deoxyribose, make up the side of the DNA ladder.

Phosphate

Deoxyribose

Nitrogen bases make up the rungs.

Guanine (G)

Adenine (A)

Thymine (T)

Cytosine (C)

A DNA molecule is similar in shape to a ladder.

**1.** How many types of nitrogen bases does DNA have? _____

Name them. _____

_____

**2.** What are the sides of the DNA ladder made of?

_____

**3.** What are the steps of the DNA ladder made of?

_____

**4.** What kind of bonds hold the chains of building blocks together?

_____

## Chapter 11 DNA and Genes, *continued*

### Study the Diagram

When the DNA ladder replicates, or copies itself, the ladder breaks apart. You can think of the ladder breaking apart as a zipper unzipping. When the two sides of the ladder are apart, free nucleotides attach to the nucleotides already on the sides of the ladder, and two copies of the DNA are formed. The copies are the same as the original because adenine (A) usually pairs with thymine (T). Cytosine (C) usually pairs with guanine (G).

**The diagram below shows an unzipped strand of DNA. Write the letters (A, T, C, or G) of the bases that will pair with the bases on the strand. Some of the bases have been paired for you.**

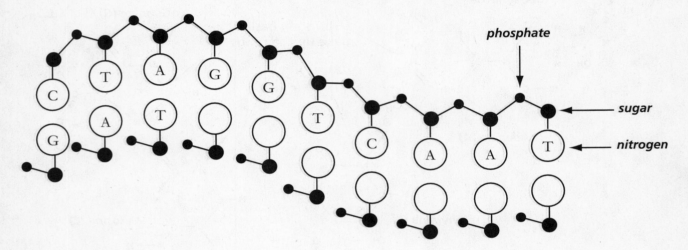

1. **True or false?** Nucleotide bases already attached to proteins form the copied side of the DNA ladder.

_____

2. **True or false?** The process of DNA replication results in a copy of the original strand of DNA.

_____

3. **True or false?** Sugar and phosphates provide the energy for DNA replication.

_____

4. **True or false?** The final result of DNA replication is two copies of the original DNA strand.

_____

**Content Mastery**

*Section 11.2  From DNA to Protein*
*Section 11.3  Genetic Changes*

## Study the Diagram

The mRNA strand shown below is in the process of synthesizing, or making, proteins from amino acids. tRNA molecules bring the amino acids to the mRNA strand. Circle the tRNA molecule that will attach to the codon shown on the mRNA strand. Remember, cytosine (C) pairs with guanine (G), and adenine (A) pairs with uracil (U).

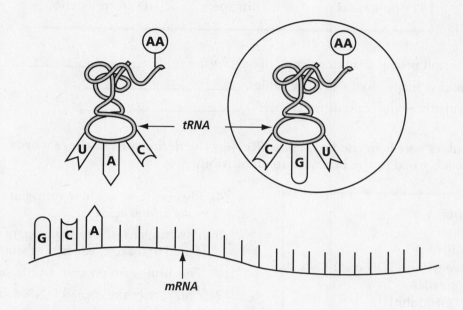

**Now look at the diagram again and answer the questions.**

**1.** How did you know which tRNA molecule would attach to the codon shown?

_____

_____

**2.** Suppose one of the bases on the mRNA was changed. Would the same tRNA molecule still attach to the strand? Explain your answer.

_____

_____

_____

**3.** What would happen to the mRNA strand if an incorrect amino acid was inserted?

_____

_____

**Chapter 11** **DNA and Genes,** *continued*

## Review the Vocabulary

Review the Chapter 11 vocabulary words in the box below. Then write <u>true</u> or <u>false</u> after each statement.

| | | |
|---|---|---|
| double helix | nitrogen | DNA replication |

**1.** DNA replication produces an exact copy of a DNA molecule. _____

**2.** A double helix is shaped like a straight ladder. _____

**3.** DNA has only three different nitrogen bases. _____

Use the vocabulary words in the box below. Review the definitions of these words. Then draw a line to match each word in the box with its definition.

**a.** transcription
**b.** translation
**c.** transfer RNA
**d.** ribosomal (ri buh SOH mul) RNA
**e.** messenger RNA
**f.** codon (KOH dahn)

**4.** This is the set of three nitrogen bases used to make amino acids.

**5.** This happens when a sequence of bases in mRNA is used to make a sequence of amino acids.

**6.** This brings amino acids to ribosomes.

**7.** This carries the copied DNA code out to the cytoplasm.

**8.** This happens when DNA unzips and makes an RNA copy of itself.

**9.** This is the part of the RNA that makes up ribosomes.

Use the vocabulary words in the box below to fill in the blanks in the statements. You will not use all the words.

| | |
|---|---|
| frameshift mutation<br>  (FRAYME shihft • mew TAY shun)<br>chromosomal mutation<br>mutagen (MYEWT uh jun) | nondisjunction<br>point mutation<br>mutation |

**10.** A ____P_____ is a change in a single base pair in DNA.

**11.** Broken chromosomes are one cause of _____ch_____m_____ .

**12.** ____N_____ happens when homologous chromosomes fail to separate properly.

**13.** A _____m_____ is any agent that can cause a change in DNA.

CONTENT MASTERY

## Chapter 12 Patterns of Heredity and Human Genetics

### Get the Big Picture

Find the red and blue headings in Chapter 12 of your textbook. Use the red headings to fill in the rectangles in the idea map below. Use the blue headings to fill in the ovals. Some of the rectangles and ovals have been filled in for you.

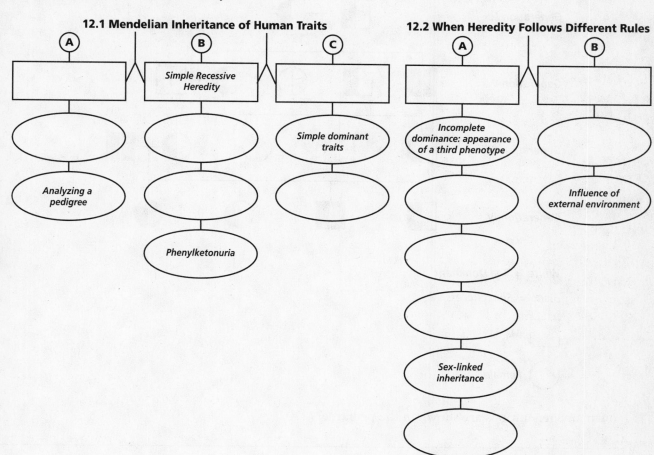

**12.1 Mendelian Inheritance of Human Traits**

**12.2 When Heredity Follows Different Rules**

A ☐

B ☐ *Simple Recessive Heredity*

C ☐

A ☐

B ☐

*Analyzing a pedigree*

*Simple dominant traits*

*Incomplete dominance: appearance of a third phenotype*

*Influence of external environment*

*Phenylketonuria*

*Sex-linked inheritance*

Each statement below goes with one of the headings in the rectangles above. Write the letter of each heading on the line in front of the statement it goes with.

_____  Scientists use pedigrees to find the genetic makeup of a related group of organisms.

_____  Many inheritance patterns are more complex than those studied by Mendel.

_____  Most genetic disorders are caused by recessive alleles.

_____  Both internal and external factors affect how a gene shows up.

## Analyze the Pedigree

Below is a pedigree for a group of dogs. Some of the dogs in this group are tall, and some are short. Some are tall but carry the recessive short trait.

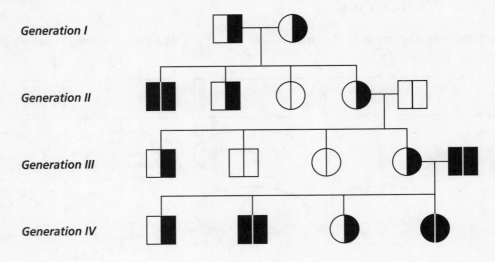

White = Tall Dominant

Black = Short Recessive

☐  Male

◯  Female

**1.** How many generations are shown in the pedigree?

_____

**2.** How many offspring did the parents in the first generation have?

_____

**3.** What does the square in generation I stand for? Why is it half shaded?

_____

_____

**4.** Which dog was the first in the family to be short?

_____

**5.** A female dog from generation III has four puppies. How many of these offspring carry the short trait? How many of the offspring are short?

_____

**Chapter 12** **Patterns of Heredity and Human Genetics,** *continued*

**Content Mastery**

*Section 12.2  When Heredity Follows Different Rules*

*Section 12.3  Complex Inheritance of Human Traits*

## Study the Diagram

This diagram shows the mating of a human male (XY) and a human female (XX). Use the diagram to answer the questions.

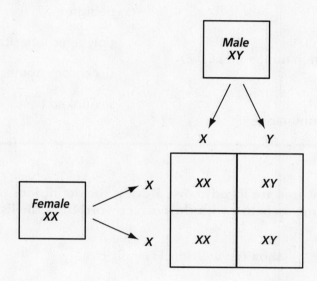

**1.** What do the letters X and Y stand for?

_____

**2.** Which chromosome is found only in the male?

_____

**3.** **True or false?** A person having two X chromosomes is female.

_____

**4.** In the mating shown in the diagram, which statement is **true?** Circle the letter.
   **a.** All the offspring are female.
   **b.** All the offspring are male.
   **c.** One-half the offspring are male.
   **d.** Three of the four offspring are female.

**5.** What happens to offspring with an extra sex chromosome, such as XXX or XXY?

_____

_____

## Review the Vocabulary

| | |
|---|---|
| autosomes | multiple alleles |
| carrier | pedigree |
| codominant alleles<br>  (koh DAH muh nunt • uh LEELZ) | polygenic inheritance |
| | sex chromosomes |
| fetus | sex-linked trait |
| incomplete dominance | |

**The Chapter 12 vocabulary words are listed above. Review the definitions of these words. Then fill in each blank in the statements below with the correct word from the list. You will not use all the words.**

1. A(n) _____ shows an individual's family tree.

2. Some genes are located on sex chromosomes. A(n) _____ is a trait controlled by these genes.

3. In humans, the 22 pairs of matching homologous chromosomes are called _____ .

4. Traits controlled by more than two alleles are said to have _____ .

5. An individual with a recessive allele for an undesirable trait is called a(n) _____ .

6. In _____ , the phenotype of the heterozygote is intermediate between those of the two homozygotes.

7. _____ are chromosomes that determine the sex of an individual.

8. _____ cause the phenotypes of both homozygotes to be produced in the heterozygote.

## Chapter 13 Genetic Technology

## Get the Big Picture

**Study the paragraphs in the boxes and answer the questions.**

> Scientists have learned how to move genes from one organism to another. This process is called **genetic engineering**. Genetic engineering can be used to give an organism new traits. For example, certain bacteria have been developed with the ability to clean up oil spills. They can break down oil into harmless substances. Scientists also use genetically engineered bacteria to improve agriculture and to treat human disease.

**1.** In genetic engineering, what is moved from one organism to another one?

_____

**2.** Give two examples of how genetic engineering can help humans.

_____

_____

_____

_____

> The human genome is made up of all the genes on the 46 human chromosomes. Scientists are now mapping the human genome. They intend to use this map to detect, treat, and cure genetic disorders. DNA fingerprinting is another use of this technology. Every person's DNA is unique. Therefore, DNA from blood, skin, or hair found at a crime scene may be compared with the DNA of a crime suspect. This evidence could give clues about the guilt or innocence of a suspect.

**3.** What is the human genome made of?

_____

_____

**4.** Why is the mapping of the human genome important?

_____

_____

_____

_____

**Chapter 13** **Genetic Technology,** *continued*

## Complete the Idea Map

Find the red heading *Applications of DNA Technology* in Chapter 13 of your textbook. Then find the blue headings and fill in the rectangles in the idea map below. They describe ways that DNA technology can be used. Next, write an example of each use in the circle below it. Two rectangles and one circle have been filled in for you.

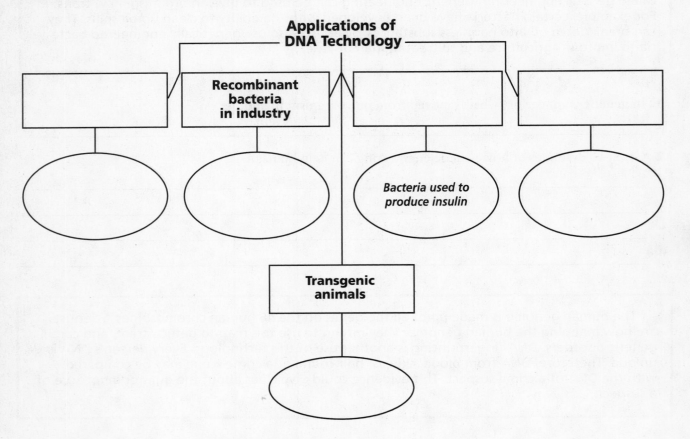

**Applications of DNA Technology**

Recombinant bacteria in industry

Bacteria used to produce insulin

Transgenic animals

**Use the idea map to answer the questions.**

1. True or false? Some bacteria are used in industry to break down pollutants. _____

2. True or false? Bacteria are all harmful organisms that should be eliminated. _____

3. True or false? Some plants produce their own insecticides that keep pests away. _____

4. What is genetic technology?

_____

_____

**Chapter 13 Genetic Technology,** *continued*

**Content Mastery**

*Section 13.3 The Human Genome*

## Complete the Idea Map

Find the red heading *Applications of the Human Genome Project* in Chapter 13 of your textbook. Then find the blue headings and fill in the rectangles in the idea map that describe ways that the Human Genome Project can be used. Next, write an example of each use in the circle below it. One rectangle and one circle have been filled in for you.

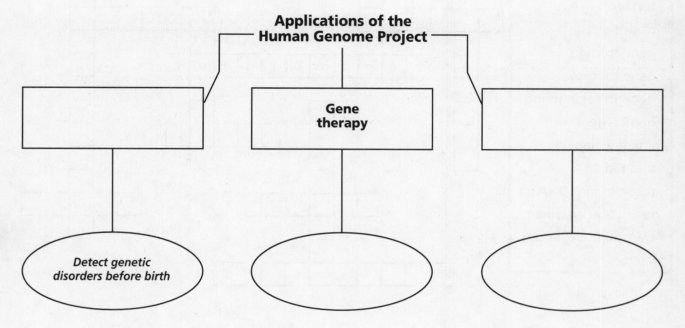

**Applications of the Human Genome Project**

Gene therapy

Detect genetic disorders before birth

**Use the idea map to answer the questions.**

**1. True or false?** Parents who want to know if their children may be genetically inclined towards certain disorders can have their children DNA fingerprinted before birth.

_____

**2. True or false?** People suspected of particular types of crimes may have their DNA examined for evidence.

_____

**3. True or false?** Some genetic disorders may be treated with proper detection and diagnosis.

_____

**Chapter 13** **Genetic Technology,** *continued*

## Review the Vocabulary

Use the Chapter 13 vocabulary words to complete the crossword puzzle. One vocabulary word has been filled in for you.

test cross
clones
gene splicing
gene therapy
genetic engineering
human genome
linkage map
plasmid
recombinant DNA
restriction enzyme
transgenic organism
vector

**Across**

**3.** organisms that are genetically identical

**5.** the thousands of genes that make up the 46 human chromosomes

**6.** DNA made by connecting pieces of DNA from different sources

**8.** small ring of DNA

**9.** A mechanical or biological _____ is used to transfer DNA.

**10.** A test _____ involves an individual of unknown genotype and an individual of known genotype.

**11.** An organism that has been changed by genetic engineering is a(n) _____ organism.

**Down**

**1.** therapy that can be used to correct genetic disorders

**2.** enzymes used to cut DNA molecules

**4.** map showing the location of genes on a chromosome

**5.** engineering used to move genes from one organism to another

**7.** Gene _____ is used to reconnect pieces of DNA.

CONTENT MASTERY

## BioDigest 4 Genetics

### Get the Big Picture

**Read the paragraphs in the boxes. Then answer the questions.**

> From the smallest, simplest bacterium to you, all organisms have DNA. DNA is a chemical that stores the blueprints for each individual organism. DNA determines what each organism looks like and how it functions.

> DNA is passed from parent to offspring. For example, ducks pass the information required to grow into ducklings to their young in DNA molecules. Your parents passed all the information needed for you to grow into a human adult to you in DNA molecules. The information about the color of your eyes is contained in DNA you received from your parents. This process is called heredity.

**1.** What is DNA and why is it important?

_____

_____

_____

_____

**2.** Explain why ducks produce ducklings and not piglets when they reproduce.

_____

_____

_____

_____

_____

**3.** List three traits that you probably inherited from your parents. Explain why you think you inherited these things from your parents.

_____

_____

_____

_____

_____

**Genetics,** *continued*

## Study the Diagram

Study the diagram. Then answer the questions.

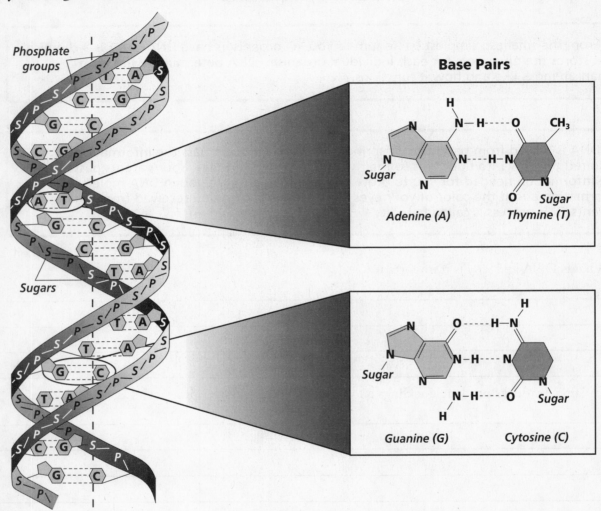

Phosphate groups

**Base Pairs**

Sugar

Adenine (A)    Thymine (T)

Sugars

Sugar

Guanine (G)    Cytosine (C)

**1.** The diagram above shows the shape of a DNA molecule. How would you describe the shape of this molecule?

_____

_____

**2.** If the DNA molecule were compared to a spiral staircase, which parts would make up the rails of the staircase? _____

**3.** If the DNA molecule were compared to a spiral staircase, which parts would make up the steps of the staircase? _____

**4.** Which bases tend to pair together?

_____

**BioDigest**
**4** **Genetics,** *continued*

**Content Mastery**

## Study the Diagram

**Read the paragraph in the box and study the diagram. Then answer the questions.**

> How does DNA convey its information? It converts its information into chemical messengers, called messenger RNA (mRNA), which are then translated into proteins. These proteins affect the appearance and the internal workings of an organism.

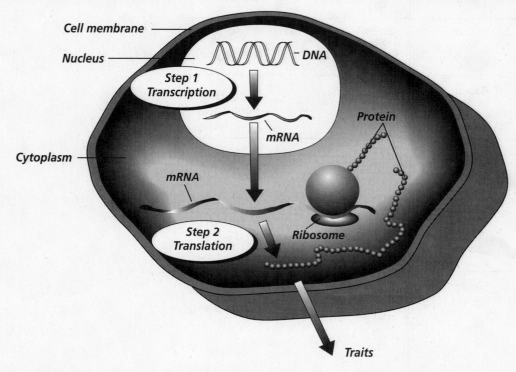

**1.** List two steps that are needed to convert information in DNA to proteins.

_____

**2.** Where does transcription take place in a cell?

_____

**3.** Where does translation take place in a cell?

_____

**4.** If your eyes are brown and your brother's eyes are blue, what can you conclude about your and your brother's DNA for eye color and proteins?

_____

_____

**Content Mastery**

**BioDigest**
**4**   **Genetics,** *continued*

## Study the Table

Study the table. Then answer the questions.

### Dominant vs. Recessive

| Trait | | | | | F₁ Offspring |
|-------|---|---|---|---|--------------|
| Flower color | Purple | × | White | = | Purple (purple flower) |
| Pea color | Yellow | × | Green | = | Yellow (yellow pea) |
| Pea texture | Round | × | Wrinkled | = | Round (round pea) |
| Pod color | Green | × | Yellow | = | Green (green pea pod) |
| Pod texture | Round | × | Constricted | = | Round (round pea pod) |
| Flower height | Tall | × | Short | = | Tall (tall pea plant) |

1. Look at the crosses shown in the table above. Do the offspring favor the pea plant with the dominant trait or the recessive trait? _____

2. What happens to the alleles for the recessive traits in the offspring? Are they still represented in the offspring's DNA?

   _____

   _____

3. How could you demonstrate whether the purple-flowering offspring have the allele for white flowers?

   _____

   _____

4. If you crossed two tall offspring, how many pea plants would be short? _____

**Chapter**
# 14 The History of Life

## Get the Big Picture

**Study the picture and read the paragraph in the box. Then answer the questions that follow.**

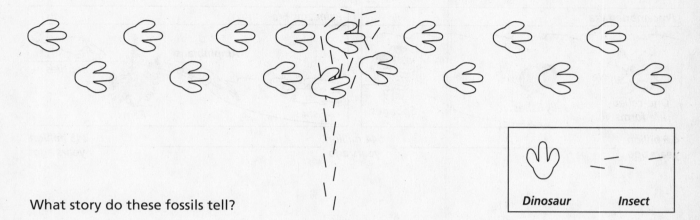

What story do these fossils tell?

Dinosaur          Insect

---

   Scientists study fossils to learn more about living things that lived long ago. Leaf prints, hardened shells, dinosaur tracks, and bones are examples of fossils. Fossils tell biologists how plants and animals looked millions of years ago. Fossils also help scientists recreate the history of life on Earth.

---

**1.** Why are fossils important to biologists?

_____

_____

**2.** List two examples of fossils.

_____

_____

**3.** Look at the picture. What story does it tell?

_____

_____

**4.** Scientists use fossils to recreate the history of life. When future scientists find fossils from our time on Earth, what do you think they will learn about present-day life?

_____

_____

## Study the Diagram

Study the diagram. Then complete the sentences below with the correct era.

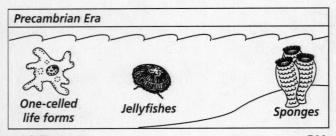

**Precambrian Era**

One-celled life forms  Jellyfishes  Sponges

4.6 billion
years ago

544 million
years ago

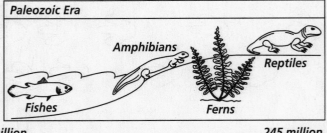

**Paleozoic Era**

Amphibians  Reptiles

Fishes  Ferns

544 million
years ago

245 million
years ago

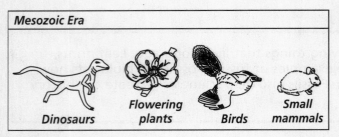

**Mesozoic Era**

Dinosaurs  Flowering plants  Birds  Small mammals

245 million
years ago

66 million
years ago

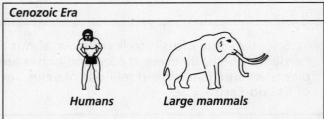

**Cenozoic Era**

Humans  Large mammals

66 million
years ago

present

**1.** Ferns and reptiles appeared in the _____ era.

**2.** Humans and other large mammals appeared in the _____ era.

**3.** Dinosaurs, birds, and flowering plants appeared in the _____ era.

**4.** The earliest life forms appeared in the _____ era.

**Chapter 14** **The History of Life,** *continued*

**Content Mastery**

**Study the diagram below. Then answer the questions that follow.**

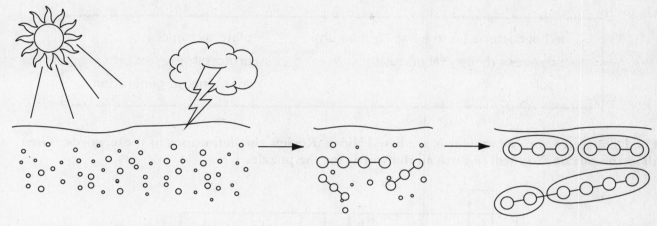

Energy from the sun and lightning strikes molecules in the sea.

Molecules combine to form simple organic molecules.

Larger molecules continue to form, making simple amino acids.

> Amino acids are the building blocks of life. Early protocells were probably made of groups of amino acids.

**5.** Where did the energy to make organic molecules come from?

_____

_____

**6.** What type of larger organic molecules formed? Why are these larger molecules important?

_____

_____

**7.** What do scientists believe was formed from groups of amino acids?

_____

_____

Content Mastery

## Review the Vocabulary

| | |
|---|---|
| archaebacteria (ar kee bac TIHR ee uh) | plate tectonics |
| biogenesis (bi oh JEN uh sus) | protocell |
| fossil | spontaneous generation |

**The Chapter 14 vocabulary words are listed above. Review the definitions of these words. Then fill in the puzzle. You will not use all the words for the puzzle.**

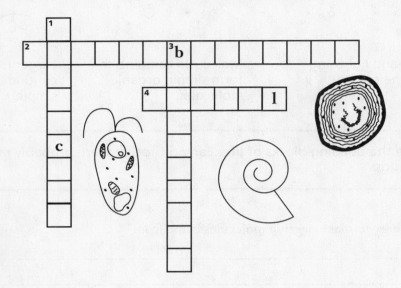

**Across**

**2.** unicellular life forms that live with little sunlight or oxygen

**4.** evidence of an organism that lived long ago

**Down**

**1.** structure that carries out some life activities such as growth or division

**3.** idea that living things come only from other living things

## Fill in each blank with the correct vocabulary word.

**5.** The idea that life can come from something nonliving is called _____ .

**6.** The theory of _____ explains how continents move.

CONTENT MASTERY

**Chapter**

# 15   The Theory of Evolution

## Get the Big Picture

Find the blue headings in Section 15.1 of your textbook. Use a blue heading to fill in the rectangles in the organizer below. One rectangle has been filled in for you.

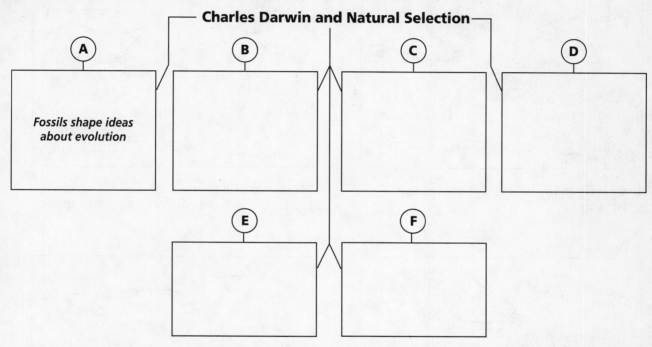

**Charles Darwin and Natural Selection**

**A**

*Fossils shape ideas about evolution*

**B**

**C**

**D**

**E**

**F**

Each statement below goes with one of the headings in the rectangles above. Write the letter of each heading on the line in front of the statement it goes with.

_____ **1.** Darwin saw many life forms on the Galápagos Islands. He was convinced that species change over time.

_____ **2.** Darwin's theory of evolution by natural selection explains how populations change over time.

_____ **3.** Fossil records made scientists wonder if plant and animal species changed over time.

_____ **4.** In 1831, Darwin became a naturalist on a ship called HMS *Beagle*.

_____ **5.** Back in England, Darwin did more research. He learned that some plants and animals have traits that help them survive.

_____ **6.** Some people consider the fossil evidence for natural selection to be inconclusive because the fossil record is incomplete.

**Chapter 15** **The Theory of Evolution,** *continued*

Section 15.1 *Natural Selection and the Evidence for Evolution*

Section 15.2 *Mechanisms of Evolution*

## Study the Diagrams

Study the diagrams. Then answer the questions that follow.

1.

In nature, many animals overproduce offspring.

2.

Members of a population have a variety of traits. These fishes differ in size and speed.

3.

Fishes that are slow and small usually get eaten by predators. Faster, larger fishes can get away from predators.

4.

Offspring of surviving fishes make up a larger part of the new population.

**1.** Why is a fast fish more likely to survive than a slow fish?

_____

_____

**2. True or false?** Natural selection happens when traits that help an organism survive are passed from generation to generation.

_____

_____

**Chapter 15**  **The Theory of Evolution,** *continued*

Study the diagrams. Then answer the questions that follow.

## Flower Population

### First Generation

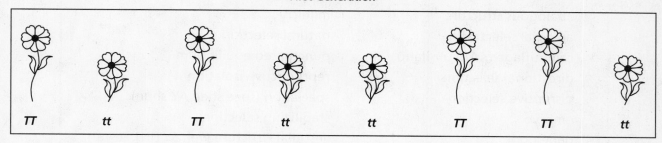

### Second Generation

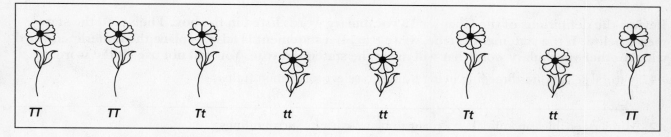

**3.** Two genotypes—gene types—are present in the first generation population. One is *TT*. What is the other?

_____

> **Allelic frequency** tells how often an allele occurs in a population. In the first generation, 8 out of 16 alleles are the *T* allele. The *T* allele is present one-half of the time, so the allelic frequency for the *T* allele is 50%. The allelic frequency for the *t* allele is also 50%.

**4.** What is the allelic frequency for each allele in the second generation?

**a.** *T* _____

**b.** *t* _____

## Review the Vocabulary

| | |
|---|---|
| adaptive radiation | genetic equilibrium |
| allelic frequency | homologous structure |
| analogous structure | mimicry |
| artificial selection | natural selection |
| camouflage (KAM uh flahj) | punctuated equilibrium |
| directional selection | reproductive isolation |
| disruptive selection | speciation (spee shee AY shun) |
| embryo | stabilizing selection |
| gene pool | vestigial structure (veh SYTIHJ ee yul) |
| genetic drift | |

**Review the definitions of the Chapter 15 vocabulary words listed in the box. Then read the statements below. If the statement is true, write _true_. If a statement is false, replace the underlined word with another vocabulary word that will make the statement true. You will not use all the words.**

1. <u>Natural selection</u> is breeding living things to select for certain traits.

_____

2. <u>Mimicry</u> enables an animal or a plant to blend with its surroundings.

_____

3. <u>Homologous structures</u> are similar structures found in groups of related organisms.

_____

4. <u>Genetic equilibrium</u> happens when allelic frequencies stay the same from generation to generation.

_____

5. The <u>allelic frequency</u> is the entire collection of genes in a population.

_____

**Use the vocabulary words in the box below. Review the definitions of these words. Then draw a line to match each word in the box with its definition.**

| |
|---|
| **a.** divergent evolution |
| **b.** geographic isolation |
| **c.** convergent evolution |
| **d.** polyploid |
| **e.** gradualism |

6. When a physical barrier divides a population into groups

7. Any organism that has multiple sets of chromosomes

8. The idea that species form by gradual change over time

9. When two or more similar species become more unlike each other over time

10. When distantly related life forms develop similar traits

## Chapter 16 Primate Evolution

### Get the Big Picture

**Study the picture. Then answer the questions that follow.**

Opposable thumbs help primates grasp objects.

The primate's large brain helps it remember, think, and communicate.

Keen vision in primates helps them watch for predators and spot food sources.

Primates have flexible joints for easy movement.

Primate feet are adapted for grasping.

**1.** What traits help some primates live in trees?

_____

**2.** What traits do humans share with other primates?

_____

**3.** What are some ways in which humans use their opposable thumbs?

_____

## Chapter 16 Primate Evolution, *continued*

**Section 16.1 Primate Adaption and Evolution**
**Section 16.2 Human Ancestry**

## Study the Idea Map

Use the idea map to answer the questions that follow.

**Primates**

**Prosimians**
- Live in trees
- Mostly active at night
- No larger than house cat
- Eat insects, seeds, fruits

**Anthropoids**
- Large brains
- Complex skeleton

**New World Monkeys**
- Central and South America
- Live in trees
- Can grab things with their tails

**Old World Monkeys**
- Africa and Asia
- Live in trees or on the ground
- Some live in cold regions.
- Use tails for balance

**Hominoids**
- Do not have tails
- Largest primate brains
- Can use simple tools
- Includes humans and apes

1. Suppose you found a small primate climbing in a tree at night. What type of primate would it most likely be? Explain.

_____

_____

_____

2. How could you tell whether an anthropoid was a hominoid or an Old World monkey?

_____

_____

_____

3. **True or false?** New World monkeys are an important part of the African rain forest ecosystem.

_____

## Chapter 16 — Primate Evolution, *continued*

Study the diagram. Then answer the questions that follow.

### Evolution of *Homo Sapiens*

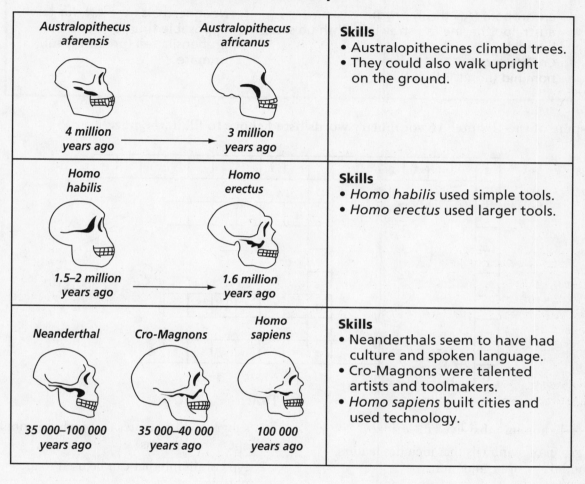

**Australopithecus afarensis**
4 million years ago

**Australopithecus africanus**
3 million years ago

**Skills**
• Australopithecines climbed trees.
• They could also walk upright on the ground.

**Homo habilis**
1.5–2 million years ago

**Homo erectus**
1.6 million years ago

**Skills**
• *Homo habilis* used simple tools.
• *Homo erectus* used larger tools.

**Neanderthal**
35 000–100 000 years ago

**Cro-Magnons**
35 000–40 000 years ago

**Homo sapiens**
100 000 years ago

**Skills**
• Neanderthals seem to have had culture and spoken language.
• Cro-Magnons were talented artists and toolmakers.
• *Homo sapiens* built cities and used technology.

**4.** Which primate species was the first to use simple tools?

_____

**5.** Which primate species spent some of their time in trees?

_____

_____

**6.** The *Homo sapiens* skull is much larger than the *Australopithecus* skull. What can you say about these two groups, using skull size as evidence?

_____

_____

## Review the Vocabulary

| | |
|---|---|
| anthropoid (AN thruh poyd) | Neanderthals (nee AN dur tawl) |
| australopithecine (ah stray loh pihth uh sine) | opposable thumb |
| bipedal | prehensile tail (pree HEN sul) |
| Cro-Magnon | primate |
| hominid (hoh MIHN ud) | |

Use some of the Chapter 16 vocabulary words listed above to fill in the puzzle.

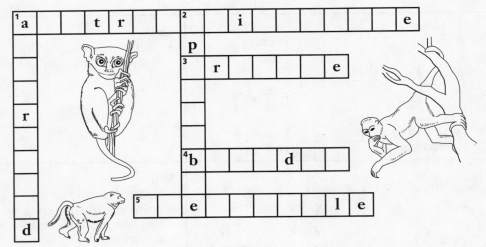

**Across**

**1.** early hominid that lived in Africa

**3.** group of mammals that includes lemurs, monkeys, apes, and humans

**4.** ability to walk upright on two legs

**5.** type of tail that can grasp tree branches

**Down**

**1.** subgroup of primates that includes monkeys, apes, and humans

**2.** type of thumb that can be used to grasp objects

Use the rest of the vocabulary words to finish the words in the sentences.

**6.** _____ lived from 35 000 to 100 000 years ago.
   Ne

**7.** _____ are humanlike primates that walk on two legs.
              ids

**8.** _____ - _____ people lived in Europe 35 000 to
              o
40 000 years ago.

## Chapter 17 — Organizing Life's Diversity

### Get the Big Picture

Read the paragraph in the box and study the picture. Then answer the questions that follow.

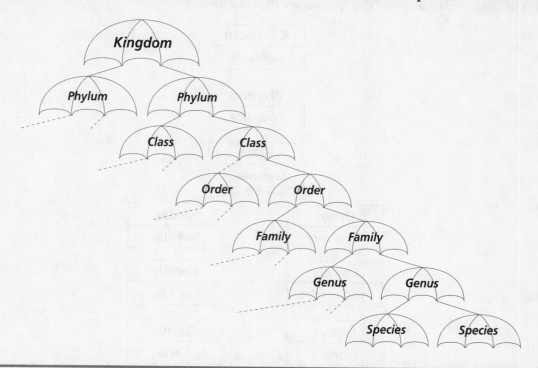

The classification of organisms into groups is based on similarities and differences of the organisms' traits. Organisms that are placed in the same group have more traits in common than those in different groups. All the organisms on Earth belong to one of six kingdoms. Each kingdom is divided into two or more smaller groups (each called a phylum). Those groups are divided into two or more smaller groups (each called a class), and so on. Each smaller group includes a smaller number of different types of organisms.

**1.** What are the seven kinds of groups that make up the above classification system?

_____

**2.** In the above classification system, two or more families make up a(n) _____ .

**3.** Do you think there are more species or more families of organisms on Earth? Explain.

_____

_____

**4.** What is the basis for classifying organisms into groups?

_____

**Chapter 17** **Organizing Life's Diversity,** *continued*

*Section 17.1*
*Classification*

## Study the Diagram

Study the diagram, which shows the classification of the northern raccoon and the pet guinea pig. Then use the diagram to answer the questions that follow.

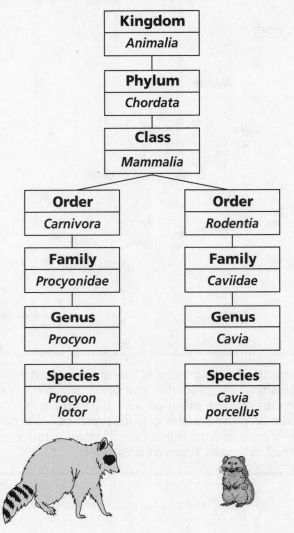

**Kingdom**
*Animalia*

**Phylum**
*Chordata*

**Class**
*Mammalia*

**Order**
*Carnivora*

**Order**
*Rodentia*

**Family**
*Procyonidae*

**Family**
*Caviidae*

**Genus**
*Procyon*

**Genus**
*Cavia*

**Species**
*Procyon lotor*

**Species**
*Cavia porcellus*

**1.** To which of the same groups do the raccoon and the guinea pig belong?

_____

**2.** What two orders are included in class Mammalia? _____

**3.** What is the scientific name of the northern raccoon? The pet guinea pig?

_____

**4.** How is the common name *guinea pig* misleading? _____

## Study the Drawings

Use the drawings to answer the questions that follow.

### The Six Kingdoms

**Archaebacteria**
- one-celled
- some make their own food, others consume food
- found in extreme environments

**Eubacteria**
- one-celled
- some make their own food, others consume food
- found in many kinds of environments

**Protists**
- one-celled or many-celled
- some make their own food, others consume food
- found only in moist environments

**Fungi**
- one-celled or many-celled
- consume food
- stay in one place

**Plants**
- many-celled
- make their own food
- stay in one place

**Animals**
- many-celled
- consume food
- most can move from place to place

**1.** Name the six kingdoms.

_____

_____

**2.** In which kingdom(s) are all of the organisms many-celled?

_____

_____

**3.** Compare how a mushroom and a fern get the food they need.

_____

_____

**4.** How are eubacteria and archaebacteria different?

_____

_____

## Review the Vocabulary

Use the Chapter 17 vocabulary words listed in the box to fill in the blanks in the sentences. You will not use all the words.

| | |
|---|---|
| binomial nomenclature | phylogeny (fi LAW juh nee) |
| cladistics | protists |
| division | taxonomy |
| eubacteria | |

**1.** The naming system called _____ gives each species a two-word name.

**2.** _____ is a classification system based on the derived traits of organisms.

**3.** _____ are prokaryotes.

**4.** _____ is the branch of biology that groups and names living things.

**5.** _____ is the history of the evolution of a species.

**Draw a line to match each vocabulary word in the box with its definition.**

| | |
|---|---|
| **a.** family | **6.** Group of related orders |
| **b.** order | **7.** Group of related genera |
| **c.** genus (JEE nus) | **8.** Group of related species |
| **d.** phylum (FI lum) | **9.** Group of related families |
| **e.** class | **10.** Group of related phyla |
| **f.** kingdom | **11.** Group of related classes |

**BioDigest**
**5**  ## Change Through Time

### Get the Big Picture

Find the red and blue headings in Biodigest 5. Use the blue headings to fill in the rectangles in the idea map below. Use the red headings to fill in the ovals. One rectangle and one oval have been filled in for you.

**Change Through Time**

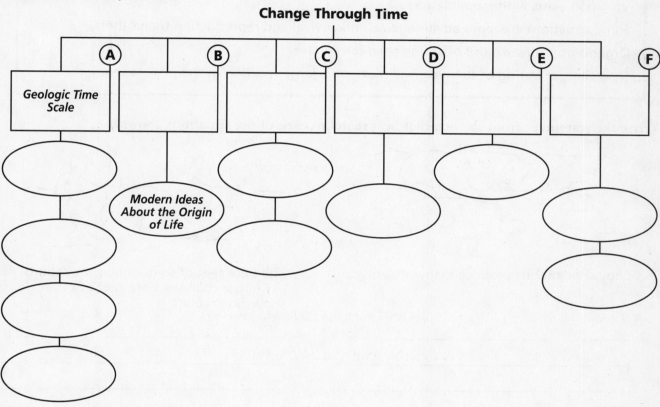

Each statement below goes with one of the headings in the rectangles above. Write the letter of each heading on the line in front of the statement it goes with.

_____  Possible shared ancestry between different organisms may be indicated by similar anatomical structures.

_____  The most recent era of the Geologic Time Scale is the Cenozoic era.

_____  The first true cells may have evolved from protocells, which were formed from clusters of organic molecules.

_____  If a change in the genetic equilibrium of a population takes place, evolution occurs.

_____  Fossils indicate that possible human ancestors walked on two legs and climbed trees.

_____  Biologists use criteria such as body structure, breeding behavior, geographic distribution, and biochemical similarities to explain relationships among organisms.

**BioDigest 5**  **Change Through Time,** *continued*

## Study the Pictures

**Evolution by natural selection can be summarized in four statements.**

> Variation exists within populations.
>
> Some variations are more advantageous for survival and reproduction than others.
>
> Organisms produce more offspring than can survive.
>
> Over time, offspring of survivors will make up a larger portion of the population.

**Write the statement from the box that best matches each of the situations shown.**

Snowshoe rabbits produce many offspring.

1. _____

_____

_____

The back feet of some snowshoe rabbits are larger than the back feet of other snowshoe rabbits.

2. _____

_____

_____

Snowshoe rabbits with large back feet can run across snow faster than those with small back feet and escape predators, such as wolves, more often.

3. _____

_____

_____

More snowshoe rabbits with larger feet survive in the population and reproduce.

4. _____

_____

_____

## Study the Graphs

Each graph compares the normal distribution of a characteristic in the original population with the distribution of the characteristic in a population altered by natural selection.

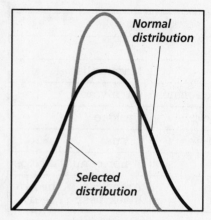

**Graph A**

More individuals in the altered population have the average value of the characteristic than in the original population.

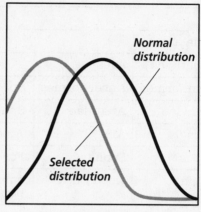

**Graph B**

The distribution of the characteristic in the altered population differs from the distribution of the characteristic in the original population.

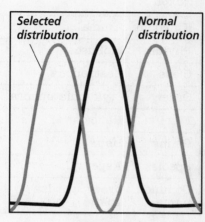

**Graph C**

Two altered populations appear—each having a distribution of a characteristic distinct from the characteristic of the original population.

**In the space at the left, write the letter of the graph that illustrates the type of natural selection described.**

_____ **5.** Directional selection: natural selection that results in a regular change in a population in one direction

_____ **6.** Disruptive selection: natural selection that results in two separate populations that have distinct characteristics

_____ **7.** Stabilizing selection: natural selection that favors the average individuals in a population

**In the space at the left, write the letter of the graph that illustrates each of the following situations.**

_____ **8.** A large valley is flooded and a population of lizards is divided into two smaller populations that can no longer interbreed.

_____ **9.** A population of penicillin-resistant bacteria develops from a population of bacteria (some of which were resistant to penicillin), which was treated with penicillin.

_____ **10.** In a large population of grass plants, variation in the height of grass decreases over time.

**BioDigest 5** **Change Through Time,** *continued*

## Study the Table

The table shows the phylogenetic classification of six organisms.

| Taxon | Name | | | | | |
|---|---|---|---|---|---|---|
| Kingdom | Animalia | | | | | |
| Phylum | Mollusca | Chordata | | | | |
| Class | Gastropoda | Osteichthyes | Aves | | Mammalia | |
| Order | Stylommatophora | Cypriniformes | Anseriformes | Sphenisciformes | Carnivora | |
| Family | Helicidae | Cyprinidae | Anatidae | Spheniscidae | Ursidae | |
| Genus | Helix | Carassius | Aix | Aptenodytes | Ursus | |
| Species | Aspersa | Auratus | Spona | Forsteri | Americanus | Arctos |
| Common name | brown garden snail | goldfish | wood duck | emperor penguin | American black bear | brown bear |

**In the space at the left, write the letter of the word or phrase that best completes each statement.**

_____ **11.** The largest taxon, or classification group, is

         **a.** class.       **b.** kingdom.       **c.** phylum.       **d.** species.

_____ **12.** All of the organisms in the table are

         **a.** animals.       **b.** autotrophs.       **c.** vertebrates.       **d.** warm-blooded.

_____ **13.** The two most closely related organisms are the

         **a.** brown garden snail and goldfish.
         **b.** emperor penguin and goldfish.
         **c.** American black bear and wood duck.
         **d.** American black bear and brown bear.

_____ **14.** The binomial nomenclature name of the brown garden snail is

         **a.** *Gastropoda helicidae.*             **b.** *Gastropoda helix.*
         **c.** *Helix aspera.*                   **d.** *Mollusca gastropoda.*

_____ **15.** The number of taxa that the wood duck and emperor penguin have in common is

         **a.** zero.       **b.** one.       **c.** two.       **d.** three.

## Chapter 18 Viruses and Bacteria

## Get the Big Picture

Study the pictures. Then write **B** after each sentence below that describes bacteria. Write **V** after each sentence that describes viruses.

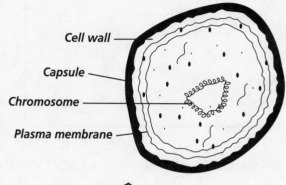

Cell wall

Capsule

Chromosome

Plasma membrane

**Bacteria** are the oldest form of life on Earth. Bacteria grow, reproduce, and carry out respiration. They are used to make yogurt, cheese, and some other foods. Bacteria can cause diseases, such as tuberculosis and strep throat.

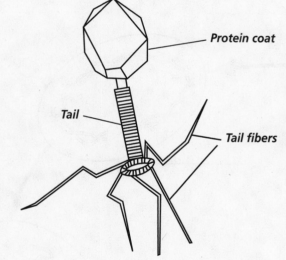

Protein coat

Tail

Tail fibers

**Viruses** are much smaller than bacteria. Most biologists agree that viruses are not alive. Viruses do not move, grow, or carry out respiration. Viruses need living host cells to reproduce. Viruses can cause diseases, such as the flu or chicken pox.

**1.** They cause chicken pox. _____

**2.** They can grow, reproduce, and carry out respiration. _____

**3.** They are the oldest life form on Earth. _____

**4.** Most biologists agree they are not alive. _____

**5.** They cause strep throat. _____

**6.** They do not move, grow, or carry out respiration. _____

**7.** They need a living host to reproduce. _____

**8.** They are used to make some foods. _____

*Section 18.1 Viruses*

## Study the Cycle

Viruses use a host cell to make new viruses, then destroy the cell. This process is called the **lytic cycle.**
Here are the steps of the lytic cycle.

> **1.** The virus attaches to the cell.
>
> **2.** DNA from the virus enters the cell.
>
> **3.** The cell makes new viral DNA and proteins.
>
> **4.** New viruses are assembled from the proteins and DNA.
>
> **5.** The cell breaks open and the viruses are released.

**The steps of the lytic cycle are shown in the diagram below. Use the list above to number the steps.**

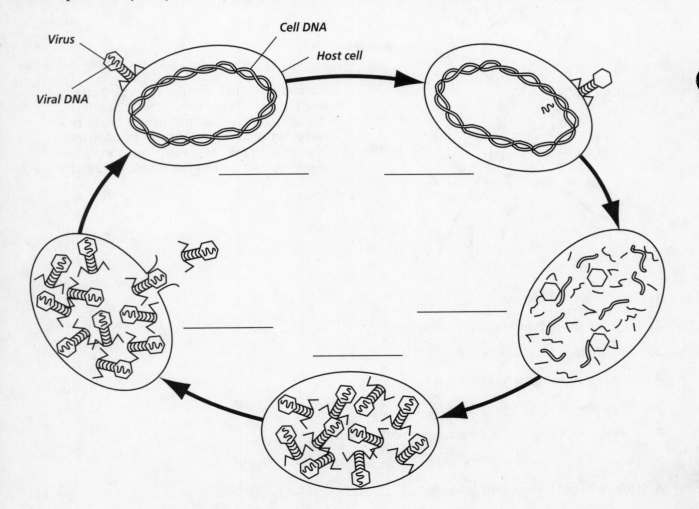

**CONTENT MASTERY**

**Chapter 18** **Viruses and Bacteria,** *continued*

 **Content Mastery**

*Section 18.2 Archaebacteria*
*and Eubacteria*

## Study the Shapes

Bacteria are the smallest and simplest living things. They come in three basic shapes: spheres, rods, and spirals. The figures below show the three shapes. Write the name of the shape below each figure.

1. _____

2. _____

3. _____

Bacteria usually live in groups. The names of bacteria often tell how the bacteria are grouped. If the name starts with *Diplo-*, the bacteria live in pairs. If the name starts with *Staphylo-*, they live in clusters like grapes. If the name starts with *Strepto-*, they live in chains. The figures below show these three groups. Write the prefix of the name of the bacteria below each figure.

4. _____

5. _____

6. _____

**Content Mastery**

## Chapter 18   Viruses and Bacteria, *continued*

## Review the Vocabulary

Use the Chapter 18 vocabulary words in the box to fill in the puzzle.

| | | |
|---|---|---|
| virus (VI rus) | bacteriophage (bak TEER ee yuh fayj) | retrovirus |
| provirus | toxin | endospore |

### Across

**3.** virus that infects only bacteria

**5.** poison produced by some bacteria

**6.** virus whose DNA has been inserted into the host cell's chromosome

### Down

**1.** virus that has RNA

**2.** tiny, nonliving particle

**4.** bacterium with a tough outer covering

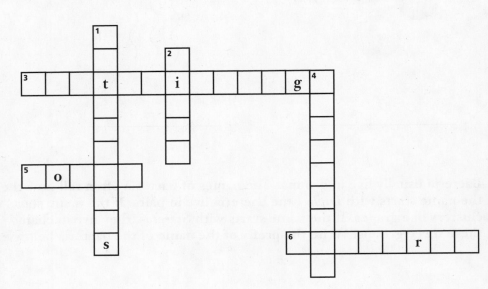

Look at each vocabulary word in the box below. If the word is related to bacteria, write it in the table under *Bacteria*. If the word is related to viruses, write it in the table under *Viruses*.

| | |
|---|---|
| lytic cycle (LI tihk) | |
| lysogenic cycle (li suh JEN ihk) | |
| capsid | |
| reverse transcriptase | |
| obligate aerobe | |
| binary fission | |
| conjugation | |
| obligate anaerobe | |
| nitrogen fixation | |

| Bacteria | Viruses |
|---|---|
| | |
| | |
| | |
| | |

## Chapter 19 Protists

### Get the Big Picture

Read the paragraphs in the boxes and study the picture. Then answer the questions that follow.

> Protists are all around us. There are more than 200 000 species in the kingdom Protista. Protists come in many different shapes, sizes, and colors. Some protists have traits like animals. Protozoans are animal-like protists. Other protists have traits like plants. Algae are plantlike protists. Still other protists have traits like fungi. Slime molds, water molds, and downy mildews are examples of funguslike protists.

> Protists are important to nearly all ecosystems. Some protists produce large amounts of oxygen. Other protists form the first link in aquatic food chains. Protists live in almost every moist habitat on Earth.

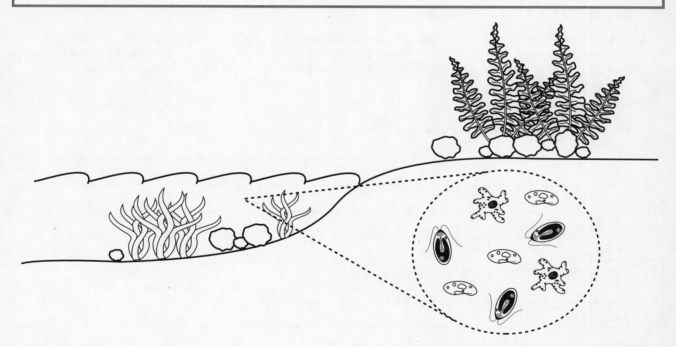

**1.** What are protozoans?

_____

**2.** Why are protists important to other living things on Earth? Give two reasons.

_____

_____

**3. True or false?** Protists live mostly in dry habitats. _____

**Chapter**
**19** **Protists,** *continued*

## Study the Diagram

Use the diagram to answer the questions that follow.

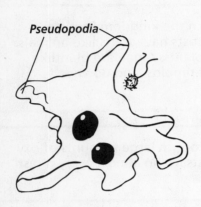

*Pseudopodia*

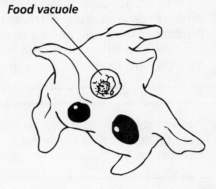

*Pseudopodia*      *Food vacuole*
                   *forming*

*Food vacuole*

**A.** An amoeba senses food
   nearby. It extends
   pseudopodia toward
   the food.

**B.** The amoeba captures the
   food and forms a food
   vacuole around it.

**C.** Digestive enzymes in
   the food vacuole break
   down the food.

**1.** What does an amoeba use its pseudopodia for?

_____

_____

_____

_____

**2.** Where does an amoeba digest its food?

_____

_____

_____

_____

*Section 19.2 Algae: Plantlike Protists*

*Section 19.3 Slime Molds, Water
Molds, and Downy Mildews*

## Study the Idea Maps

Use the idea map to answer the questions that follow.

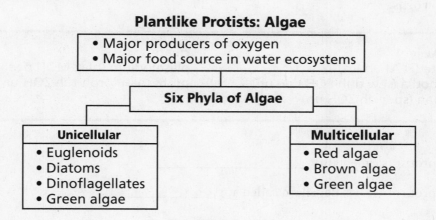

**Plantlike Protists: Algae**

• Major producers of oxygen
• Major food source in water ecosystems

**Six Phyla of Algae**

**Unicellular**
• Euglenoids
• Diatoms
• Dinoflagellates
• Green algae

**Multicellular**
• Red algae
• Brown algae
• Green algae

**1.** Why are plantlike protists important to all living things?

_____

**2.** How many cells does a dinoflagellate have? _____

Use the idea map to answer the questions that follow.

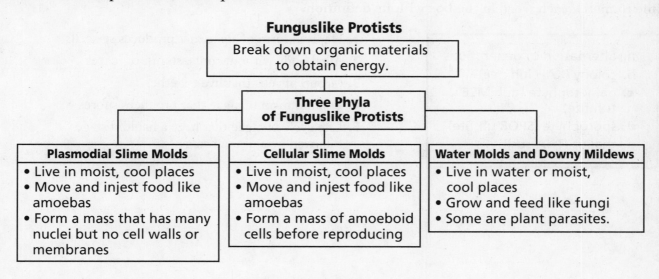

**Funguslike Protists**

Break down organic materials
to obtain energy.

**Three Phyla
of Funguslike Protists**

**Plasmodial Slime Molds**
• Live in moist, cool places
• Move and injest food like
  amoebas
• Form a mass that has many
  nuclei but no cell walls or
  membranes

**Cellular Slime Molds**
• Live in moist, cool places
• Move and injest food like
  amoebas
• Form a mass of amoeboid
  cells before reproducing

**Water Molds and Downy Mildews**
• Live in water or moist,
  cool places
• Grow and feed like fungi
• Some are plant parasites.

**3.** How are slime molds and cellular slime molds different?

_____

_____

**4.** How are some funguslike protists harmful to plants?

_____

_____

## Review the Vocabulary

Use the Chapter 19 vocabulary words in the box below to fill in the blanks in the sentences. You will not use all the words.

| |
|---|
| algae (AL jee)                         ciliate |
| flagellate (FLAJ uh lut)          plasmodium (plaz MOH dee um) |
| pseudopodia (sew duh POH dee uh)    protozoan (proh tuh ZOH un) |
| sporozoan (spor uh ZOH un) |

**1.** An animal-like protist is called a(n) _____ .

**2.** An animal-like protist that has flagella is called a(n) _____ .

**3.** A(n) _____ is a protist that produces spores.

**4.** Some protists use _____ to move and to capture food.

**5.** A(n) _____ is a protist that has cilia.

Use the vocabulary words in the box below. Review the definitions of these words. Then draw a line to match each word in the box with its definition.

| |
|---|
| **a.** alternation of generations |
| **b.** colony (KAH luh nee) |
| **c.** gametophyte (guh MEE tuh fite) |
| **d.** sporophyte (SPOR uh fite) |
| **e.** thallus (THAL us) |

**1.** Haploid form of algae that produces sex cells

**2.** Algal body without roots, stems, or leaves

**3.** Group of cells that live together

**4.** Diploid form of algae that produces spores

**5.** Life cycle of algae that have a haploid stage followed by a diploid stage

**Chapter**
## 20 Fungi

## Get the Big Picture

Study the diagram. Then answer the questions that follow.

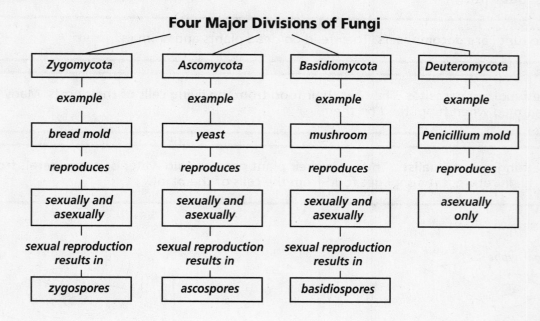

**Four Major Divisions of Fungi**

1. What are the four major divisions of fungi?

   _____

2. In which divisions do the fungi reproduce sexually?

   _____

3. How does the *Penicillium* mold reproduce?

   _____

4. When yeasts reproduce sexually, what kind of spore do they produce?

   _____

5. What is an example of a fungus that belongs to the division Basidiomycota?

   _____

**Chapter 20** **Fungi,** *continued*

## Match the Diagrams with the Statements

The statements in each box go with one of the diagrams. Write the letter of the box under the diagram it goes with.

**A.** Some fungi are **decomposers**. They feed on dead plants and animals.

**B.** Some fungi are **parasites**. They get their food from the living cells of their hosts. Many hosts are harmed when fungi feed on them.

**C.** Some fungi are **mutualists**. They help their plant partner hold water or get minerals from the soil. In return, the fungi get food from the cells of the plant.

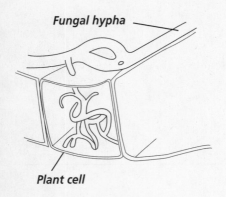

_____

This fungus gets food from the plant cell. The fungus helps the plant get minerals from the soil.

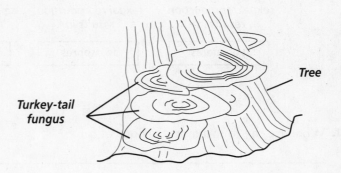

_____

A turkey-tail fungus feeds on a dead tree.

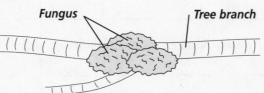

_____

Some fungi get food from the cells of living trees. Many of the trees die when the fungi attack them.

**Chapter 20** **Fungi,** *continued*

*Section 20.2 The Diversity of Fungi*

## Match the Steps

The drawing below shows the steps in the life cycle of a mushroom. Write the numbers from the drawing next to the matching life-cycle steps that follow.

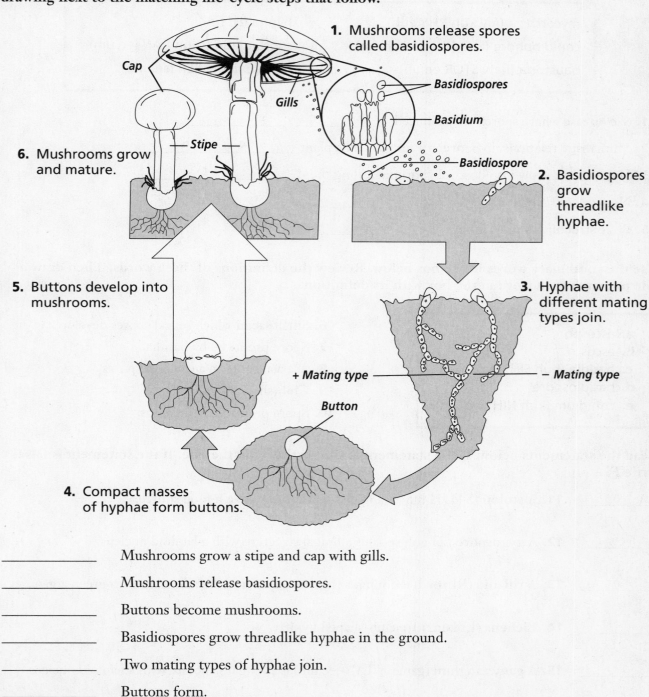

**1.** Mushrooms release spores called basidiospores.

*Cap*

*Basidiospores*

*Gills*

*Basidium*

**6.** Mushrooms grow and mature.

*Stipe*

*Basidiospore*

**2.** Basidiospores grow threadlike hyphae.

**5.** Buttons develop into mushrooms.

**3.** Hyphae with different mating types join.

*+ Mating type*        *– Mating type*

*Button*

**4.** Compact masses of hyphae form buttons.

_____ Mushrooms grow a stipe and cap with gills.

_____ Mushrooms release basidiospores.

_____ Buttons become mushrooms.

_____ Basidiospores grow threadlike hyphae in the ground.

_____ Two mating types of hyphae join.

_____ Buttons form.

**Content Mastery**

**Chapter 20** **Fungi,** *continued*

## Review the Vocabulary

Use the Chapter 20 vocabulary words in the box to fill in the puzzle. You will not use all the words.

---
mycorrhiza (my kuh RHY zuh)          hypha (HI fuh)

conidiophore (kuh NIH dee uh for)    sporangium (spuh RAN jee um)

haustoria (haw STOR ee uh)           mycelium (mi SEE lee um)
---

1. Sac or case where spores are produced _____ r _____ g _____

2. Mutualistic relationship between a fungus and a plant _____ c _____ h _____

3. Hyphae that grow into host cells without killing them _____ t _____

4. Network of filaments _____ y _____

5. Basic structural unit of fungi _____ p _____

Use the vocabulary words in the box below. Review the definitions of these words. Then draw a line to match each word in the box with its definition.

---
**a.** ascospore

**b.** ascus

**c.** basidia (buh SIH dee uh)

**d.** basidiospore

**e.** conidium (kuh NIH dee um)
---

6. Small sac in which sexual spores develop

7. Spore produced by basidia

8. Asexual spore in a chain of spores

9. Club-shaped hyphae

10. Spore produced in an ascus

Read the statements below. If the statement is true, write <u>T</u> on the line. If the statement is false, write <u>F</u>.

_____ **11.** A **stolon** (STOH lun) is a hypha that grows across a food source.

_____ **12.** A **zygospore** (ZI goh spor) is a fungal structure with a haploid nucleus.

_____ **13.** A **rhizoid** (RI zoyd) is a fungus that has a symbiotic relationship with green algae.

_____ **14.** **Lichens** (LI kunz) are club-shaped hyphae.

_____ **15.** A **gametangium** (gam uh TAN jee um) is a fungal structure with a haploid nucleus.

CONTENT MASTERY

**BioDigest 6**

# Viruses, Bacteria, Protists, and Fungi

## Get the Big Picture

After you have read the Biodigest, look at the pictures below. Then answer the questions that follow.

**A.** *Virus*　　　**B.** *Bacterium*　　　**C.** *Protist*　　　**D.** *Fungus*

**1.** Which pictures show eukaryotes?

_____

**2.** Which picture shows a prokaryote?

_____

**3.** Which picture does not show a living organism?

_____

**4.** Identify the shape of the bacterium in picture B.

_____

**5.** Which organism is animal-like?

_____

**6.** Which organism is multicellular?

_____

**7.** Identify the protist shown in picture C.

_____

**8.** Identify the fungus shown in picture D.

_____

## BioDigest 6  Viruses, Bacteria, Protists, and Fungi, *continued*

**Content Mastery**

## Study the Diagram

Read the paragraph in the box and study the diagram. Then answer the questions that follow.

> Sometimes when a virus infects a host cell, it does not destroy the cell to make new viruses. Instead, the virus's DNA is inserted into the DNA of the host cell. When the host cell reproduces, the virus's DNA is copied along with the cell's DNA. This method of viral replication is called the **lysogenic cycle**.

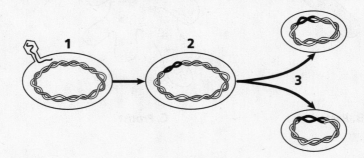

**1.** Which numbered step in the diagram shows that the virus's DNA has been copied along with the DNA of the host cell?

_____

**2.** In which step is the virus infecting the host cell?

_____

**3.** Which step shows that the virus's DNA has just been inserted into the DNA of the host cell?

_____

## Label the Diagram

Label the main parts of the bacterium. Use these labels: *cytoplasm, cell wall, chromosome, plasma membrane.*

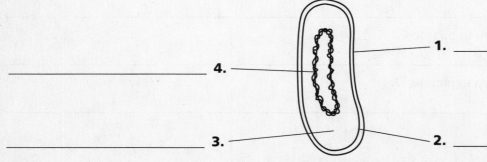

**Bacterium**

1. _____

2. _____

3. _____

4. _____

**BioDigest 6**  **Viruses, Bacteria, Protists, and Fungi,** *continued*

## Matching

Match the pictures of the different kinds of protists with their descriptions below. Write the number of the correct description below each picture.

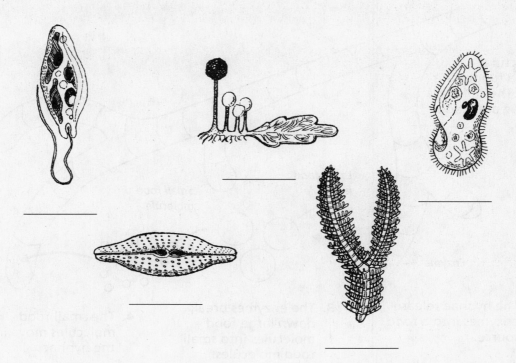

1. Paramecia are unicellular animal-like protists that use tiny hairlike cilia to move and collect food.

2. Red algae are multicellular plantlike protists that can grow in deep ocean water where there is little sunlight.

3. Diatoms are unicellular plantlike protists that have shells made of two pieces.

4. Slime molds are funguslike protists that obtain food by decomposing dead plants and animals.

5. Euglena are unicellular protists that use whiplike flagella to move. They usually make their own food and sometimes obtain food by feeding on other organisms.

## Study the Diagram

Study the diagram that shows how fungi obtain food. Then use the diagram to complete the sentences and answer the questions that follow.

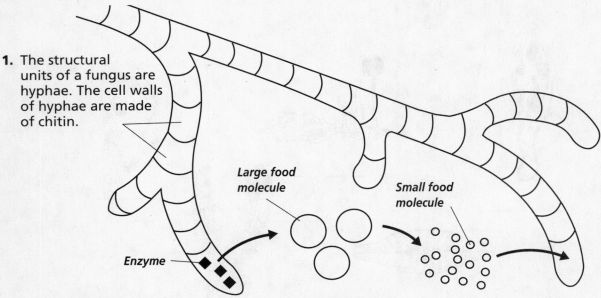

**1.** The structural units of a fungus are hyphae. The cell walls of hyphae are made of chitin.

*Large food molecule*

*Small food molecule*

*Enzyme*

**2.** The hyphae release enzymes into a food source.

**3.** The enzymes break down large food molecules into small food molecules.

**4.** The small food molecules move into the hyphae.

**1.** _____ release enzymes.

**2.** The enzymes break down _____ into small food molecules.

**3.** The small food molecules move into the _____ .

**4.** Hyphae are the structural units of a _____ .

**5.** _____ makes up the cell walls of hyphae.

**6.** Why is it necessary for a fungus to release enzymes that break down large food molecules?

_____

_____

**7.** Why can a fungus with many hyphae absorb more food than a fungus with few hyphae?

_____

_____

## Chapter 21 — What Is a Plant?

### Get the Big Picture

**Read the paragraph in the box. Then answer the questions that follow.**

> Plants were some of the earliest living things on land. When they moved to land, plants faced challenges to get water, food, and energy. Some plants, like giant redwood trees, formed deep roots. These roots helped the trees get water and food from deep below the surface of Earth. Other plants, like some desert cacti, formed shallow roots like bicycle spokes. These roots help desert plants capture water near the ground over a great distance. Most plants have leaves that capture energy from the sun. The leaves of many plants are covered with a waxy coating called a cuticle that helps them hold water. Plants have adapted to many types of land environments.

**1.** How does each plant structure below help plants live on land?

   **a.** Roots: _____

   **b.** Leaves: _____

   **c.** Waxy coating: _____

**2.** Why are the roots of many desert plants very shallow?

_____

_____

_____

_____

**3.** What trait of plants helps prevent water loss from their leaves?

_____

_____

_____

_____

## Chapter 21 What Is a Plant?, *continued*

## Study the Diagram

Use the diagram to answer the questions.

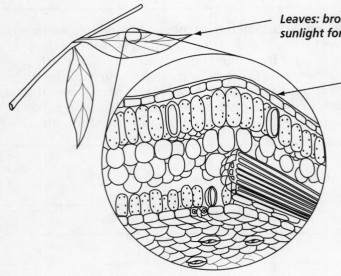

Leaves: broad, flat organs that trap sunlight for photosynthesis.

Cuticle: waxy coating on fruits, leaves, and stems. It helps plants hold water.

**1.** What is a cuticle?

_____

_____

_____

**2.** What is the purpose of a plant's cuticle?

_____

_____

_____

**3.** What is the purpose of leaves?

_____

_____

_____

**Chapter 21**  **What Is a Plant?,** *continued*

*Section 21.2   Survey of the Plant Kingdom*

## Study the Idea Map

Use the idea map to answer the questions.

**Plants**

Plants are divided into two groups based on whether or not a plant produces seeds.

- There are seven divisions of non-seed plants.
- These plants release hard-walled reproductive cells called spores.
- Non-seed plants may be either vascular or nonvascular.

- There are five divisions of seed plants.
- Seed plants release seeds.
- Seeds are made up of an embryonic plant and a food supply covered by a hard protective seed coat.
- All seed plants are vascular.

**4.** How are plants divided into two groups?

_____

_____

_____

_____

**5.** How do non-seed plants and seed plants reproduce?

_____

_____

_____

_____

_____

**6. True or false?** Non-seed plants are always nonvascular plants.

_____

**Chapter 21** **What Is a Plant?,** *continued*

## Review the Vocabulary

Use the Chapter 21 vocabulary words in the box to label the parts of the plant.

| | |
|---|---|
| cuticle (KYEW tih kul) | seed |
| leaf | stem |
| root | |

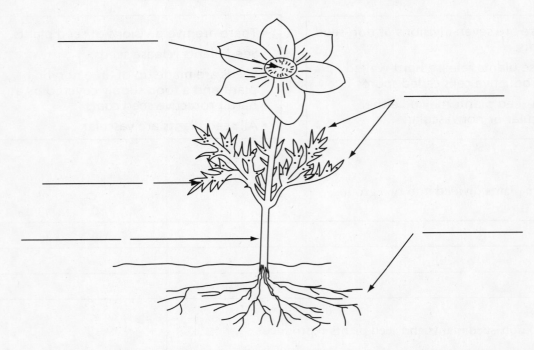

**Look at the vocabulary statements below. If the statement is true, write T on the line. If the statement is false, write F.**

_____ **1.** **Nonvascular plants** possess vascular tissues.

_____ **2.** A **frond** is the leaf found on ferns that vary in length from 1 cm to 500 cm.

_____ **3.** Tubelike, elongated cells through which water, food, and other materials are transported make up **vascular tissues**.

_____ **4.** **Cuticles** are scaly structures that support male or female reproductive structures.

_____ **5.** Plants that possess vascular tissues are known as **vascular plants**.

CONTENT MASTERY

## Chapter 22 — The Diversity of Plants

### Get the Big Picture

**Nonvascular plants** lack vascular tissue and reproduce by releasing spores. They usually live in moist, cool environments. There are three divisions of nonvascular plants: mosses, liverworts, and hornworts.

The **non-seed vascular plants** require a continuous film of water through which sperm swim to the egg. These plants have vascular tissues that transport water and nutrients throughout the plant. Vascular tissues also provide the structural support that enables vascular plants to grow taller than nonvascular plants.

**Seed plants** include vascular plants that produce naked seeds, as well as plants that produce flowers and have seeds enclosed in a fruit. Fertilization in most seed plants does not require a continuous film of water.

**Label the pictures below. Use these choices: nonvascular plant, non-seed vascular plant, seed plant that produce naked seeds, seed plant that produces fruit.**

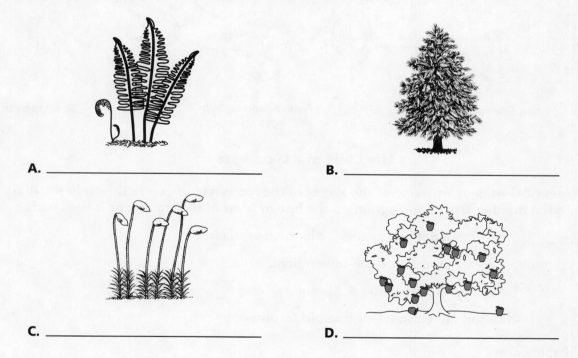

A. _____

B. _____

C. _____

D. _____

**Each statement below goes with one of the pictures. Write the letter of each picture on the line in front of the statement it goes with.**

_____ These plants were prominent members of Earth's ancient forests.

_____ These plants are divided into two classes: monocotyledons and dicotyledons.

_____ The gametophyte generation is dominant.

_____ This group is sometimes referred to as gymnosperms, meaning "naked seed."

**Chapter**
**22** **The Diversity of Plants,** *continued*

**Content Mastery**

*Section 22.1 Nonvascular Plants*
*Section 22.2 Non-seed Vascular Plants*

## Study the Diagram

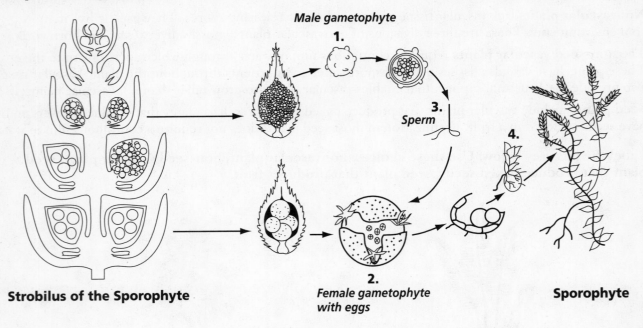

Male gametophyte
1.
3.
*Sperm*
4.
2.
Female gametophyte
with eggs

**Strobilus of the Sporophyte**

**Sporophyte**

### Life Cycle of a Lycophyte

Each statement below goes with one of the stages of the lycophyte life cycle shown in the diagram. Write the number from the diagram on the line in front of the statement it goes with.

_____ Sperm swim to the eggs, and fertilization takes place.

_____ Sperm are produced in the antheridium.

_____ Eggs are produced in the archegonium.

_____ New sporophyte develops from the fertilized egg.

**Answer the questions.**

**1. True or false?** Nonvascular plants do not need water for reproduction.

_____

**2. True or false?** All non-seed vascular plants have a gametophyte stage.

_____

**3. True or false?** Nonvascular plants reproduce by releasing spores.

_____

**4. True or false?** Fertilization in non-seed vascular plants requires a continuous surface film of water through which sperm swim to the egg.

_____

CONTENT MASTERY

**Chapter 22** **The Diversity of Plants,** *continued*

*Section 22.3  Seed Plants*

## Study the Diagram

**A.** *Spruce tree*

**B.** *Maple tree*

**Each statement below goes with one of the pictures. Write the letter of the picture on the line in front of the statement it goes with.**

_____ This tree is a conifer.

_____ This tree is often found where the warm growing season is short, so keeping leaves year-round gives it a head start on growth.

_____ This tree is a deciduous tree.

_____ This tree loses all of its leaves at once.

_____ Although individual leaves drop off as they age or are damaged, this tree never loses all its leaves at once.

**Answer the following questions.**

**1. True or false?** Dicotyledons make up the majority of flowering plants.

_____

**2. True or false?** There are only two living species of Ginkgophytes.

_____

**3. True or false?** Most annuals are herbaceous, which means their stems are green and do not contain woody tissue.

_____

**4. True or false?** Biennials have a life span that lasts half a year.

_____

**5. True or false?** Anthophytes are the only division of plants that produce fruits.

_____

**Chapter 22** **The Diversity of Plants,** *continued*

**Content Mastery**

## Review the Vocabulary

| | |
|---|---|
| archegonium | frond (FRAWND) |
| antheridium | monocotyledon |
| cotyledon (kah tuh LEE dun) | perennial |
| deciduous plant (dih SIH juh wus) | prothallus |
| dicotyledon | rhizome (RI zohm) |
| fruit | sorus (SOR us) |

**Use the Chapter 22 vocabulary words listed above to fill in the blanks in the statements.**

**1.** A fern leaf is called a _____ .

**2.** A(n) _____ has one seed leaf, leaves with parallel veins, and flower parts in multiples of three.

**3.** A plant that lives for several years is called a(n) _____ . It produces flowers and seeds periodically, usually once a year.

**4.** A(n) _____ has two seed leaves, leaves with branched veins, and flower parts in multiples of four or five.

**5.** A(n) _____ loses all its leaves at one time.

**6.** The part of the seed plant embryo that functions to store food is the _____ .

**7.** The thick underground stem in ferns is the _____ .

**8.** A(n) _____ is a male reproductive structure in which sperm are produced.

**9.** The spores released from a strobilus then grow to form a gametophyte, called a(n) _____ .

**10.** A group of sporangia on the back of a fern frond is called a(n) _____ .

**11.** A(n) _____ is the ripened ovary of a flower

**12.** The female reproductive structure in which eggs are produced is called a(n) _____ .

## Chapter 23 Plant Structure and Function

### Get the Big Picture

Read the following summary paragraphs and fill in the blanks using the word lists given for each section.

| | |
|---|---|
| collenchyma | phloem |
| dermal tissue | sclerenchyma |
| ground tissue | vascular tissue |
| parenchyma | xylem |

Most plant tissues are composed of three types of cells. **(1)** _____ cells are thin-walled cells that can carry on photosynthesis and store food. **(2)** _____ cells, with unevenly thickened cell walls, provide structure for growing tissue. **(3)** _____ cells, with their thick walls, provide structural support. **(4)** _____ is the protective covering of a plant. **(5)** _____ transports materials. **(6)** _____ moves water and minerals up the stems. **(7)** _____ transports sugars and organic compounds throughout the plant. **(8)** _____ is found between the dermal tissue and the vascular tissue and often functions in food production and storage.

| | | |
|---|---|---|
| leaves | roots | stems |

**(9)** _____ have chloroplasts and perform photosynthesis.
**(10)** _____ grow downward into the soil as cells elongate. **(11)** _____ support leaves and upright growth and transport water and food from one part of the plant to another.

| | |
|---|---|
| auxins | gibberellins |
| cytokinins | nastic responses |
| ethylene | tropisms |

Three major plant hormones that affect plant growth and development by promoting cell division and cell elongation are **(12)** _____ , **(13)** _____ , and **(14)** _____ . Another hormone called **(15)** _____ speeds up the ripening of fruit. **(16)** _____ are plants' responses to external stimuli that result in a growth response. **(17)** _____ are not dependent on the direction of the stimulus but are often the result of changes in cell pressure.

## Study the Diagrams

Use the diagram of the tree trunk to answer the questions.

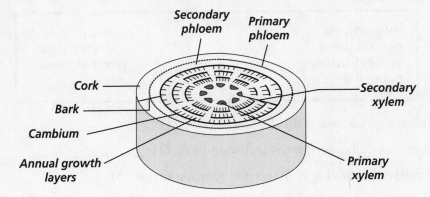

1. What tissue makes up the annual growth rings in a tree? _____

2. Vascular cambium produces new xylem and phloem. The newest growth is closest to the cambium. Which is older, primary phloem or secondary phloem? _____

3. The inner part of bark is made of phloem. The outer layer of bark is made of _____.

Use the diagram of the leaf to answer the questions.

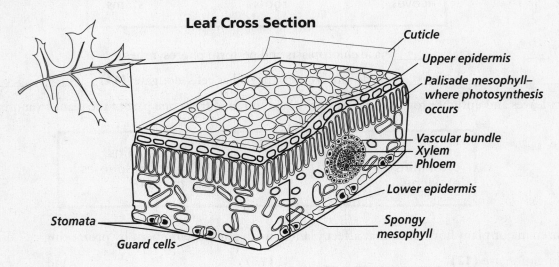

**Leaf Cross Section**

4. **True or false?** Only a stem has xylem and phloem. _____

5. As well as being coated with a waxy cuticle, leaves prevent water loss by controlling the size of the stomata. This is done by surrounding cells called _____.

6. In which leaf cells does most photosynthesis take place? _____

**Chapter 23** **Plant Structure and Function,** continued

**Content Mastery**

*Section 23.2  Roots, Stems, and Leaves*
*Section 23.3  Plant Responses*

## Study the Diagram

Use the diagram of the root to answer the questions.

Mineral ions and water molecules enter root hair cells and travel through the cells of the cortex by osmosis (A). Water may also flow between the cells of the cortex.

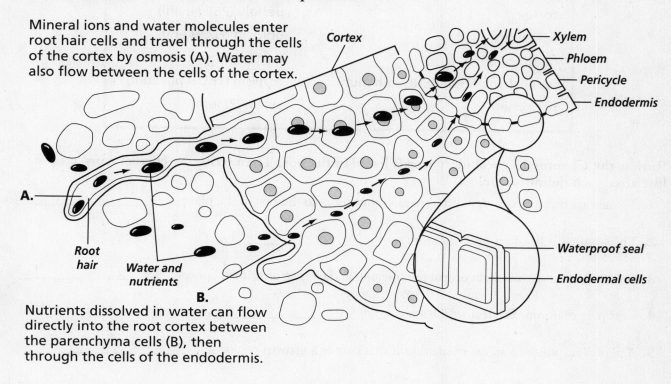

Nutrients dissolved in water can flow directly into the root cortex between the parenchyma cells (B), then through the cells of the endodermis.

**1. True or false?** Water and minerals can be absorbed by root hairs.

_____

**2. True or false?** Water and minerals travel through the cortex to the cells of the phloem.

_____

**3. True or false?** The endodermis forms a seal that controls the flow of water.

_____

**Answer the following questions about plant responses.**

**4. True or false?** Gibberellins cause plants to grow taller.

_____

**5. True or false?** The growth of a plant toward light is called phototropism.

_____

**6. True or false?** The sudden closing of a Venus's flytrap is an example of a nastic movement.

_____

## Review the Vocabulary

| | |
|---|---|
| cortex | petiole (PET ee ohl) |
| epidermis | phloem (FLOH em) |
| guard cells | transpiration |
| parenchyma (puh RENG kuh muh) | tropism (TROH pih zum) |
| pericycle | xylem (ZI lum) |

**Review the Chapter 23 vocabulary words listed in the box. Then write the correct word on the line after each definition below.**

1. Tissue that transports water and minerals from roots to the rest of the plant _____

2. Thin-walled cells often used for storage _____

3. Cells in leaf epidermis that control the opening and closing of stomatal pores _____

4. Leaf part that joins the leaf to the stem _____

5. A plant's response to an external stimuli that causes a growth response _____

6. Outermost layer of cells in plants _____

7. Plant tissue that helps form lateral roots _____

8. Tissue found in plant stems and roots between the epidermis and vascular core _____

9. Evaporation of water from the stomata of leaves _____

10. Tissue that transports sugar from the leaves to all parts of the plant _____

## Chapter 24 Reproduction in Plants

### Get the Big Picture

Use the information from Section 24.1 to fill in the rectangles in the idea map below. Some of the rectangles have been filled in for you.

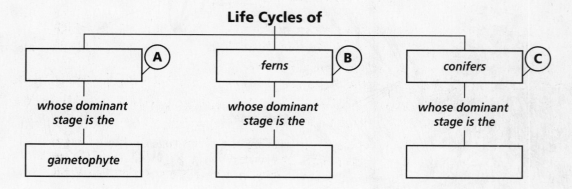

**Life Cycles of**

| A | ferns | B | conifers | C |

whose dominant stage is the

gametophyte

whose dominant stage is the

whose dominant stage is the

Use the information from Section 24.2 to fill in the rectangles in the idea map below. Some of the rectangles have been filled in for you.

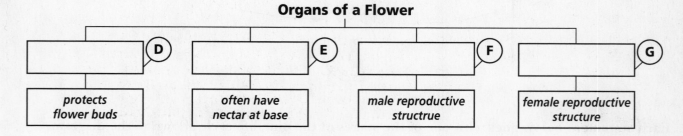

**Organs of a Flower**

| D | E | F | G |

protects flower buds

often have nectar at base

male reproductive structrue

female reproductive structure

**Each statement below goes with one of the words in the rectangles above. Write the letter of the rectangle on the line in front of the statement it goes with. Not all the words in rectangles will be used.**

_____ Protonema develops into a small green filament of cells that develop into either a male or female gametophyte.

_____ Anther is at the top of this structure.

_____ Fronds grow from the underground stem called the rhizome.

_____ The bottom of this structure enlarges to form an ovary.

**Chapter 24** **Reproduction in Plants,** *continued*

*Section 24.1 Life Cycles of Mosses, Ferns, and Conifers*

## Study the Diagram

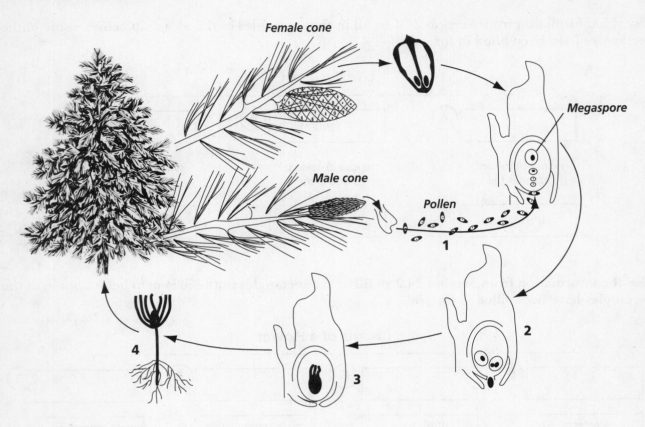

Female cone

Megaspore

Male cone

Pollen

1

2

3

4

**Each statement below goes with one of the stages of the pine life cycle shown in the diagram. Write the number from the diagram on the line in front of the statement it goes with.**

_____ Male gametophytes form a pollen tube that grows into the ovule, and the sperm fertilize the eggs.

_____ Pollen grains—the male gametophytes—are carried by the wind to the female cones.

_____ Inside the seed coat, the food is stored for the developing embryo.

_____ When the seed germinates, a new seedling is formed.

CONTENT MASTERY

**Chapter 24** **Reproduction in Plants,** *continued*

*Section 24.2  Flowers and Flowering*
*Section 24.3  The Life Cycle of a Flowering Plant*

## Study the Diagram

Use the diagram to answer the questions.

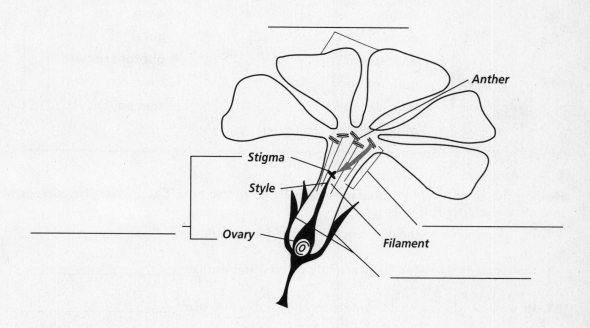

1. Label the diagram with the following parts of a flower.
   Stamen—male part of the flower; pollen is made in the anther
   Pistil—female part of the flower; the ovary will become the fruit
   Petals—often brightly colored to attract insects and birds
   Sepals—protect the flower bud

2. Complete flowers have all four parts, but some flowers are incomplete. Some plants have separate male and female flowers. Draw an incomplete female flower next to the complete flower in the diagram.

3. Some plants produce fruits and seeds that are attractive to animals. How does it help a plant to have an animal eat its fruits?

   _____

   _____

   _____

4. **True or false?** Seeds require water to germinate.

   _____

## Review the Vocabulary

| | |
|---|---|
| anther | ovary |
| dormancy | petal |
| endosperm | photoperiodism |
| germination | short-day plant |
| long-day plant | stamen |
| micropyle (MI kruh pile) | |

**Review the Chapter 24 vocabulary words listed in the box. Then write the correct word on the line after each definition below.**

1. Plant's response to the difference in day and night length _____

2. Flower parts that are usually brightly colored and leaflike _____

3. Process by which a seed begins to develop into a new plant _____

4. Period of seed inactivity _____

5. Tiny opening in the ovule through which sperm enter _____

6. Plant that flowers when exposed to a long night _____

7. Food-storage tissue used by developing anthophyte embryo _____

8. Female reproductive organ formed at lower end of pistil _____

9. Consists of an anther and a filament _____

10. Plant that flowers when the nights are short _____

11. Male reproductive structure that contains pollen grains _____

## BioDigest 7 Plants

### Get the Big Picture

Review all of the headings and photos in the BioDigest. Then look at the following pictures and answer the questions.

**A.** *Fern sporophyte*

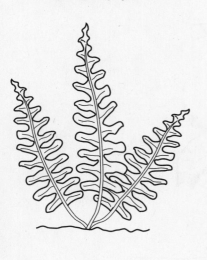

**B.** *Pine tree*

**C.** *Dogwood flowers*

**1.** Which picture shows a non-seed plant?

_____

**2.** Which picture shows a flowering plant?

_____

**3.** Which picture shows a plant adapted for cold?

_____

**4.** Which picture shows a plant that produces fruits?

_____

**5.** Vascular tissues let plants grow tall. Which pictures show plants with vascular tissue?

_____

**6.** Some insects are attracted to plants with brightly colored flowers or fragrances.. Which picture shows a plant that is pollinated by insects?

_____

## Study the Picture

Study the picture of the vascular plant. Then answer the questions.

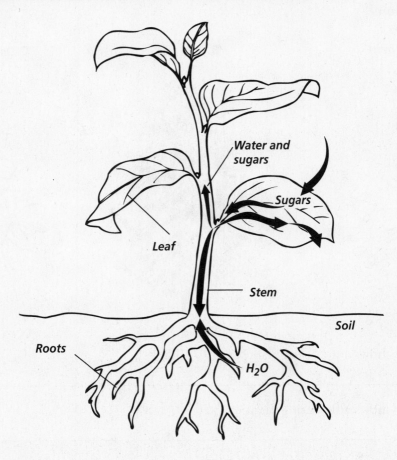

Water and sugars

Sugars

Leaf

Stem

Soil

Roots

$H_2O$

**1.** Where does the plant produce energy in the form of sugars?

_____

**2.** What part of the plant takes in water?

_____

**3.** Vascular tissues move sugars and water throughout the plant and provide some support. Which part of the plant provides support and allows the plant to grow taller?

_____

**BioDigest 7**  **Plants,** continued

## Study the Picture

Study the picture of the flower. Then fill in the blanks in the statements. **The pistil is the female reproductive part of the flower. The stamen is the male reproductive part of the flower.**

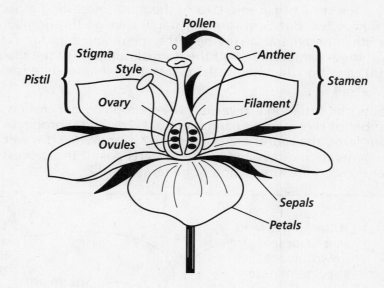

1. Flowering plants attract animal pollinators with nectar, perfumes, or brightly colored

   _____ .

2. Pollen from the _____ rubs off onto the animal as it drinks the nectar.

3. Egg cells develop at the base of the pistil inside the _____ .

4. Pollen sticks to the _____ and forms a pollen tube to reach the egg.

## Matching

**Fruits provide flowering plants with different ways to disperse their seeds. Draw a line to match each fruit in the box with its method of dispersal.**

> **a.** The fruit of a coconut floats.
> **b.** The fruit of a maple is wing-shaped.
> **c.** The fruit of a grape vine is edible.
> **d.** Some fruits, like burrs, have hooks.

5. The seed falls out while the fruit is eaten.
6. The fruit is carried by the wind.
7. The fruit sticks to the fur of animals.
8. The fruit is carried by ocean currents.

## Study the Diagrams

**Read the paragraphs in the box and study the diagrams. Then answer the questions.**

Plants are very interesting organisms. One of the most interesting aspects of plant life is that most of them have two different forms or stages they go through during their lifetime. The gametophyte stage or generation is where the sperm and eggs are formed. The number of chromosomes in these gametes are half the normal number for the plant species. This is called a haploid (**n**) condition. In nonvascular plants, the gametophyte is the larger, more visible form of the plant.

In vascular plants, the situation is reversed. The sporophyte generation is the larger form. It has the full number of chromosomes and is diploid (**2n**). The sporophyte generation produces spores. In ferns, the spores are dispersed by wind. When it is wet and warm enough, the gametophyte generation grows and the cycle starts again. The process of one plant stage following another is called the alternation of generations.

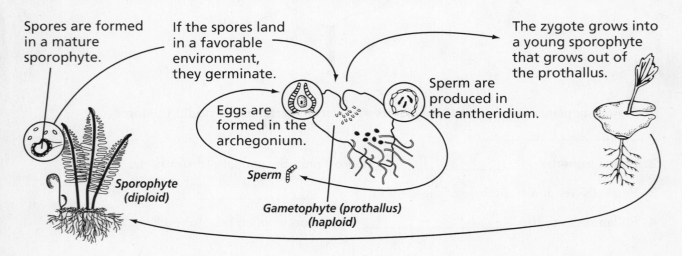

Spores are formed in a mature sporophyte.

If the spores land in a favorable environment, they germinate.

The zygote grows into a young sporophyte that grows out of the prothallus.

Sperm are produced in the antheridium.

Eggs are formed in the archegonium.

**Sporophyte (diploid)**

*Sperm*

*Gametophyte (prothallus) (haploid)*

1. Which form of a plant produces spores? _____

   Which form produces gametes? _____

2. In nonvascular plants, which generation is the largest?

   _____

3. Give two examples of gametes.

   _____

4. Which generation is haploid and which is diploid?

   _____

**Chapter 25**

**Content Mastery**

# What Is an Animal?

## Get the Big Picture

**Read the paragraph in the box. Then study the picture and answer the questions.**

> There are so many kinds of animals that it is nearly impossible to describe just what an animal is. All animals, however, have some things in common. All animals have some kind of shape. Scientists often identify animals by their shape and symmetry—the balance in their body proportions. All animals go through a developmental stage when they go from a single cell to an adult. They also have a life cycle they pass through as they grow. All animals have some way to reproduce. Most animals interact with their environment in some way. And all animals must reproduce if their species is going to survive.

### Some Characteristics of Animals

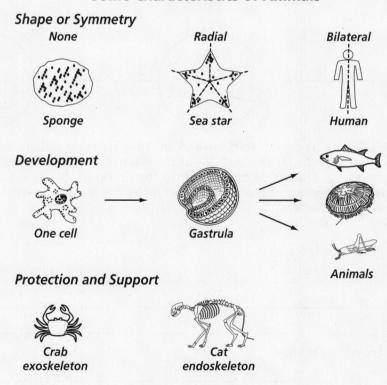

*Shape or Symmetry*

None — Sponge

Radial — Sea star

Bilateral — Human

*Development*

One cell → Gastrula → Animals

*Protection and Support*

Crab exoskeleton

Cat endoskeleton

**1.** What do all adult animals develop from?

_____

**2.** A sea urchin is related to a sea star. What kind of symmetry do you think a sea urchin would have?

_____

**3.** What kind of skeleton do you have? Explain.

_____

**Chapter 25** **What Is an Animal?,** *continued*

**Content Mastery**

*Section 25.1 Typical Animal Characteristics*

## Study the Diagram

Use the diagram to answer the questions.

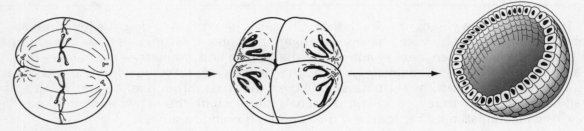

Soon after fertilization, the cell begins to divide. Each new cell divides over and over again until a hollow ball called a blastula is formed.

One side of the blastula begins to fold inward, making an inner pouch. At this point, the embryo is called a gastrula. The outside of the gastrula eventually becomes the animal's outer covering. The inside develops into the lining of the digestive system. In some animals, the opening of the gastrula becomes the mouth. In other animals, the mouth develops elsewhere.

**1.** What is a blastula? How does it form?

_____

_____

_____

**2.** What is a gastrula? How does it form?

_____

_____

_____

**3.** Why is it important to determine whether an animal is a protostome or a deuterostome?

_____

_____

_____

## Study the Diagram

**Read the paragraph in the box. Then study the diagram and answer the questions.**

> One way scientists can identify an animal is by the presence and type of body cavity. Two types of body cavities are a **pseudocoelom** and a **coelom** (SEE lome). Simple animals, such as flatworms, have no body cavity. More complex animals, such as roundworms, have a pseudocoelom, a body cavity filled with fluid that provides support. In more complex animals with a coelom, the internal organs are suspended within the coelom and are completely surrounded by the **mesoderm**.

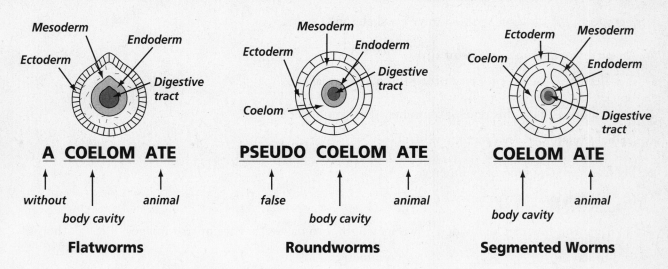

1. What type of animals have no body cavity? Give an example of this type of animal.

   _____

   _____

2. What type of animal is a roundworm? How do you know?

   _____

   _____

3. Why is an earthworm a coelomate?

   _____

   _____

4. What does the coelom do?

   _____

   _____

## Review the Vocabulary

**Circle the Chapter 25 vocabulary word in brackets that best matches each description.**

1. A sponge is an example of a(n) _____ organism.

   [sessile (SES sile) / dorsal / ventral / anterior]

2. hollow ball made up of a single layer of cells

   [gastrula (GAS truh luh) / deuterostome (DEW tuh roh stohm) / blastula / coelom]

3. layer of cells on the outer surface of the gastrula

   [ectoderm / endoderm / mesoderm / exoskeleton]

4. An earthworm is an example of a(n) _____ .

   [acoelomate / pseudocoelom / protostome / gastrula]

5. Most sponges have this type of symmetry (SIH muh tree).

   [radial / bilateral / asymmetry / ventral]

6. Hydras have this type of symmetry.

   [radial / bilateral / asymmetry / dorsal]

7. An organism that can be divided down its length into halves that are mirror images of each other is

   said to have _____ symmetry.

   [radial / bilateral / ventral/ dorsal]

8. head end of a flatworm

   [posterior / dorsal / ventral / anterior]

9. an animal that has three cell layers with a digestive tract but no body cavity

   [pseudocoelomate / coelomate / acoelomate (uh SEE luh mayt) / protostome]

10. Humans, insects, and fishes have this type of body cavity.

    [coelom (SEE lum) / pseudocoelom (sew duh SEE lum) / acoelom / gastrula]

11. An internal skeleton is called a(n) _____ .

    [exoskeleton / endoskeleton / blastula / protostome (PROH tuh stohm)]

Copyright © Glencoe/McGraw-Hill, a division of The McGraw-Hill Companies, Inc.

**Content Mastery**

# Chapter 26 Sponges, Cnidarians, Flatworms, and Roundworms

## Get the Big Picture

**Read the paragraphs in the boxes. Then answer the questions.**

> Organisms similar to the sponges, cnidarians, flatworms, and roundworms of today were Earth's earliest animals. Scientists sometimes study these animals to find out how animal bodies have evolved. Sponges have a simple body. They have an irregular shape with only one body opening. Most sponges live in the ocean. The body of a cnidarian also has only one opening. However, their body is shaped like the wheel of a bicycle. The body of the cnidarian is the hub, or center, of the wheel. Their body parts extend outward from the hub like spokes. Most cnidarians also live in the oceans.

> Flatworms have a thin body with only one opening. If you drew a line lengthwise down the center of a flatworm's body, the left half would be the mirror image of the right half. Some flatworms live in the water. Others are parasitic and live in other animals. Roundworms have a round body with a mirror-image form similar to the flatworm. Unlike flatworms, roundworms have two body openings. Most roundworms live in soil or water. Some are parasites.

**1.** Where can sponges, cnidarians, flatworms, and roundworms all be found?

_____

_____

**2.** To what can you compare the body of a cnidarian?

_____

_____

**3.** Which three types of animals have only one body opening?

_____

_____

**4.** How is the body of a sponge different from the body of a roundworm?

_____

_____

_____

**Chapter 26** Sponges, Cnidarians, Flatworms, and Roundworms, *continued*

## Interpret the Diagrams

Study the diagrams and read the paragraphs. Then complete the table. Part of the table has been completed to help get you started.

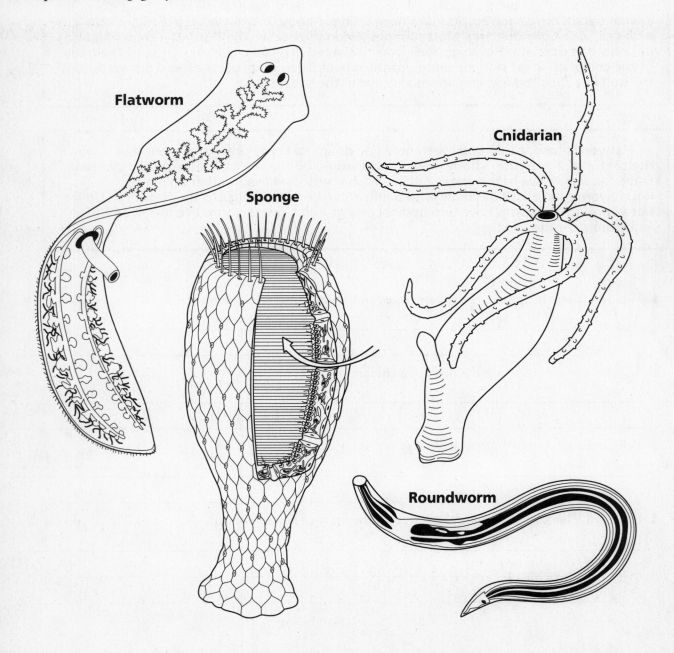

Flatworm

Sponge

Cnidarian

Roundworm

**Sponges, Cnidarians, Flatworms, and Roundworms,** *continued*

> The animals shown are all simple animals with distinct traits. The **sponge** is the simplest. Sponges have only one body opening. Sponges belong to a group of animals that evolved entirely in the water. They live alone or in colonies.

> The **cnidarian** is a soft-bodied animal that lives in water. Cnidarians evolved a wide variety of body shapes. They have one body opening in which they digest their food. Most species of cnidarians use stinging cells to capture their prey. Jellyfishes and hydras are cnidarians.

> The **flatworm** has a more complex body than the sponge or the cnidarian, but it still has only one body opening. The two eye spots on a flatworm's head are made up of cells that can tell the difference between light and dark. Some flatworms, such as planarians, are scavengers. Others, such as tapeworms, are parasites. Some flatworms spend their entire lives under rocks in the water, whereas others live on land.

> The fourth animal is a **roundworm**. Roundworms have two body openings—one for eating and one for excretion. They often live as parasites in plants, humans, and other animals. Roundworms can live on land or in water.

| Name of Animal | Example | One or Two Openings in Body? | Do They Live on Land or in Water? | Are Any Species Parasites? |
|---|---|---|---|---|
| Sponge | | one | | |
| Cnidarian | hydra | | | |
| Flatworm | | | land and water | |
| Roundworm | *Ascaris* | | | yes |

## Review the Vocabulary

**a.** external fertilization

**b.** filter feeding

**c.** gastrovascular cavity (gas troh VAS kyuh lur)

**d.** hermaphrodite (hur MAF ruh dite)

**e.** internal fertilization

**f.** medusa

**g.** nematocyst (nuh MAT uh sihst)

**h.** nerve net

**i.** pharynx (FAYR ingks)

**j.** polyp (PAH lup)

**k.** proglottid (proh GLAH tud)

**l.** scolex (SKOH leks)

**Write the letters of the Chapter 26 vocabulary words on the lines after the definitions. One word has been matched with its definition to help you get started.**

**1.** Reproduction in which the eggs are fertilized inside the animal's body _____e_____

**2.** Reproduction in which the eggs are fertilized outside the animal's body _____

**3.** Conducts nerve impulses in cnidarians _____

**4.** Individual, repeating sections of a tapeworm _____

**5.** The way in which sponges get their food _____

**6.** Tubelike organ used by planarians to suck food into the digestive system _____

**7.** Structure used by cnidarians to capture or poison their prey _____

**8.** Individual that can produce both eggs and sperm _____

**9.** Stage of cnidarian life cycle in which its body is shaped like a tube _____

**10.** Cavity in which cnidarian digestion takes place _____

**11.** Head of a tapeworm _____

**12.** Stage of cnidarian life cycle in which its body is shaped like an umbrella _____

## Chapter 27 Mollusks and Segmented Worms

### Get the Big Picture

Read the paragraphs in the boxes and study the pictures. Then answer the questions.

> Did you know that the simple garden snail is a close relative of the squid? Both these animals are **mollusks**, one of the largest groups of animals on Earth. Some mollusks, like the clam and the beautiful sea snails named gastropods, have shells. Most mollusk shells are secreted by the mantle. The mantle cavity may have gills for gas exchange. Mollusks usually have a large hump that holds the intestines. Their mouthparts look like a tongue and are called a **radula**. All mollusks have a free-swimming larval stage. Most adult mollusks have a foot that can be used in a variety of ways, including movement. Most mollusks live in the ocean or in other wet environments. Mollusks will die if they dry out.

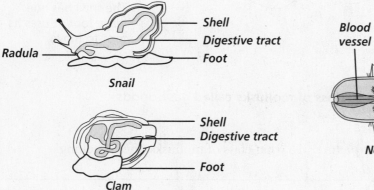

Snail

Clam

**Two Members of the Mollusk Group**

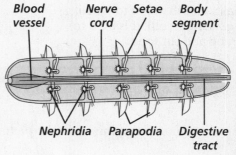

**A Generalized Annelid Worm**

> **Annelid** worms are found in the ocean and on land. The term **annelida** means "ringed," and the bodies of these animals have repeating body segments. Some worms have footlike projections on their segments, called **parapodia**, for movement. Others, like the earthworm, have very small hairs called **setae**. Most marine annelids are filter feeders. These annelids live in tubes in the mud and extend feathery arms into the water to capture floating organic food. Annelids need to live in moist environments because they will die if they dry out.

**1.** How are mollusks and annelids similar?

_____

_____

**2.** How are mollusks and annelids different?

_____

_____

**Chapter 27** **Mollusks and Segmented Worms,** *continued*

## Study the Figure

Use the figure to answer the questions.

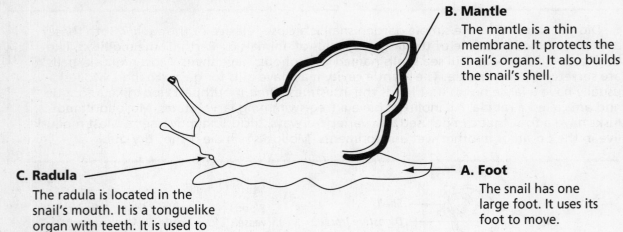

**B. Mantle**
The mantle is a thin membrane. It protects the snail's organs. It also builds the snail's shell.

**C. Radula**
The radula is located in the snail's mouth. It is a tonguelike organ with teeth. It is used to scrape and cut food.

**A. Foot**
The snail has one large foot. It uses its foot to move.

**The snail belongs to the class of mollusks called gastropods.**

**1.** What is the name of the animal in the picture? To what class of mollusks does it belong?

_____

_____

_____

**2.** What is the name of the structure labeled *A*?

_____

_____

**3.** What is the name of the structure labeled *B*? What is its function?

_____

_____

_____

**4.** What is the name of the structure labeled *C*? For what does the snail use it?

_____

_____

_____

**Chapter 27**   **Mollusks and Segmented Worms,** *continued*

**Content Mastery**

*Section 27.2 Segmented Worms*

## Study the Figure

Use the figure to answer the questions.

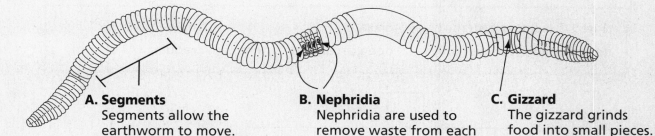

**A. Segments**
Segments allow the earthworm to move. A group of segments may perform a certain task.

**B. Nephridia**
Nephridia are used to remove waste from each segment.

**C. Gizzard**
The gizzard grinds food into small pieces.

**The earthworm belongs to the phylum Annelida.**

**1.** What is the name of the animal in the figure? To what phylum does it belong?

_____

_____

_____

**2.** What is the name of the structures labeled *A*? Why are these structures important?

_____

_____

_____

**3.** What is the name of the structures labeled *B*? What do these structures do?

_____

_____

_____

**4.** What is the name of the structure labeled *C*? For what is this structure used?

_____

_____

_____

**Content Mastery**

## Chapter 27 Mollusks and Segmented Worms, continued

## Review the Vocabulary

Use the Chapter 27 vocabulary words to fill in the puzzle.

| closed circulatory system | gizzard | mantle |
| nephridia (ne FRIH dee uh) | open circulatory system | radula (RAJ uh luh) |

**ACROSS**

**2.** Blood moves into open spaces around an animal's organs. This is called an

open _____ system.

**5.** thin membrane that protects a mollusk's organs

**6.** structures that remove waste from an animal's body

**DOWN**

**1.** tonguelike organ used to scrape or cut food

**3.** annelid organ that grinds food

**4.** The blood in an animal's body stays in the blood vessels. This is called

a(n) _____ circulatory system.

## Chapter 28 Arthropods

### Get the Big Picture

**Read the paragraphs in the boxes and study the picture. Then answer the questions.**

> The arthropods are the largest group of animals in the world. This group includes crabs, spiders, insects, and many extinct fossil forms. Arthropods have many different body shapes and sizes, but they all have:
> 1. paired, jointed legs or appendages
> 2. a hard, armored exoskeleton that protects them and prevents water loss
> 3. segmented bodies
> 4. an open circulatory system with a dorsal heart

> In order to grow, arthropods shed their exoskeletons in a process called **molting**. Arthropods live both in water and on land. Although some arthropods are considered pests, many of them, including shrimp and crabs, can be eaten by humans. Many arthropods eat other arthropods and help keep Earth from being overrun by these successful animals.

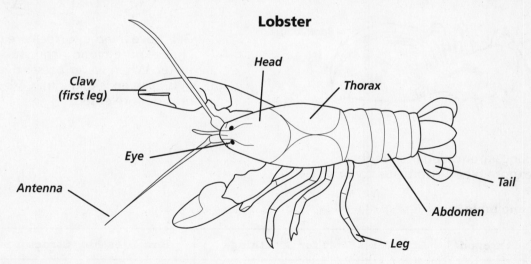

**Lobster**

Claw (first leg)  Head  Thorax  Eye  Antenna  Tail  Abdomen  Leg

**1.** Name one characteristic of arthropods.

_____

_____

**2.** How do arthropods grow?

_____

**3. True or false?** Arthropods are all herbivores (eat only plants).

_____

## Identify the Arthropods

Write the names of the arthropods shown in the figure.

**A.** _____

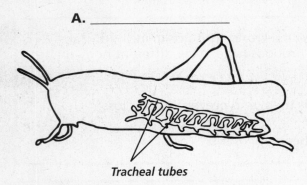

*Tracheal tubes*

Tracheal tubes are inside the body. They carry air close to each cell.

**B.** _____

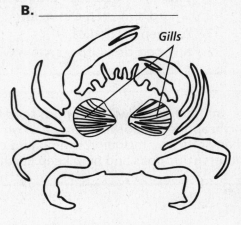

*Gills*

Gills have a large surface area. They expose blood-rich tissue to water. When water passes over the gills, oxygen is taken in. Carbon dioxide is released.

**C.** _____

*Heart*

*Book lung*

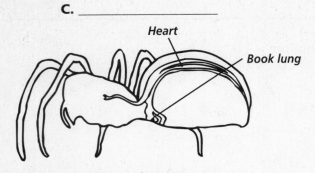

Book lungs are folded membranes. They expose blood-rich tissue to air.

Complete the table.

| Name of Arthropod | Structures Used for Breathing | How Breathing Structures Work |
|---|---|---|
| Grasshopper | | |
| Crab | | |
| Spider | | |

## Chapter 28 Arthropods, continued

*Section 28.2 Diversity of Arthropods*

## Sequence the Diagram

The diagram below shows the four stages of metamorphosis of a butterfly. Number the stages to put them in order.

_____ **Egg stage.** Insects begin life as a fertilized egg.

_____ **Adult stage.** Out comes an adult. The adult can now reproduce.

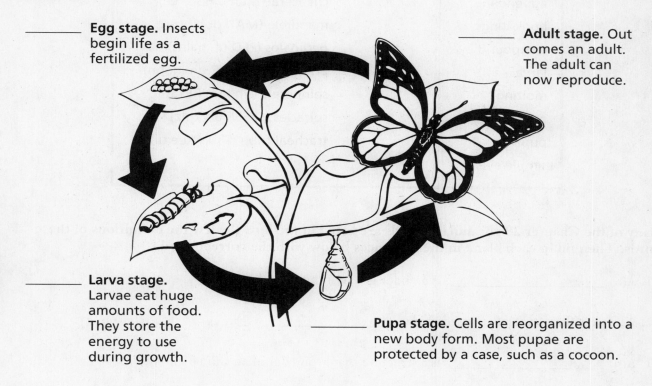

_____ **Larva stage.** Larvae eat huge amounts of food. They store the energy to use during growth.

_____ **Pupa stage.** Cells are reorganized into a new body form. Most pupae are protected by a case, such as a cocoon.

Complete the table. Part of the table has been filled in for you.

| Stage of Complete Metamorphosis | Description of Each Stage |
|---|---|
|  |  |
| Larva |  |
|  |  |
|  | Out comes an adult. The adult can reproduce. |

## Review the Vocabulary

| | |
|---|---|
| appendage | chelicerae (kuh LIH sur ee) |
| book lungs | mandible (MAN duh bul) |
| compound eyes | pedipalps (PED uh palps) |
| larva | pheromone (FAYR uh mohn) |
| molting | spinnerets (sih nuh RETS) |
| nymph (NIHMF) | spiracles (SPEER uh kulz) |
| pupa | tracheal tube (TRAY kee ul) |
| simple eye | |

**Many of the Chapter 28 vocabulary words are listed in the box. Review the definitions of these words. Then fill in each blank in the sentences below with the correct word.**

**1.** A(n) _____ is an odor given off by animals.

**2.** The wormlike stage of an insect is the _____ .

**3.** A(n) _____ is a structure that grows out of an animal's body.

**4.** Arachnids use _____ for holding food and for sensing.

**5.** The biting appendages of arachnids are called _____ .

**6.** Spiders use _____ to spin silk into thread.

**7.** Spiders and their relatives use _____ to breathe.

**8.** A(n) _____ hatches from an egg during incomplete metamorphosis.

**9.** Many arthropods see with a pair of large _____ .

**10.** The mouthpart an arthropod uses to hold, chew, suck, or bite food is called

a(n) _____ .

## Chapter 29 Echinoderms and Invertebrate Chordates

**Content Mastery**

### Get the Big Picture

**Read the paragraphs in the boxes. Then answer the question that follow.**

> Echinoderms have characteristics that make them different from other animals. Echinoderms move by hundreds of tiny suction cups on their tube feet. They have hard, spiny skeletons that are covered by a thin layer of skin. They also have a water vascular system. This system controls how they move, eat, respire, and get rid of waste. You can find echinoderms in all the oceans of the world.

> Invertebrate chordates are ocean animals that do not have a hard skeleton. These chordates share some characteristics with echinoderms and animals with backbones. For example, echinoderm embryos look similar to embryos of invertebrate chordates. An ancient invertebrate chordate may have been the ancestor of all animals with backbones.

**1.** How are echinoderms and invertebrate chordates similar?

_____

_____

_____

_____

_____

**2.** How are echinoderms and invertebrate chordates different?

_____

_____

_____

_____

_____

## Chapter 29 — Echinoderms and Invertebrates Chordates, *continued*

**Content Mastery**

*Section 29.1 Echinoderms*

## Study the Diagram

**Read the paragraph in the box. Then use the diagram to answer the question that follows.**

> ### How Do Sea Stars Move?
>
> All sea stars have hundreds of tube feet. Each tube foot has a suction cup on the end. Sea stars use their tube feet to creep along the ocean floor. Sea stars also use their tube feet to pry open the shells of mollusks to get food. The tube feet are part of a sea star's water vascular system. One of the main uses of this system is to create water pressure to move the tube feet.

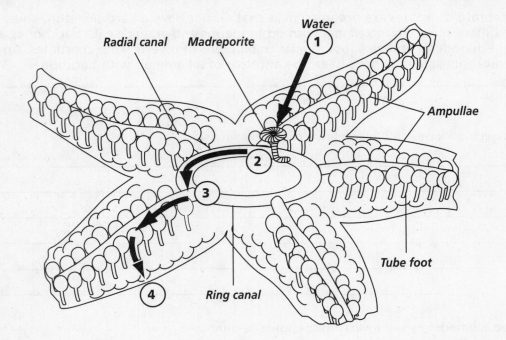

1. Write numbers to order the steps of water flow from the madreporite to the sea star's tube feet.

   _____ Ampullae contract to squeeze water into the tube feet.

   _____ Water enters the madreporite.

   _____ Water flows from the ring canal into the radial canals.

   _____ Water flows from madreporite to the ring canal.

## Study the Diagrams

Read what is in the boxes and study the diagrams below them. Then answer the questions that follow.

> All **chordates** share certain characteristics at some time during their development. They have a dorsal hollow nerve cord, a notochord, gill slits, a tail that extends beyond the anus, and muscles that are found in blocks along the body.

**Typical Chordate Characteristics**

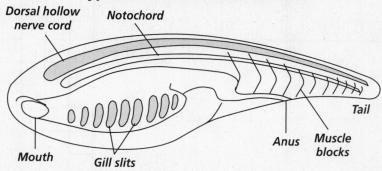

> Sea squirts, or **tunicates**, are considered to be chordates because their larvae have traits that are found in other chordates. The figure below shows the change of a larval tunicate into an adult. The larva is free-swimming, but the adult remains attached to rocks in the sea.

**Tunicate Metamorphosis**

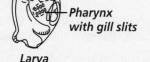
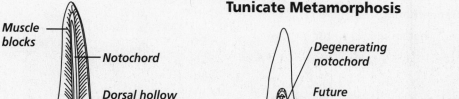
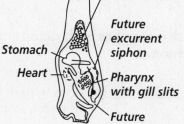
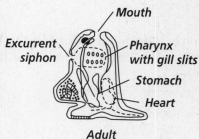

**1.** What are five characteristics common to all chordates? _____

_____

**2.** What tunicate body traits shown in the diagrams indicate that tunicates are chordates?

_____

## Chapter 29 — Echinoderms and Invertebrates Chordates, continued

## Review the Vocabulary

Use the Chapter 29 vocabulary words in the box to fill in the puzzle.

> ampulla (am POOL uh)
> madreporite (MAD ruh por ite)
> notochord (NOH tuh kord)
> pedicellaria (ped uh suh LAYR ee uh)
> ray

**Across**

**3.** disk-shaped opening in an echinoderm's body that lets water in and out

**4.** long, tapering arm of an echinoderm

**5.** round, muscular structure that squeezes water into or out of tube feet

**Down**

**1.** long, rodlike structure in all chordates

**2.** pincerlike appendage on an echinoderm

Find the vocabulary word in the box that matches each definition. Then write the letter of the word on the line in front of the definition.

> **a.** dorsal hollow nerve cord
> **b.** gill slits
> **c.** tube feet
> **d.** water vascular system

_____ **6.** System in echinoderms that helps them move, respire, eat, and get rid of waste

_____ **7.** Hollow, thin-walled tubes with a suction cup on the end

_____ **8.** Tube of cells surrounding a fluid-filled canal above the notochord

_____ **9.** Paired openings located behind the mouth

**BioDigest**
**8**   **Invertebrates**

**Content Mastery**

## Get the Big Picture

**Read the paragraph in the box. Then answer the questions that follow.**

How are sponges and grasshoppers alike? Both animals are **invertebrates**—animals without backbones. The ancestors of modern invertebrates had simple body plans. They lived in water and got food, oxygen, and other materials from their surroundings. Some modern invertebrates, such as sponges, have simple body plans like their ancestors. Sponges do not have tissues, organs, or organ systems. They live in the ocean and stay in one place. Other modern invertebrates are adapted to live in different environments. Arthropods such as spiders and grasshoppers developed tissues, organs, organ systems, and legs. These invertebrates live on land and can move from one habitat to another.

**1.** What is the main difference between invertebrates and other animals?

_____

_____

_____

_____

**2.** Describe the ancestors of modern invertebrates.

_____

_____

_____

_____

**3.** Name a modern invertebrate that is very different from its ancestors. Describe the difference.

_____

_____

_____

_____

**4.** Name a modern invertebrate that has a simple body plan like its ancestors. What makes this body plan simple?

_____

_____

_____

_____

## Study the Table

Study the table. Then answer the questions that follow.

| Animal | Parts of the Nervous System |
|--------|------------------------------|
| Sponges | • none |
| Cnidarians | • no brain or control center<br>• simple nervous system<br>• Nerve net carries impulses to and from all parts of the body.<br>• Impulses from the nerve net cause muscles to contract. |
| Flatworms | • ganglion—brainlike structure that receives messages along nerve cords from eyespots and sensory pits<br>• two nerve cords that run the length of the body |
| Arthropods | • brain<br>• at least one ganglion per body segment<br>• double nerve cord that runs along the ventral side of the animal |

**1.** Which animals have the most complex nervous system?

_____

**2.** Which animals have the least complex nervous system?.

_____

**3.** Summarize the nervous system of each type of animal.

Cnidarians: _____

_____

Flatworms: _____

_____

Arthropods: _____

_____

**BioDigest 8** **Invertebrates,** *continued*

**Content Mastery**

**Study the table. Then answer the questions.**

| Animal | Parts of the Digestive System |
|---|---|
| Sponges | • no mouth; opening at the top through which water leaves the body <br> • pores through which water and food enter the body <br> • no special cavity or space for digestion |
| Cnidarians | • single body opening through which food enters and wastes leave <br> • gastrovascular cavity—space inside the body where enzymes break down food |
| Flatworms | • single body opening through which food enters and wastes leave <br> • pharynx—muscular tube that begins digesting food outside the body <br> • gastrovascular cavity |
| Arthropods | • mouth—opening through which food enters the body <br> • stomach—organ where enzymes break down food <br> • intestine—tube that absorbs water from food and moves waste toward the anus <br> • anus—opening through which waste leaves the body |

**4.** Which animals have the most complex digestive system?

_____

**5.** Which animals have the least complex digestive system?

_____

**6.** How are the cnidarian digestive system and the arthropod digestive system similar?

_____

_____

**7.** How are the cnidarian digestive system and the arthropod digestive system different?

_____

_____

**Content Mastery**

## Complete the Sentences

Read the paragraphs in the box. Then use the words in bold type in the paragraphs to complete the sentences that follow.

---

**Invertebrates** are animals without a backbone. How do invertebrates keep their shape without a skeleton?

Many invertebrates, including **cnidarians** such as jellyfishes, live in the ocean. Jellyfishes use properties of the water, such as water pressure and density, to keep their shapes.

**Mollusks** (including, snails, slugs, clams, octopuses, and squids) can have a hard, external shell or a very muscular, flexible body.

**Echinoderms**—such as sea stars—have a hard, bumpy endoskeleton. *Endo-* means "inside," so an *endoskeleton* is a skeleton inside the body. Unlike the skeleton of a vertebrate, the echinoderm skeleton is not very flexible and cannot support much weight.

There are several kinds of worms. All are invertebrates. The earthworms you dig up in the garden are **segmented worms**. Segmented worms are the most complex kind of worm. Each segment has its own muscles. The muscular segments allow the worm to keep its shape on land.

Other worms, such as **roundworms** and **flatworms**, are usually very small compared to segmented worms. Because they are small, roundworms and flatworms do not need special adaptations to maintain their shape.

**Arthropods**, including insects, spiders, and crabs, are some of the most successful and varied animals on Earth. Arthropods have an armored shell, called an **exoskeleton**. *Exo-* means "outside," so an *exoskeleton* is a skeleton on the outside of the body. An arthropod's exoskeleton is a lot like a knight's suit of armor, with joints that can bend and allow movement.

---

1. Octopuses and squids are _____ ks .

2. _____ worms and _____ t are often very small.

3. Sea stars have an endoskeleton. They are a kind of _____ derm .

4. _____ teb are animals without a backbone.

5. A s_____ worm is made up of many units, each of which has its own muscles.

6. Jellyfishes are _____ da .

7. Insects are a_____ . They keep their shape by having an armored shell, called an _____ skeleton .

CONTENT MASTERY

# Chapter 30 Fishes and Amphibians

## Get the Big Picture

**Study the diagrams. Then answer the questions that follow.**

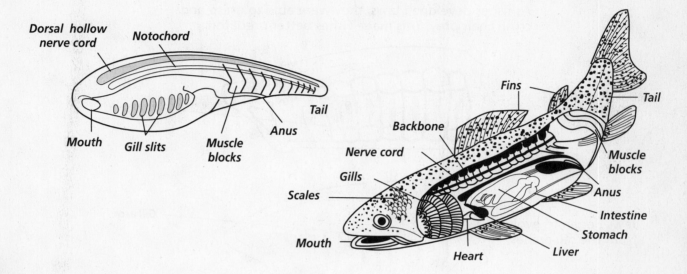

**1.** What structures do fishes share with invertebrate chordates?

_____

_____

**2.** What structures do fishes have that invertebrate chordates don't have?

_____

_____

**Read the paragraph in the box. Then answer the question that follows.**

> **Tadpoles** are young amphibians. They share many characteristics with fishes. Like fishes, tadpoles have a two-chambered heart, gill slits, and fins. As tadpoles grow, they develop features they need to live on land. These features include legs, lungs, a three-chambered heart, and moist skin.

**3.** Name four characteristics that adapt amphibians for living on land.

_____

_____

## Study the Diagram

**Study the diagram. Then answer the questions that follow.**

As fishes developed jaws, they were able to grasp and crush their prey. This made fishes better predators.

Jawless, filter-feeding fish.

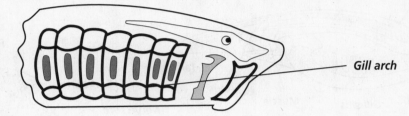

Gill arch

Jaws began to evolve from the gill arches.

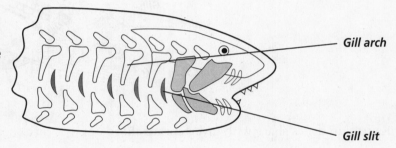

Gill arch

Gill slit

Fish with jaws. Teeth evolved from skin.

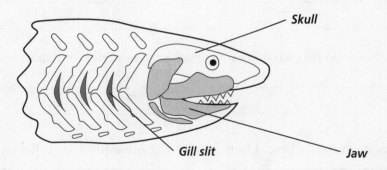

Skull

Gill slit

Jaw

**1.** From what structure did the jaws of fishes evolve?

_____

_____

**2.** How did the evolution of jaws help fishes survive?

_____

_____

**Chapter 30** **Fishes and Amphibians,** continued

*Section 30.2 Amphibians*

## Study the Idea Maps

Use the idea maps to answer the questions.

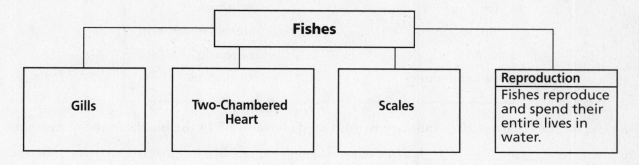

| Fishes | | | |
|---|---|---|---|
| **Gills** | **Two-Chambered Heart** | **Scales** | **Reproduction** Fishes reproduce and spend their entire lives in water. |

| Amphibians | | | | |
|---|---|---|---|---|
| **Gills** Young amphibians have them. Most adults develop lungs. | **Two-Chambered Heart** Young amphibians have this. Adult amphibians have a three-chambered heart. | **Moist, Smooth Skin** Adult amphibians rely on their skin for respiration more than their lungs. | **Life Stages** Most young amphibians live in water. Adults live in water and on land. Most adults lay their eggs in water. | **Legs** Most adult amphibians use legs to move on land. |

**1.** Name two characteristics that young amphibians share with fishes.

_____

_____

_____

_____

**2.** Name four characteristics that adult amphibians have that fishes don't have.

_____

_____

_____

_____

## Review the Vocabulary

| | |
|---|---|
| cartilage | ectotherm |
| fin | lateral line system |
| scale | spawning |
| swim bladder | vocal cords |

**Use three of the Chapter 30 vocabulary words listed above to fill in the blanks in the statements.**

**1.** The _____ is a line of canals along the side of a fish that help it detect movements and find its way in the dark.

**2.** A(n) _____ is a gas-filled sac in bony fishes that helps them control their depth.

**3.** _____ are bands of tissue in the throats of frogs and mammals. These bands enable animals to make sounds.

**Use the rest of the vocabulary words to fill in the puzzle.**

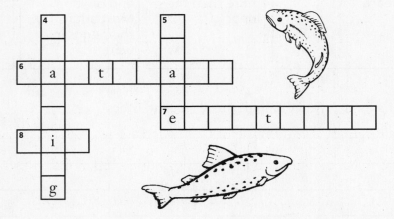

**Across**

**6.** tough, flexible material that forms the skeleton in some fishes

**7.** animal whose body temperature is controlled by the environment

**8.** fan-shaped membrane used by fishes for balance

**Down**

**4.** kind of breeding in fish and some other animals

**5.** one of many thin, bony plates that cover the skin of a fish

## Chapter 31 Reptiles and Birds

### Get the Big Picture

**Read the paragraph in the box. Then answer the questions that follow.**

> Unlike amphibians, most reptiles spend their entire life on land. Instead of smooth, moist skin, reptiles have a thick skin covered with scales. The thick skin protects them and helps them adjust to life on land. Like amphibians, most reptiles have a three-chambered heart. Large reptiles such as crocodiles need a greater oxygen supply than smaller reptiles and have a four-chambered heart. The legs of reptiles are set farther under their bodies than are the legs of amphibians. This difference in leg position helps reptiles move on land. Reptiles reproduce by laying eggs with shells on land.

**1.** Circle the letter of the sentence that states the main idea of the paragraph.

   **a.** Reptiles have scales, three-chambered hearts, and legs.

   **b.** Reptiles reproduce by laying eggs on land.

   **c.** Reptiles have a variety of structures that adapt them to life on land.

   **d.** Reptiles have thick skin that adapts them to climate changes.

**2.** Large reptiles need more oxygen than small reptiles. How are the hearts of large reptiles different from the hearts of small reptiles?

_____

_____

**Read the paragraph in the box. Then answer the questions.**

> Birds and reptiles share some characteristics. Many birds have claws and scaly feet. Like reptiles, birds reproduce by laying eggs. Unlike reptiles, birds evolved feathers and wings that adapted them for flight. Because they can fly, birds can find food in many different places. Life in the air also helps birds avoid land predators.

**3.** What is the main difference between birds and reptiles?

_____

_____

**4.** Name one way that flying helps birds survive.

_____

_____

## Study the Idea Map

Use the idea map to answer the questions that follow.

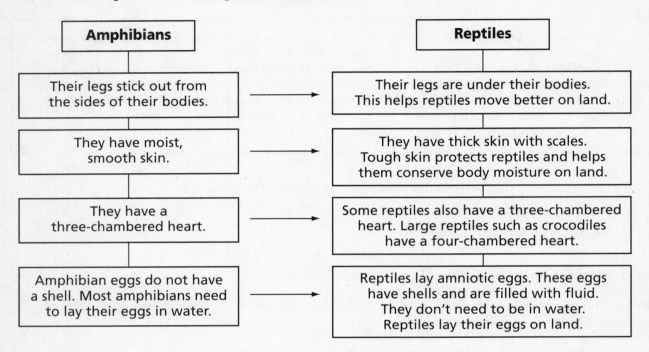

**1.** Choose two reptile adaptations. How did these adaptations help reptiles to live on land?

_____

_____

_____

_____

_____

**2.** Why are amniotic eggs important to reptiles?

_____

_____

_____

_____

_____

**Chapter 31** **Reptiles and Birds,** *continued*

*Section 31.2 Birds*

## Study the Idea Map

Use the idea map to answer the questions.

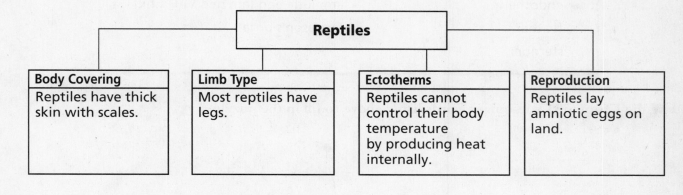

**Reptiles**

**Body Covering**
Reptiles have thick skin with scales.

**Limb Type**
Most reptiles have legs.

**Ectotherms**
Reptiles cannot control their body temperature by producing heat internally.

**Reproduction**
Reptiles lay amniotic eggs on land.

**Birds**

**Body Covering**
Birds have feathers and scaly skin on their legs and feet.

**Limb Type**
Birds have legs and wings. Wings help birds find food. Wings also help birds escape land predators.

**Endotherms**
Birds can control their body temperature by producing heat internally. They can live in different climates.

**Reproduction**
Birds lay amniotic eggs on land.

**1.** What characteristics do birds share with reptiles?

_____

_____

_____

_____

**2.** Birds are endotherms. How does this help them survive?

_____

_____

_____

_____

**Chapter**
**31** **Reptiles and Birds,** *continued*

**Content Mastery**

## Review the Vocabulary

| |
|---|
| endotherm          amniotic egg (am nee YAH tihk) |
| feather             Jacobson's organ |
| sternum |

**Use the Chapter 31 vocabulary words listed above to fill in the puzzle.**

## Across

**3.** Reptiles use their _____ organ to detect chemicals in the air.

**5.** animal that maintains a constant body temperature even if the temperature of its environment changes

## Down

**1.** kind of egg that has a shell and fluid to protect the embryo

**2.** lightweight, modified scale that provides insulation for birds and allows them to fly

**4.** breastbone

**Chapter 32 Mammals**

## Get the Big Picture

**Read the paragraphs in the boxes. Then answer the questions that follow.**

> What do a polar bear and a dolphin have in common? They are both mammals. Mammals, like birds, are **endotherms**. This means that they can maintain a constant body temperature. For example, when dolphins swim in cold water, their bodies stay warm. Most mammals also have hair or fur to help keep them warm and to protect them. The white fur of polar bears keeps them warm in very cold climates. It also helps them blend in with their snowy surroundings. In this way, they are not easily seen by their prey.

**1.** Name two characteristics of mammals that help keep them warm.

_____

_____

> Mammals have a sheet of muscle under their chest cavity. This muscle sheet is called a **diaphragm**. When the diaphragm contracts, the chest cavity expands. When the diaphragm relaxes, the cavity gets smaller. The diaphragm helps mammals take in the large amount of oxygen they need to support their active lifestyles.

**2.** What does the diaphragm help mammals do?

_____

_____

> Mammals help their young survive by feeding them milk from their **mammary glands**. Mammals also teach their young survival skills.

**3.** How do mammals help their young survive?

**4.** Review the paragraphs in the three boxes above. Then list three characteristics of mammals.

_____

_____

_____

_____

## Study the Diagrams

Read the paragraph in the box and study the diagrams. Then answer the questions that follow.

> Mammals have distinct types of teeth. Mammal teeth are adapted to eating various foods. Scientists can tell what type of food a mammal eats by looking at its teeth.

Animals use incisors to grasp and hold prey. Chisel-like incisors help beavers gnaw wood.

Meat-eaters such as tigers use sharp canine teeth to stab and hold their prey. Their jagged premolars and molars are adapted for grinding bones and chewing meat.

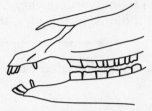

These teeth are made for crushing and grinding. Many animals with large premolars and molars eat only plants. Animals with large rounded molars include elephants.

**1.** Circle the letter of the word that best completes the following sentence.
Animals with large, rounded molars are likely to eat _____ .
 **a.** wood
 **b.** meat
 **c.** plants

**2.** Circle the letter of the kind of teeth you would expect a meat-eating wolf to have.
 **a.** large, rounded molars
 **b.** sharp canine teeth and jagged premolars and molars

Explain your choice.

_____

_____

_____

**3.** What can scientists learn about extinct mammals by studying fossils of their teeth?

_____

_____

_____

## Chapter 32 Mammals, *continued*

## Study the Idea Maps

Use the idea maps to answer the questions.

| **Monotremes** | **Marsupials** | **Placental Mammals** |
|---|---|---|
| • lay eggs<br>• Only three species exist today. | • carry partly developed young in pouches | • carry their young inside their bodies until development is nearly complete |

| **Examples** | **Examples** | **Examples** |
|---|---|---|
| Duck-billed platypus<br>Spiny anteater | Kangaroo<br>Wombat<br>Tasmanian devil | Bats, rats, dolphins, elephants, monkeys, horses, hippopotamuses |

| **Where They Live** | **Where They Live** | **Where They Live** |
|---|---|---|
| Only in Australia, Tasmania, and New Guinea | Mostly in Australia and surrounding islands | Throughout the world in the sea, on land, and in the air |

**1.** What are three ways that mammals reproduce?

_____

_____

_____

_____

**2.** Which group of mammals live in environments all over the world?

_____

**3.** How many species of living mammals lay eggs to reproduce?

_____

## Review the Vocabulary

Use the Chapter 32 vocabulary words in the box to fill in the blanks below.

| | |
|---|---|
| gestation (jes TAY shun) | mammary gland |
| marsupial | placenta |
| placental mammal | uterus (YEW tuh rus) |

**1.** Muscular, hollow organ in which offspring develop _____ t _____

**2.** Type of mammal that carries its young inside the uterus until development is nearly
complete _____ a _____ m _____

**3.** Time during which young mammals develop in the uterus _____ s _____

**4.** Organ that develops during pregnancy, provides food and oxygen to the embryo, and removes
wastes _____ l _____ e _____

**5.** Gland in female mammals that produces milk for the young _____ m _____ a _____

**6.** A kangaroo is a _____ a _____ u _____

**Draw a line to match each vocabulary word in the box with its definition.**

| |
|---|
| **a.** diaphragm (DI uh fram) |
| **b.** gland |
| **c.** monotreme (MAH nun treem) |
| **d.** therapsid (thuh RAP sud) |

**7.** Egg-laying mammal

**8.** Mammal-like reptile ancestor of all mammals

**9.** Sheet of muscle under the chest cavity that helps mammals breathe

**10.** Group of cells that secrete substances needed by an animal

**Chapter**

# 33 Animal Behavior

## Get the Big Picture

**Read the paragraph in the box and look at the pictures. Then answer the questions that follow.**

> Every animal has behaviors that help it survive. For example, vultures have social behaviors. They eat dead animals while in groups. Other animals, such as coyotes, prefer to live on their own. Some animal behaviors are innate. This means that an animal inherits genes that control certain behaviors. The genetic makeup of mallard ducks causes them to fly south for the winter. Other behaviors are learned. Learned behaviors result from practice or experience. Young birds learn to build nests by watching other birds and by using trial-and-error learning. Innate and learned behaviors help animals adapt and survive.

**1.** How are innate and learned behaviors different?

_____

_____

_____

**2.** Circle the letter of the sentence that states the main idea of the paragraph.

    **a.** Each animal has a certain way of behaving.

    **b.** Some animal behaviors are innate.

    **c.** Young birds learn to build better nests through trial-and-error learning.

    **d.** Innate and learned behaviors help animals adapt and survive.

**Content Mastery**

## Read the Words

**Read the paragraphs in the boxes. Then answer the questions that follow.**

> A **reflex** is the simplest form of innate behavior. A reflex is a quick, automatic response that happens without thought. Many reflexes can happen in less than a second. For example, you blink quickly when something passes in front of your eyes. A clam withdraws into its shell when something touches it. This reflex helps to protect the clam from predators.

> An **instinct** is a complex pattern of innate behavior. Unlike a reflex, an instinctive behavior may have several parts. It may take hours or even weeks to complete. Instinctive behavior begins when an animal recognizes a stimulus. A **stimulus** is a condition in the environment that makes an animal change its behavior. When greylag geese retrieve eggs that roll out of their nest, the stimulus is the presence of an object outside the nest. Instinctive behaviors end when an animal completes all parts of the behavior. Greylag geese retrieve the eggs one by one until they are all back in the nest. Instincts help animals survive.

**1.** What is the difference between a reflex and an instinct?

_____

_____

_____

_____

_____

**2.** Label each behavior as an instinct or a reflex.
   **a.** Geese retrieve eggs that have rolled out of their nests. _____

   **b.** You blink when something passes in front of your eyes. _____

   **c.** A clam withdraws into its shell when something touches it. _____

CONTENT MASTERY

**Chapter**
**33** **Animal Behavior,** *continued*

Content Mastery

*Section 33.2 Learned Behavior*

## Study the Diagram

**Study the pictures. Then answer the questions.**

**A.** Pavlov noted that dogs drool when they smell food. This response to food is a reflex.

**B.** Pavlov rang a bell whenever the dogs smelled food. After a while, the dogs connected the sound of the bell with the smell of food.

**C.** Later, the dogs drooled at the sound of the bell alone. The dogs were conditioned to respond to a stimulus they did not usually connect with food.

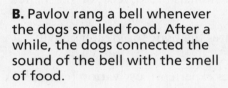

**1.** What reflex did Pavlov's dogs have before the experiment?

_____

_____

**2.** How did Pavlov condition the dogs to drool when they heard a bell?

_____

_____

## Chapter 33 Animal Behavior, continued

## Review the Vocabulary

Review the definitions of the Chapter 33 vocabulary words in bold type in the statements below. If the statement is true, write <u>true</u>. If the statement is false, write <u>false</u>.

_____ **1.** An **instinct** is anything an animal does in response to a stimulus in the environment.

_____ **2.** **Innate behavior** is inherited behavior.

_____ **3.** **Courtship behavior** takes place before male and female animals mate.

_____ **4.** **Aggressive** behavior is not threatening to other animals.

_____ **5.** A **territory** is a physical space where animals breed, feed, or get shelter.

_____ **6.** The **fight-or-flight response** prepares the body for greater activity.

_____ **7.** Animals that live in very cold climates experience **estivation** (es tuh VAY shun).

_____ **8.** A 24-hour cycle of behavior is called a **circadian** (sur KAY dee un) **rhythm**.

_____ **9.** During **hibernation**, animals have a great need for oxygen and energy.

_____ **10.** A **dominance hierarchy** is a social order with several levels.

Draw a line to match each word in the box with its definition.

| |
|---|
| **a.** communication |
| **b.** conditioning |
| **c.** habituation (huh bih chuh WAY shun) |
| **d.** imprinting |
| **e.** insight |
| **f.** language |
| **g.** motivation |
| **h.** trial-and-error learning |

**11.** Internal need that causes an animal to act

**12.** Occurs when an animal is given a stimulus without punishment or reward

**13.** Attachment to an object during a certain time in an animal's life

**14.** Kind of learning in which an animal is rewarded for a particular response

**15.** kind of learning in which an animal uses its experience to respond to something new

**16.** kind of learning in which an animal connects a new stimulus to a certain behavior

**17.** Using symbols to represent ideas

**18.** Sharing of information that results in a change of behavior

## BioDigest 9 Vertebrates

### Get the Big Picture

**Read the paragraphs in the box. Then answer the questions that follow.**

> A vertebrate is an animal with a backbone. Some vertebrates, such as fishes, live in water. Others, such as reptiles and birds, live mostly on land. In these land animals, lungs and legs evolved. Birds also evolved wings. Wings provided birds with the adaptation for flight.
>
> When vertebrates moved from the water to the land and air, there was a change in the way they reproduced. In reptiles and birds, eggs evolved with shells that hold fluid inside. These eggs protect the growing embryos. Vertebrates that lay shelled eggs can reproduce on land instead of in water. In some female vertebrates, a uterus evolved. Animals with a uterus can carry their young inside their body until development is nearly complete.

**1.** What is a vertebrate?

_____

_____

**2.** Name three places a vertebrate might live.

_____

_____

_____

_____

**3.** Name two kinds of vertebrates. How did the bodies of these vertebrates change to allow the animals to live in new environments?

_____

_____

_____

_____

_____

_____

## BioDigest 9 Vertebrates, continued

## Study the Table

**Read the following definitions and study the table. Then answer the questions that follow.**

**Endothermy:** Endothermic animals use their own energy to heat their bodies. Birds and mammals are the only endothermic vertebrates.

**Ectothermy:** Ectothermic animals use an external source of heat, like a warm rock, to heat their bodies.

**Amniotic Egg:** This egg has a thick shell and contains fluid, yolk for food, and the developing embryo. Amniotic eggs can be laid on land instead of in the water.

| Class | Example | Description |
|-------|---------|-------------|
| Reptile | Green sea turtle | • spends most of its life in water<br>• must surface to breathe with its lungs<br>• Females lay eggs on the beach. |
| Bird | Kentucky warbler | • migrates long distances across the Gulf of Mexico<br>• has feathers and hollow bones<br>• Females lay eggs in a nest. |
| Mammal | Arctic fox | • lives in northern Canada and Alaska<br>• has thick fur and short ears |
| Amphibian | Dusky salamander | • lives along streams and near springs<br>• breathes through its skin<br>• Females lay eggs in the water. |
| Fish | Pacific salmon | • lives in the ocean<br>• gets oxygen from the water with its gills<br>• Females lay eggs in freshwater streams. |

**1.** What adaptations does the arctic fox have to keep it from losing heat?

_____

_____

_____

**2.** A green sea turtle will sometimes bask at the surface of the water. Its body temperature rises as it does this. Is the turtle endothermic or ectothermic? What is its source of heat?

_____

_____

**3.** Which animals in the table lay amniotic eggs?

_____

_____

**4.** The vertebrates in the table get oxygen—breathe—in different ways. List three ways, and give an example of an animal that uses each way.

   **a.** _____

   **b.** _____

   **c.** _____

**5.** Kentucky warblers make long migrations in the spring and fall. What are some of the adaptations these warblers have that help them fly?

_____

_____

_____

## Study the Diagram

**Read the paragraphs in the box and study the diagram. Then answer the questions that follow.**

Although fishes, amphibians, reptiles, birds, and mammals are all vertebrates—animals with a backbone—they are different in many ways. One important difference is the way in which they keep their body temperature at a safe level. Birds and mammals can keep their temperature constant throughout the day and the seasons. Because of this ability, they are called **endotherms**. Animals that have a body temperature that changes with the outside temperature are called **ectotherms**.

Because you are a mammal, you are an endotherm—you can keep your body temperature constant. Even on a hot day, your body temperature is usually the same as it is on a cold day. You have an internal "thermostat" that cools you when the outside temperature gets too high and warms you when it gets too low. Endotherms can cool themselves by sweating and panting, and they can warm themselves by shivering. Some endotherms also use fur or feathers to keep themselves warm.

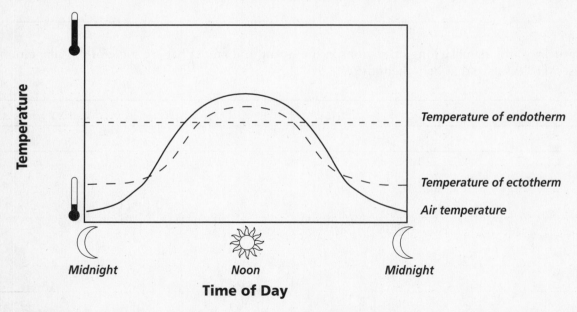

**Read each description below. Decide whether it describes an endotherm or an ectotherm. Then circle the correct word inside the brackets.**

**1.** An animal wakes up on a cold winter morning and is hungry. It sits on a rock in the sun until it warms up enough to go hunting. [endotherm / ectotherm]

**2.** An animal is moving around on a very warm day. It begins to sweat, and the sweat cools it down so that it feels comfortable. [endotherm / ectotherm]

**3.** On a cold day, an animal keeps warm by using a layer of feathers to keep the cold wind out. [endotherm / ectotherm]

# Chapter 34 Protection, Support, and Locomotion

## Get the Big Picture

**Read the paragraph in the box. Then answer the questions.**

> Vertebrates have bones, muscles, and skin to give their bodies support, movement, and protection. Bones form a skeleton that supports body tissues. The skeleton also helps protect organs such as the heart, lungs, and brain. Muscles help to move the skeleton. Muscles are protein fibers attached to bones. Skin surrounds and protects the skeleton and muscles. Skin also helps keep the body in a balanced internal state called **homeostasis**. For example, sweat glands and sweat help to prevent the body from overheating.

**1.** What are the two functions of the skeleton?

_____

_____

_____

**2.** What do muscles do?

_____

_____

_____

**3.** What are two functions of skin?

_____

_____

_____

**4.** What is the purpose or function of sweat glands in the body?

_____

_____

_____

**5.** Other than support for body tissues, what else do the bones provide?

_____

_____

_____

**Chapter 34** Protection, Support, and Locomotion, *continued*

Content Mastery

Section 34.1 *Skin: The Body's Protection*
Section 34.2 *Bones: The Body's Support*
Section 34.3 *Muscles for Locomotion*

## Study the Idea Maps

Study the idea maps. Then answer the questions.

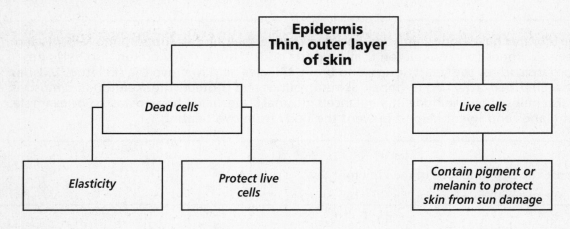

1. What are the two kinds of cells that make up the epidermis? What does each kind of cell do?

_____

_____

_____

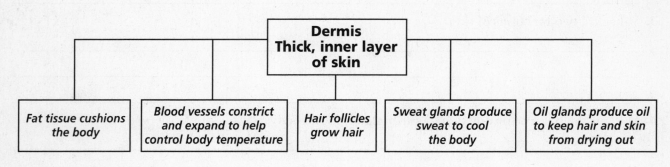

2. **a.** What is the dermis?

_____

   **b.** Name one kind of gland found in the dermis. What does it do?

_____

_____

_____

**Chapter 34** **Protection, Support, and Locomotion,** *continued*

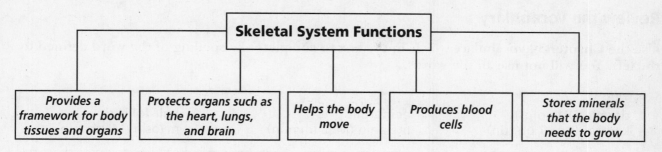

**Skeletal System Functions**

| Provides a framework for body tissues and organs | Protects organs such as the heart, lungs, and brain | Helps the body move | Produces blood cells | Stores minerals that the body needs to grow |

**3.** What are the five functions of the skeleton?

_____

_____

_____

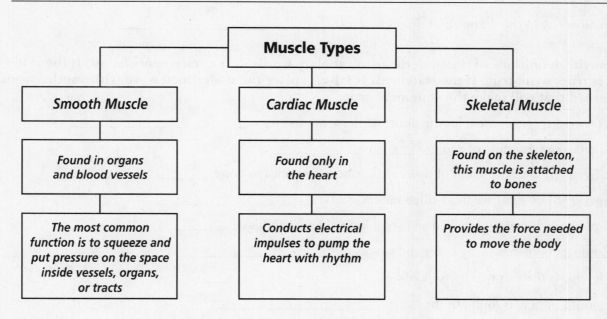

**Muscle Types**

| Smooth Muscle | Cardiac Muscle | Skeletal Muscle |
| --- | --- | --- |
| Found in organs and blood vessels | Found only in the heart | Found on the skeleton, this muscle is attached to bones |
| The most common function is to squeeze and put pressure on the space inside vessels, organs, or tracts | Conducts electrical impulses to pump the heart with rhythm | Provides the force needed to move the body |

**4.** Fill in the table to give the location and the function of each muscle type.

| Muscle Type | Location | Function |
| --- | --- | --- |
| Smooth | | |
| Cardiac | | |
| Skeletal | | |

## Review the Vocabulary

Use the Chapter 34 vocabulary words in the box to complete the spelling of the word defined to the left. You will not use all the words.

| | | |
|---|---|---|
| dermis (DUR mus) | epidermis | hair follicle |
| keratin (KAYR uh tun) | melanin (MEL uh nun) | myosin (MI uh sun) |

**1.** thin, outer layer of skin _____ d _____

**2.** protein in dead epidermal cells _____ at _____

**3.** cell pigment that colors the skin and protects it from sun damage _____ el _____

**4.** thick, inner layer of skin _____ is _____

**5.** small cavity in the dermis that grows hair ___ h ___ f ___

Review the definitions of the underlined vocabulary words in the statements below. If the statement is true, write <u>true</u>. If the statement is false, replace the underlined word with another vocabulary word that will make the statement true.

**6.** The <u>axial skeleton</u> includes the bones of the arms and legs. _____

**7.** A knee is an example of a <u>joint</u>. _____

**8.** A <u>ligament</u> is a thick band of tissue that attaches muscles to bone. _____

**9.** <u>Bursae</u> (BUR sigh) are fluid-filled sacs in joints. _____

**10.** A potential bone cell is called an <u>osteoblast</u> (AH stee uh blast). _____

**11.** <u>Compact bone</u> has many holes and spaces. _____

**12.** <u>Marrow</u> is the soft tissue inside of bones. _____

**13.** <u>Smooth muscle</u> is found in the heart. _____

**14.** <u>Skeletal muscle</u> is attached to bones and moves the skeleton. _____

**15.** <u>Involuntary muscle</u> contracts when you try to contract it. _____

**16.** A small fiber that makes up larger muscle fibers is called a <u>myofibril</u> (mi yuh FI brul).

_____

**17.** Thick filaments in myofibrils are made of the protein <u>actin</u>. _____

**18.** Each section of a myofibril is called a <u>sarcomere</u> (SAR koh meer). _____

**19.** The <u>sliding filament theory</u> states that actin filaments slide together during muscle contraction.

_____

## Chapter 35  The Digestive and Endocrine Systems

### Get the Big Picture

**Read the paragraphs in the box. Then use the pictures to answer the questions that follow.**

Your body breaks down the food you eat into sugars, proteins, vitamins, and minerals that it can use. This breaking down process is called digestion. As you eat, the food moves through your digestive system. Along the way, important tissues and organs help in the process of digestion.

The food you eat helps your body stay healthy by providing it with the nutrients it needs to function, including carbohydrates for energy and vitamins and minerals for body maintenance. If your digestive system is not working properly, your body cannot get the nutrients it needs, and serious health problems may occur.

**Explain the roles that the following items play in digestion or nutrition.**

**1.** Mouth

_____

_____

_____

**2.** Wheat bread and apple

_____

_____

_____

**3.** Diet soft drink and candy

_____

_____

_____

**4.** Liver

_____

_____

_____

**5.** Water

_____

_____

_____

## Chapter 35 The Digestive and Endocrine Systems, *continued*

Section 35.1  Following Digestion of a Meal
Section 35.2  Nutrition
Section 35.3 The Endocrine System

## Study the Diagrams

Study the diagram. Then answer the questions that follow.

### How Long Is Your Digestive System?

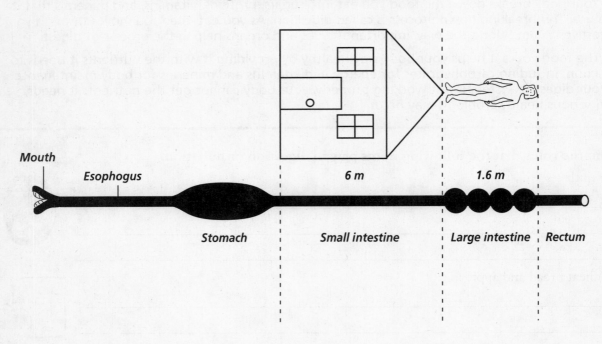

1. What part of the digestive system is the shortest? Explain your answer.

_____

_____

2. What part of the digestive system is the longest? Explain your answer.

_____

_____

3. The entire digestive system is about 9 m long. How tall are you? How can your digestive system fit inside your body?

_____

_____

_____

**Read the paragraph in the box. Then answer the questions that follow.**

> The human body works actively to maintain a balance within itself. This balance is affected by both the hormones of the endocrine system and by the food we eat. If we eat too much of one thing and not enough of another, the body falls out of balance. Similarly, if an endocrine gland produces too much or too little of a certain hormone, the body can also lose its balanced inner state.

**4.** Is eating very little food good for your body? Explain.

_____

_____

_____

_____

**5.** Do sugary foods give you a lot of long-term energy? Explain.

_____

_____

_____

_____

**6.** What kind of control mechanism does the endocrine system use to maintain balance within the body? How does it work?

_____

_____

_____

_____

_____

_____

## Review the Vocabulary

| | |
|---|---|
| amylase (AM uh lays) | pancreas (PANG kree us) |
| bile | peristalsis (payr uh STAWL sus) |
| pituitary | small intestine |
| endocrine | stomach |
| gallbladder | villus (VIH lus) |
| negative feedback | vitamin (VI tuh mun) |

**Use the Chapter 35 vocabulary words in the box to fill in the blanks in the sentences.**

1. The pouchlike, muscular organ that secretes acids and digestive enzymes is

   the _____ .

2. _____ is a chemical produced by the liver that helps break down fats.

3. The endocrine system is regulated by a _____ system.

4. _____ is a digestive enzyme that breaks starches into sugars.

5. The _____ gland controls many other glands of the endocrine system.

6. _____ is a wave of muscular contractions that moves food through the

   digestive system.

7. The organ that stores bile is the _____ .

8. A _____ is a fingerlike projection in the lining of the small intestine.

9. The gland that produces both hormones and digestive enzymes is the _____ .

10. Digestion is completed in the organ called the _____ .

11. A _____ is an organic substance that regulates body processes.

12. _____ glands release hormones directly into the bloodstream.

## Chapter 36 The Nervous System

### Get the Big Picture

Read the paragraphs in the boxes and look at the diagram. Then answer the questions that follow.

The **nervous system** gives directions to all the other systems in your body. It also gets information from your senses and keeps track of how well the different parts of your body are working together. The nervous system is made up of two parts: the **central nervous system** (CNS), and the **peripheral nervous system** (PNS). Peripheral means "not central." Your brain and spinal cord make up your CNS and send and receive messages through your PNS.

Your senses allow you to perceive the world by seeing, hearing, feeling, tasting, and smelling. Your sense organs collect information about the world and send it to your brain. The brain decodes the signals and makes them meaningful.

Many drugs act to disrupt the normal functioning of the nervous system. Drugs can change your brain's ability to think and to control the rest of your body.

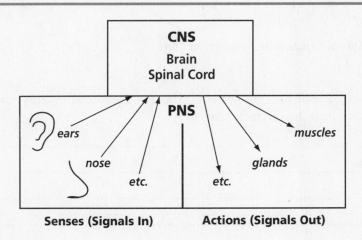

1. How does your central nervous system receive information?

2. Which part of the nervous system do the nerves in your skin belong to?

3. You may not think that caffeine is a drug, but it is. When you drink a soft drink that contains caffeine, you may feel jittery. Why do you think this is so?

**Chapter 36  The Nervous System,** *continued*

## Study the Diagram

**Read the paragraph in the box and study the diagram. Then answer the questions that follow.**

Electrical signals travel throughout your nervous system, carrying information from one place to another. The nervous system is made up of nerve cells, or **neurons**. The neurons have gaps between them, called **synaptic spaces,** which an electrical signal has to jump across in order to continue. In some electrical machinery, electrical signals jump across a tiny gap as a spark. In your body, an electrical impulse is passed by a chemical signal called a **neurotransmitter**.

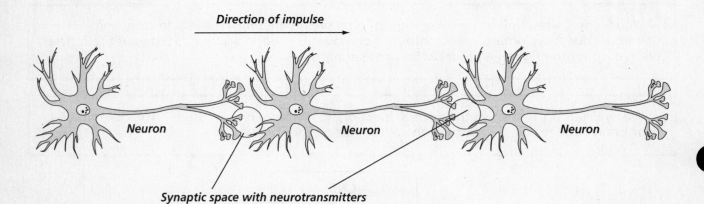

*Direction of impulse*

*Neuron*          *Neuron*          *Neuron*

*Synaptic space with neurotransmitters*

**1.** What would happen to your nervous system if the neurotransmitters in your body were suddenly blocked from passing into the synaptic spaces?

_____

_____

_____

_____

**2.** What do you think would happen if a lot of neurotransmitters were suddenly released throughout your nervous system?

_____

_____

_____

**Chapter 36** The Nervous System, *continued*

*Section 36.2  The Senses*

## Study the Diagram

Read the paragraphs in the boxes and study the diagram. Then answer the questions that follow.

> Your senses give you all of your information about the world. We receive three kinds of information through our senses: information about chemicals, information about light, and information about mechanical stimulation.

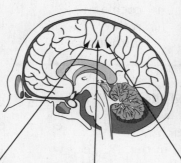

> Our senses of smell and taste tell us about chemicals in the air or in our food. Smell and taste are very similar, both in the way they work and in the way we perceive them. A lot of the time things we think we are tasting we are actually smelling.

> Our senses of touch, hearing, and balance are very closely related. The sense of touch comes from pressure directly on the skin. Pressure receptors in the ears sense changes in sound waves and allow us to hear. Organs in the ears called semicircular canals maintain our balance by detecting the movement of fluid that occurs when we move our head.

> Our sight is based on the light information received by our eyes. Our eyes have cells adapted for seeing different kinds of light. Rods allow us to see in dim light; cones work best at seeing color, as well as sharp images in bright light.

1. Which sense do you think an acrobat uses the most when walking blindfolded on a tightrope? Which organ is responsible for this sense?

_____

_____

2. Why is it hard to taste food when you have a stuffed-up nose?

_____

_____

3. Cats have many rods and few cones in their eyes. Do you think cats see well in the dark? How well do you think they see colors?

_____

_____

**Content Mastery**

## Review the Vocabulary

| | | |
|---|---|---|
| addiction | nervous system | cerebellum |
| cerebrum | cochlea | retina |
| neuron (NEW rahn) | reflex | taste bud |
| rods | withdrawal | synapse (SIH naps) |

Use the Chapter 36 vocabulary words listed above to complete the puzzle. First, write the correct word on the line after each definition. Then find the same word in the letter grid and circle it. Words may be written on horizontal, vertical, or diagonal lines.

```
f  r  a  x  e  d  h  l  u  c  e  n
c  e  r  e  b  e  l  l  u  m  t  e
e  w  i  t  h  d  r  a  w  a  l  r
r  n  l  d  j  h  e  d  m  l  c  v
e  e  g  f  i  o  f  d  r  k  o  o
b  u  t  e  e  l  i  h  n  c  u
r  r  u  i  e  e  e  c  t  g  h  s
u  o  e  m  n  e  x  t  q  l  l  s
m  n  s  h  d  a  s  i  a  j  e  y
m  a  c  w  v  e  r  o  d  s  a  s
r  g  s  y  h  e  b  n  s  d  s  t
t  a  s  t  e  b  u  d  f  a  e  e
w  f  s  a  s  y  n  a  p  s  e  m
a  d  e  b  n  l  g  i  w  n  e  q
```

**1.** Psychological or physiological drug

dependence _____

**2.** Layer of the eye containing rods and

cones _____

**3.** Body's control center

_____

**4.** Taste receptor on tongue

_____

**5.** Portion of brain that maintains balance

and muscle coordination _____

**6.** Psychological or physiological illness resulting from cessation of drug use _____

**7.** Largest portion of the brain _____

**8.** Place where neurons meet _____

**9.** Fluid-filled structure of the ear in which sound vibrations are converted into nerve

impulses _____

**10.** Light receptors in the retina responsible for vision in low light _____

**11.** Basic structural and functional unit in the nervous system _____

**12.** Rapid, automatic response to a stimulus _____

**CONTENT MASTERY**

## Chapter 37   Respiration, Circulation, and Excretion

### Get the Big Picture

**Read the paragraphs in the boxes. Then answer the questions that follow.**

> The **respiratory** system, the **circulatory** system, and the **urinary** system are very important for maintaining homeostasis—your body's constant internal environment.

> The **respiratory** system breathes in oxygen and takes it into the body. It also breathes out waste carbon dioxide.

> The **circulatory** system delivers oxygen from the respiratory system and nutrients from digestion to your body's tissues. It also picks up waste products from tissues and delivers them to the urinary and respiratory systems for removal from the body. Carbon dioxide goes out through the respiratory system. Other wastes exit through the urinary system.

> Finally, the **urinary** system removes waste products from your blood through the kidneys— two small, but powerful, filters.

**1.** Which two systems are involved in the removal of carbon dioxide from the body?

_____

**2.** Which two systems carry waste products out of the body?

_____

**3.** Which two gases does your respiratory system breathe in and breathe out?

_____

**4.** Which system delivers nutrients throughout your body?

_____

**5.** What do the circulatory, respiratory, and urinary systems of your body maintain?

_____

**Chapter**
**37** Respiration, Circulation, and Excretion, *continued*

*Section 37.1 The Respiratory System*
*Section 37.3 The Urinary System*

## Study the Diagram

**Read the paragraphs in the boxes and study the diagram. Then answer the questions that follow.**

> The **respiratory system** controls the balance between oxygen entering the body and waste carbon dioxide leaving the body. Our cells need oxygen to make energy. We inhale oxygen through our nose and mouth. This oxygen travels to the lungs and crosses into the bloodstream through thin-walled sacs called alveoli (singular: alveolus). At the same time, waste carbon dioxide passes from the blood back through the alveoli into the lungs. We then breathe it out of the body. The diaphragm—a powerful sheet of muscle below the lungs— helps pull air in and push air out of the lungs.

> The **urinary system** collects other kinds of cell waste products from the blood and stores them until they are passed out of the body in urine. The kidneys are the most important organs in the urinary system. Kidneys act like complex filters. When blood goes through the kidneys, materials that the body needs stay in the blood. Toxic waste products are removed from the blood and stored in the bladder as urine.

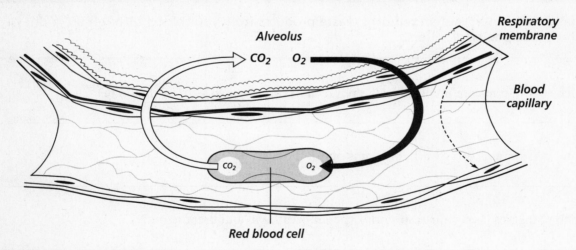

1. Does the white arrow show the transport of oxygen or of carbon dioxide?

   _____

2. Does the black arrow show the transport of oxygen or of carbon dioxide?

   _____

3. Why do you think damage to the kidneys is so dangerous?

   _____

   _____

Copyright © Glencoe/McGraw-Hill, a division of the McGraw-Hill Companies, Inc.

**Chapter 37** Respiration, Circulation, and Excretion, *continued*

**Content Mastery**

*Section 37.2 The Circulatory System*

## Study the Diagram

**Read the paragraphs in the boxes and study the diagram. Then answer the questions that follow.**

> Your **circulatory system** supplies all the different parts of your body with nutrients and oxygen. It also carries carbon dioxide and other cellular waste products away from the cells. The heart is the most important organ in the circulatory system. It pumps blood through your body all the time, all during your life. The blood is carried through vessels that are like a highway system. This system has freeways that carry large numbers of fast-moving blood, smaller roads that carry a steady stream of blood cells, and tiny vessels called **capillaries** that are like neighborhood streets. Some capillaries are so small that only one cell can pass through them at a time. Vessels called **arteries** carry blood away from the heart and lungs. Vessels called **veins** carry the blood from the body back to the heart.

> Blood is a tissue because it is made up of several different cell types. **Red blood cells** are the most common and are like delivery trucks, carrying oxygen to body cells. **White blood cells** are less common but cruise your network of blood vessels ready to identify and destroy enemy invaders. **Platelets** are sticky fragments that patch damaged vessels by forming clots.

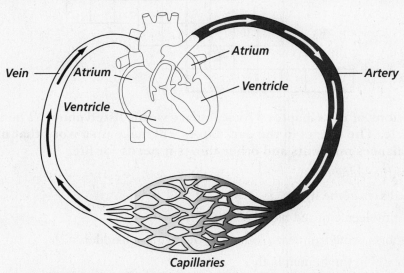

*Capillaries*

The heart constantly pumps blood to all parts of
the body through a network of blood cells.

**1.** Think about the jobs that red blood cells and white blood cells do. When you get a cold, do you think your body will make more red blood cells or more white blood cells? _____

**2.** Which blood vessels carry blood away from the heart? _____

**3.** Which blood vessels carry blood toward the heart? _____

## Review the Vocabulary

| | |
|---|---|
| alveoli (al VEE uh li) | nephron (NE frawn) |
| aorta | plasma |
| artery | pulse |
| atrium | ureter (YUR uh tur) |
| hemoglobin (HEE muh gloh bun) | vein |
| kidneys | |

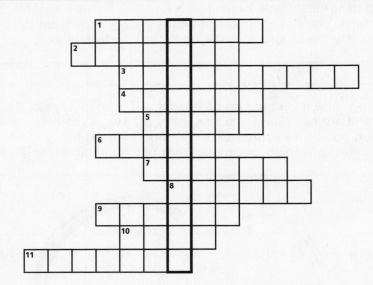

Review the definitions of the Chapter 37 vocabulary words listed above. Then use the clues to complete the puzzle. The letters in the dark boxes will make up a word that means the process by which the body balances nutrients and other things it needs for life.

1. filtering unit of the kidney

2. tiny, thin-walled sacs in the lungs

3. iron-containing molecule of red blood cells

4. tube that transports urine from each kidney to the urinary bladder

5. largest blood vessel in the human body

6. rhythmic surge of blood through an artery

7. thin-walled upper chambers of the heart

8. thick-walled blood vessel that transports blood away from the heart

9. fluid portion of the blood

10. large blood vessel that returns blood from the tissues back to the heart

11. pair of organs that filter waste from blood

**Chapter**
# 38 Reproduction and Development

## Get the Big Picture

**Read what is in the boxes. Then use the pictures to answer the questions that follow.**

> Our bodies are adapted for reproduction.

> **In a man**, this means that:
> 1. sperm is produced.
> 2. sperm passes to the female body where it can fertilize an egg.

> **In a woman**, this means that:
> 1. eggs are produced in her ovaries.
> 2. eggs are fertilized in her oviducts.
> 3. the fertilized egg is protected and nourished while it develops into a fetus.
> 4. the reproductive process delivers a fully developed baby.

> Hormones, including testosterone and estrogen, are the messengers that tell the different parts of the body what to do. In addition to controlling many body functions, they play a large role in reproduction.

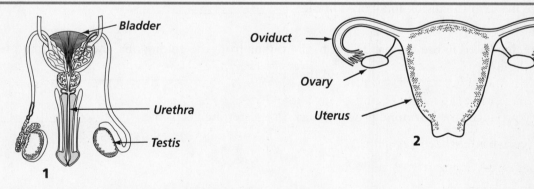

1. Which picture shows the male reproductive system?

2. Write **S** on the picture where sperm are made.

3. Write **E** on the picture where the eggs are made.

4. Write **F** on the picture where fertilization takes place.

5. Write **B** on the picture where the fertilized egg develops into a fetus.

## Study the Diagram

Study the diagram. Then fill in the blanks in the statements that follow.

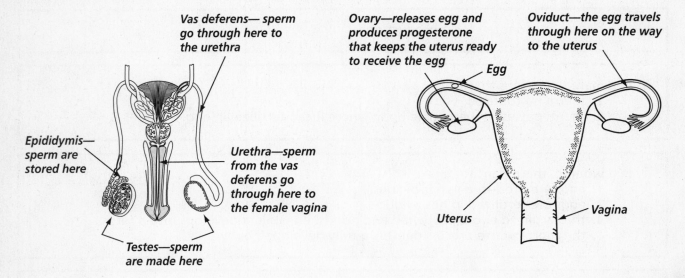

*Vas deferens— sperm go through here to the urethra*

*Ovary—releases egg and produces progesterone that keeps the uterus ready to receive the egg*

*Oviduct—the egg travels through here on the way to the uterus*

*Egg*

*Epididymis— sperm are stored here*

*Urethra—sperm from the vas deferens go through here to the female vagina*

*Uterus*

*Vagina*

*Testes—sperm are made here*

**1.** The egg travels down the _____ to the uterus.

**2.** Sperm are made in the testes and stored in the _____ .

**3.** Sperm are deposited in the vagina. To get to the vagina from the epididymis, the sperm first go through the _____ and then through the _____ .

**4.** The ovary produces the hormone progesterone. Progesterone keeps the _____ ready to receive a fertilized egg.

**Chapter 38** Reproduction and Development, *continued*

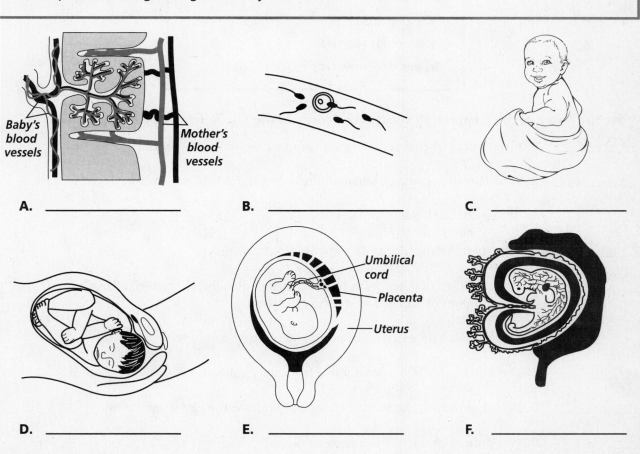Content Mastery

*Section 38.2 Development Before Birth*
*Section 38.3 Birth, Growth, and Aging*

## Match the Pictures

Some of the steps of the human reproductive and developmental cycles are given in the box. Write the number of the step on the line under the picture that illustrates it.

> **1.** When a sperm penetrates the egg, a zygote is formed.
>
> **2.** The umbilical cord attaches the embryo to the placenta.
>
> **3.** Through the placenta, nutrients from the mother's blood pass to the fetus.
>
> **4.** Body systems, like the circulatory system, develop during the first few months of pregnancy.
>
> **5.** At birth, the cervix opens so that the baby can be pushed out.
>
> **6.** People continue growing until they are adults.

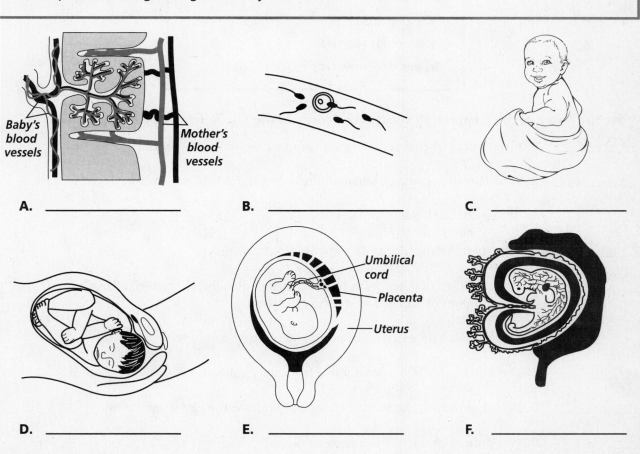

A. _____   B. _____   C. _____

D. _____   E. _____   F. _____

**Content Mastery**

## Review the Vocabulary

> **a.** first trimester
>
> **b.** cervix
>
> **c.** epididymis (ep uh DIHD uh mus)
>
> **d.** follicle (FAH lih kul)
>
> **e.** implantation
>
> **f.** labor
>
> **g.** ovulation
>
> **h.** puberty
>
> **i.** scrotum
>
> **j.** seminal vesicles
>
> **k.** vas deferens (vas • DEF uh runtz)

**Write the letter of the Chapter 38 vocabulary words in the box in front of their definitions.**

_____ **1.** Group of epithelial cells that surround a developing egg in the ovary

_____ **2.** First part of pregnancy when all the organ systems of the embryo begin to form

_____ **3.** Testes-containing sac of males

_____ **4.** Lower end of the uterus that opens into the vagina

_____ **5.** Growth stage that occurs in both males and females, characterized by the development of secondary sex characteristics

_____ **6.** Single-coiled tube in which sperm complete maturation

_____ **7.** Duct through which sperm move from the epididymis toward the urethra

_____ **8.** Process in which the follicle ruptures to release the egg from the ovary

_____ **9.** Attachment of the fertilized egg to the uterine lining

_____ **10.** Physical and psychological changes that the mother experiences during birth

_____ **11.** Paired glands at the base of the urinary bladder that produce fluid to nourish sperm

CONTENT MASTERY

**Chapter**
# 39 Immunity from Disease

## Get the Big Picture

Find the red and blue headings in Chapter 39 of your textbook. Use the blue headings to fill in the ovals in the idea map. The rectangles and some of the ovals have been filled in for you.

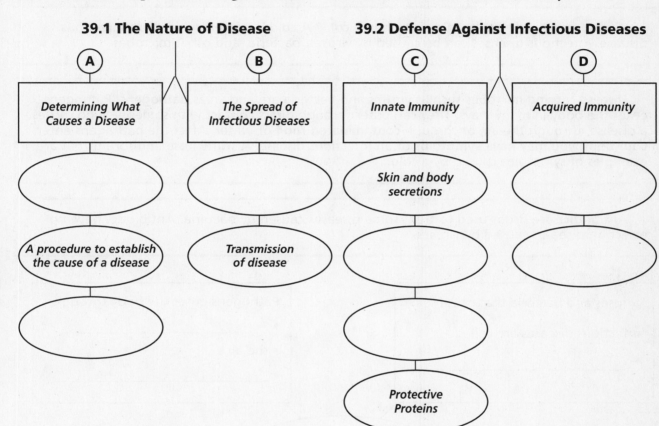

**39.1 The Nature of Disease**            **39.2 Defense Against Infectious Diseases**

A — Determining What Causes a Disease
A procedure to establish the cause of a disease

B — The Spread of Infectious Diseases
Transmission of disease

C — Innate Immunity
Skin and body secretions
Protective Proteins

D — Acquired Immunity

Each statement below goes with one of the headings in the rectangles above. Write the letter of each heading on the line in front of the statement it goes with.

_____  Infectious diseases may be spread by direct contact or through the air.

_____  The skin is the body's first line of defense.

_____  A German doctor named Robert Koch first identified that pathogens can cause diseases.

_____  The body can become immune to an infectious disease.

## Complete the Idea Map

Read the paragraphs in the boxes. Then use the terms in bold type in the paragraphs to complete the idea map.

Do you remember the last time you had a cold? A cold is one example of an **infectious disease.** Infectious diseases can be caused by viruses, bacteria, and other microbes.

Disease-causing microbes such as viruses and bacteria are known as **pathogens**. Pathogens enter the body in many ways. They can enter through **direct contact** with someone who carries a disease, through the air, or through **contaminated food or water**. After the pathogens enter your body, you may have **symptoms** of an infectious disease. A stuffy nose and sore throat are examples of symptoms caused by a cold.

**Antibiotics** are drugs used to treat some diseases caused by bacteria. Antibiotics have no effect on diseases caused by viruses.

Viruses and bacteria that cause

infectious diseases are called

_____ .

Pathogens enter the body through

• _____

• the air

• _____

**A cold is an**
**example of an**

_____ .

You know you have an infectious disease

when you have _____

such as a sore throat.

_____ can treat

diseases caused by bacteria.

**Chapter 39** **Immunity from Disease,** *continued*

*Section 39.2 Defense Against Infectious Diseases*

## Complete the Idea Map

Read the paragraphs in the boxes. Then use the terms in bold type in the paragraphs to complete the idea map.

Remember that infectious diseases are caused by pathogens. Pathogens may come in the form of viruses, bacteria, or other agents. Our bodies have two types of defenses against pathogens: (1) innate (nonspecific) defenses that are immediately ready to fight all pathogens, and (2) acquired (specific) defenses that gear up to fight against particular pathogens.

Our **skin** is one nonspecific defense. It acts like the walls of a castle to keep all foreign intruders out of our body. Our body fluids also serve as nonspecific defenses. Body fluids such as **mucus, sweat, tears, saliva,** and **stomach acid** trap or destroy pathogens. Pathogens that get past our skin and body fluids are attacked by the nonspecific defenders found in the bloodstream. These defenders are certain types of **white** blood cells and **proteins**.

While the nonspecific defenses fight pathogens, the specific defenses prepare to join the battle. After several days, the body will begin to **recognize** the pathogens as intruders. The body then adapts by acquiring specific defenses, including **antibodies** and **T cells**, that identify and destroy particular pathogens.

Body fluids

_____

_____

_____

_____

_____ is like a wall that keeps pathogens out of the body.

After several days, the body begins to _____ invading pathogens.

**Innate Nonspecific Defenses**

**Acquired Specific Defenses**

_____ blood cells and _____ are nonspecific defenses in the bloodstream.

Specific defenses include _____ and _____ .

**Content Mastery**

## Review the Vocabulary

| | | |
|---|---|---|
| antibiotic | Koch's postulates | pathogen (PATH uh jun) |
| B cell | (KAHKS • PAHS chuh lutz) | phagocyte (FAG uh site) |
| interferon | lymph (LIHMF) | pus |
| endemic disease | lymph node | T cell |
| epidemic | lymphocyte | tissue fluid |
| immunity | (LIHMF uh site) | vaccine (vak SEEN) |
| (ihm YEW nut ee) | macrophage | virus |
| infectious disease | (MAK ruh fayj) | |

**For each statement below, circle the Chapter 39 vocabulary word inside the brackets that best completes the statement. You will not use every word.**

1. Diseases are caused by the presence of [oxygen / antibiotics / a pathogen / alleles] in the body.

2. During a(n) [antibiotic / epidemic / genetic disorder / abnormality], many people have the same disease at the same time.

3. Penicillin is an example of a(n) [antibiotic / pathogen / endemic disease / lymphocyte].

4. The fluid in the lymphatic system is called [pus / blood / salt water / lymph].

5. A [lymphocyte / virus / phagocyte / macrophage] is *not* a white blood cell that protects the body against foreign substances.

6. The [B cell / C cell / D cell / F cell] is a type of lymphocyte.

7. [Pus / Skin / Mucus / A vaccine] can cause immunity to a disease.

8. Chicken pox, tetanus, tuberculosis, and AIDS are all [reproductive disorders / genetic disorders / infectious diseases / environmental diseases].

9. A disease that is continually present in the population is called a(n) [endemic disease / epidemic / plague / abnormality].

10. Lymph is filtered in the [lymph nodes / heart / brain / stomach].

11. When [calcium / carbon dioxide / blood / tissue fluid] enters the lymphatic vessels, it is called lymph.

12. The collection of dead white blood cells and different body fluids that are found around an infected area is called [an antibiotic / pus / complement / a vaccine].

CONTENT MASTERY

**Content Mastery**

**BioDigest**
# 10    The Human Body

## Get the Big Picture

Read the paragraphs in the boxes. Then complete the idea map. Part of the map has been filled in for you.

> All organisms are made of **cells**. In humans, most cells function in groups called **tissues**. The four basic tissues of the human body are epithelial tissue, muscle tissue, connective tissue, and nervous tissue. When a group of tissues works together for a single purpose, it makes up an **organ**. Organs usually receive help from other organs to accomplish a large job for the body. When organs work together, they are called an **organ system.**

> The **digestive system** is one organ system. In the digestive system, the food you eat is broken down into smaller and smaller pieces until the vitamins, proteins, minerals, and other important substances in the food are small enough to be delivered to the cells of the body. The digestive system is made up of the mouth, esophagus, stomach, small intestine, large intestine, and rectum. Other major organ systems include the skeletal system, the muscular system, the respiratory system, the circulatory system, the urinary system, the nervous system, and the reproductive system.

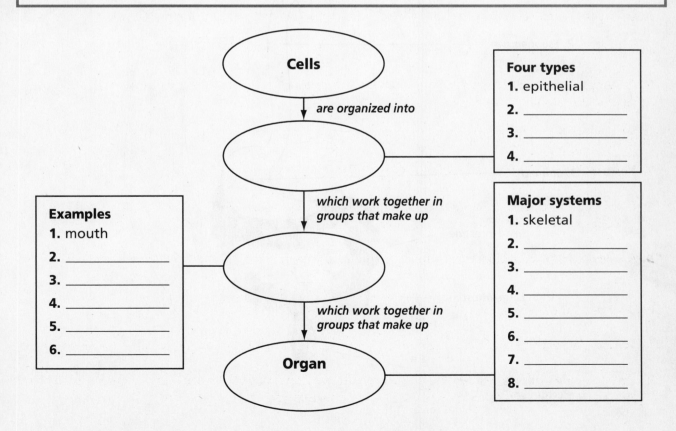

**Content Mastery**

## Study the Diagram

Read the paragraph in the box. Then study the diagram and answer the questions on the next page.

> The digestive system is a major organ system of the human body. The numbers in the diagram below show you the order in which food travels through the digestive system.

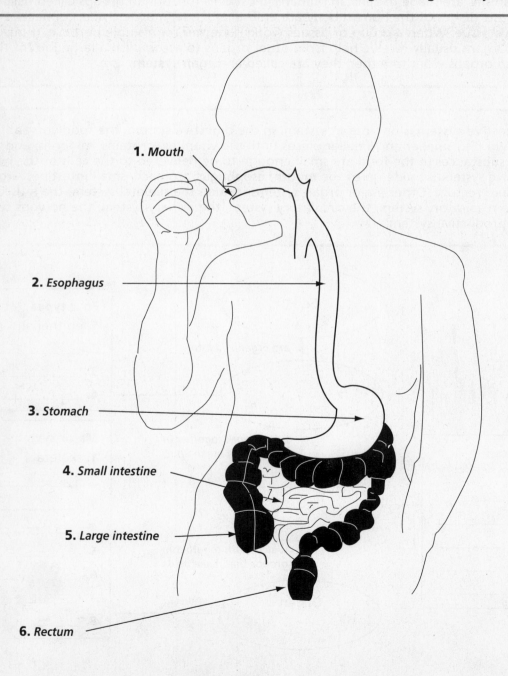

**1.** *Mouth*

**2.** *Esophagus*

**3.** *Stomach*

**4.** *Small intestine*

**5.** *Large intestine*

**6.** *Rectum*

**1.** Where does food enter the digestive system?

_____

**2.** When food travels from the mouth to the stomach, what organ does it go through?

_____

**3.** Where is the small intestine?

_____

_____

**4.** Some food materials are not absorbed or digested. These materials travel through the entire digestive system. Where do they leave the digestive system?

_____

_____

**5. True or false?** Most of the lower portion of the human body is filled with digestive organs.

_____

**6. True or false?** Digestion occurs only in the stomach.

_____

**7. True or false?** The mouth is considered part of the digestive system.

_____

**BioDigest 10**  **The Human Body,** *continued*                          **Content Mastery**

## Fill in the Organ System

| | |
|---|---|
| muscular system | skeletal system |
| respiratory system | digestive system |
| nervous system | circulatory system |
| endocrine system | reproductive system |
| urinary system | lymphatic system |

**Review the descriptions of the major human organ systems listed above. Then fill in the blanks in the sentences with the correct organ system from the list. You will not use all the systems.**

1. The cells in your body get their oxygen and nutrients from blood. Your blood is pumped through your body through the _____ system.

2. Waste products are removed from your blood by the _____ system. This system also regulates the balance of water in your blood.

3. Your brain, spinal cord, nerves, and sensory organs make up your _____ system.

4. The blood in your body receives oxygen, and carbon dioxide is removed, through your _____ system.

5. If a foreign substance enters your bloodstream, the cells that fight infection are part of the _____ system.

6. Your _____ system is responsible for breaking down the food you eat and converting it to forms that your body can use for energy.

7. The supporting framework of your body is the _____ system. This system also acts as a storehouse for calcium and phosphorus.

8. The movements you make with your arms are possible because of your _____ system.

9. The _____ system controls the metabolic activities of your other body systems. It operates by secreting hormones that affect different tissues.

# ANSWER PAGES

## Content Mastery

## Left Page

Name _____ Date _____ Class _____

**Content Mastery**

### Chapter 1 — Biology: The Study of Life

**Get the Big Picture**

Find the section titles and the red and blue headings in Chapter 1 of your textbook. Use the section titles to fill in the rectangles in the idea map below. Use the red headings to fill in the ovals. Some of the rectangles and ovals have been filled in for you.

**Biology: The Study of Life**

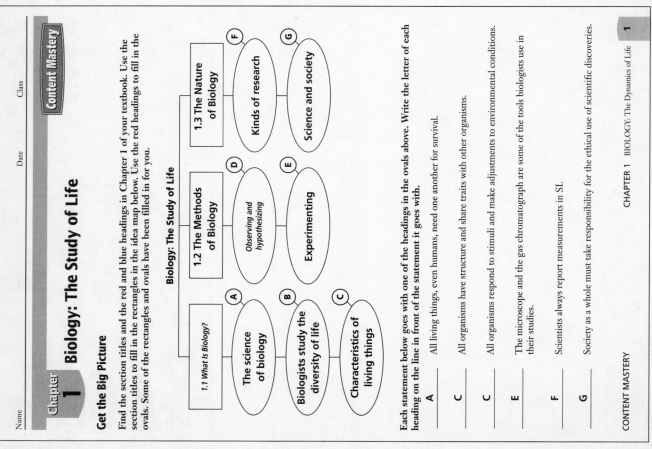

- 1.1 What Is Biology?
  - A — The science of biology
  - B — Biologists study the diversity of life
  - C — Characteristics of living things
- 1.2 The Methods of Biology
  - D — *Observing and hypothesizing*
  - E — Experimenting
- 1.3 The Nature of Biology
  - F — Kinds of research
  - G — Science and society

Each statement below goes with one of the headings in the ovals above. Write the letter of each heading on the line in front of the statement it goes with.

A _____ All living things, even humans, need one another for survival.

C _____ All organisms have structure and share traits with other organisms.

C _____ All organisms respond to stimuli and make adjustments to environmental conditions.

E _____ The microscope and the gas chromatograph are some of the tools biologists use in their studies.

F _____ Scientists always report measurements in SI.

G _____ Society as a whole must take responsibility for the ethical use of scientific discoveries.

CONTENT MASTERY CHAPTER 1 BIOLOGY: The Dynamics of Life 1

## Right Page

Name _____ Date _____ Class _____

**Content Mastery**

### Chapter 1 — Biology: The Study of Life, *continued*

*Section 1.1 What Is Biology?*

**Study the Pictures**

Write the number of the characteristic from the box above that goes best with each picture.

**Characteristics of Living Things**

1. Living things have parts that work together.
2. Living things make more living things.
3. Living things change during their lives.
4. Living things respond to their surroundings.

A __1__

B __4__

C __3__

D __2__

2 CHAPTER 1 BIOLOGY: The Dynamics of Life CONTENT MASTERY

Name                     Date                Class

**Content Mastery**

## Chapter 1  Biology: The Study of Life, *continued*

**Section 1.2  The Methods of Biology**
**Section 1.3  The Nature of Biology**

### Study the Reading

Read the paragraphs in the box and answer the question that follows.

> A biologist named Katharine Payne visited the elephants at a zoo. She felt the air around her throbbing like the rumbling of thunder. When she felt the air throb, she noticed that the skin on the foreheads of the elephants moved.
>
> Also, the elephants seemed to communicate without making any noise. They did not make a sound, but they would start and stop moving at the same time. Payne knew that some animals, such as whales, made sounds too low for humans to hear. She thought, "Maybe elephants, like whales, use low sounds to communicate with each other."

An observation is something you see or notice. A fact is something you know.

Fill in the first box with something Payne observed the elephants doing. Fill in the second box with something she observed about the air around her. Fill in the last box with a fact she knew.

*Observation:* **The elephants moved and stopped at the same time.**

→

*Observation:* **Payne could not hear any sounds. She felt the air throbbing.**

→

*Fact:* **Some animals make sounds too low for humans to hear.**

→

*Hypothesis:* Maybe elephants use low-pitched sounds to communicate with each other.

In **descriptive research**, scientists report observations in the form of observational data such as written descriptions.
In **quantitative research**, scientists report observations in the form of numerical data such as counts and measurements.

**1.** The observations made by Payne would be classified as what type of research? **descriptive research**

---

Name                     Date                Class

**Content Mastery**

## Chapter 1  Biology: The Study of Life, *continued*

### Review the Vocabulary

adaptation (ad ap TAY shun)   theory              control
data                          biology             development
energy                        dependent variable  ethics
evolution (ev uh LEW shun)    environment         growth
homeostasis (hoh me o         experiment          independent variable
STAY sus)                     hypothesis (hi PAHTH us sus)  reproduction
organism                      organization        scientific methods
response                      safety symbol       technology (tek NAHL uh jee)
species (SPEE sheez)          stimulus

The Chapter 1 vocabulary words are listed above. Review the definitions of these words. Then draw a line to match each word in the box with its definition.

**a.** biology
**b.** ethics
**c.** reproduction
**d.** homeostasis
**e.** experiment

**1.** What you do to test a hypothesis
**2.** Making of offspring
**3.** Moral principles and values held by humans
**4.** Study of living things
**5.** Living things maintaining body functions

Use the words in the box to fill in the blanks in the sentences that follow. You will not use all the words.

| response | organism | organization | control |
| stimulus | adaptation | technology | evolution |

**6.** A(n) **organism** has all four traits of life.

**7.** A(n) **stimulus** causes living things to respond.

**8.** Scientific research for society's needs or problems is called **technology** .

**9.** A(n) **control** in an experiment is used as a standard for comparison.

**10.** **Evolution** is the change in a species over time.

## What Is Biology?

**Get the Big Picture**

Find the red and blue headings in BioDigest 1. Use the blue headings to fill in the rectangles in the idea map below. Use the red headings to fill in the ovals. One rectangle and one oval have been filled in for you.

**What Is Biology?**

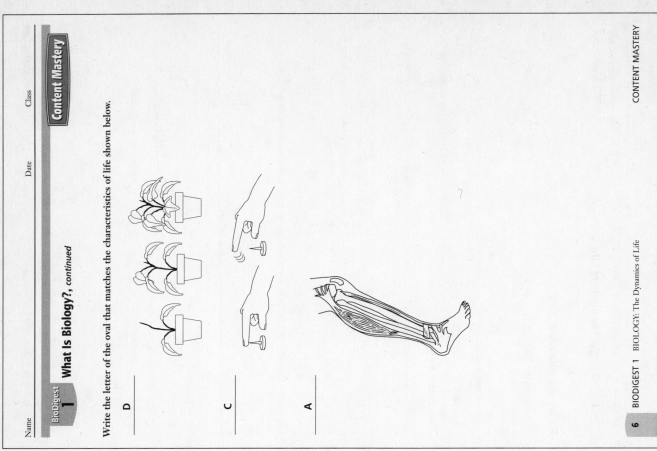

| Characteristics of Life | Scientific Methods |
|---|---|
| Ⓐ Organization | Observation |
| Ⓑ Homeostasis | Hypothesis |
| Ⓒ Response to a stimulus | Experiment |
| Ⓓ Growth and development | Theory |
| Ⓔ Reproduction | |

---

## What Is Biology?, *continued*

Write the letter of the oval that matches the characteristics of life shown below.

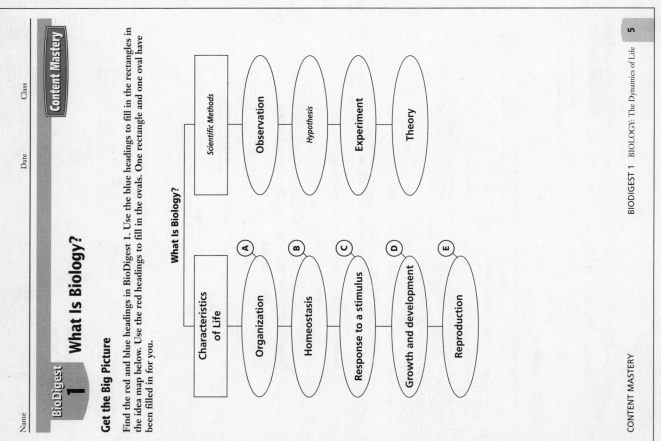

D _____

C _____

A _____

Name _____ Date _____ Class _____

## What Is Biology?, *continued*

**Content Mastery**

### Study the Graph

**18 000** —

**30** —

Sound wave frequency
(vibrations per second)

**Hearing Range of Humans and Range of Sounds Elephants Make**

Use the graph to answer the questions.

1. What is being measured on the graph?
   **the hearing range of humans and the range of sounds made by elephants**

2. According to the graph, what is the normal hearing range of humans?
   **approximately 30 to 18 000 vibrations per second**

3. Explain whether or not a human can hear all the sounds an elephant makes.
   **An elephant makes some sounds with frequencies too low for humans to hear.**

4. Is the collection of the data for the graph an example of descriptive research or quantitative research? Explain.
   **The collection of data is an example of quantitative research because the informa-
   tion was obtained as measurements.**

CONTENT MASTERY

BIODIGEST 1   BIOLOGY: The Dynamics of Life

7

# Chapter 2 Principles of Ecology

## Get the Big Picture

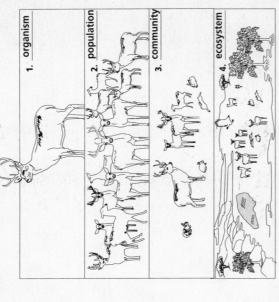

ABIOTIC FACTORS

Water
Oceans
Air
Deserts
Sunlight
Forests
Land

BIOTIC FACTORS

Plants
Animals
Decomposers
Other organisms

ECOSYSTEMS

Ecology is the study of interactions between the biotic factors and abiotic factors on Earth. Biotic factors are all living things. Abiotic factors are all nonliving things. An ecosystem is all the interactions between the biotic factors and abiotic factors in a certain place.

**Use the diagram to answer the following questions.**

1. What things make up the biotic factors on Earth? Give examples. **Biotic factors are all living things, such as plants, animals, and decomposers.**

2. What things make up the abiotic factors on Earth? Give examples. **Abiotic factors are all nonliving things, such as air, water, sunlight, and land.**

3. What is an ecosystem? Give examples. **An ecosystem is the interactions between the biotic factors and abiotic factors in a certain place. Deserts, oceans, and forests are examples of ecosystems.**

4. During the carbon cycle, plants take in carbon dioxide gas from the air and use it to make food. So the carbon cycle involves the air and plants. Where on the diagram does the carbon cycle belong? **in the section labeled Ecosystems**

---

# Chapter 2 Principles of Ecology, continued

**Section 2.1 Organisms and Their Environment**

## Study the Pictures

Label each drawing with one of these words: community, ecosystem, organism, population.

1. organism

2. population

3. community

4. ecosystem

1. Define a population. Give an example of a population of animals from the drawings above. **A population is a group of organisms that mate with one another and live in the same place at the same time. Sample answer: The deer are a population.**

2. Define a community. Give an example of a community from the drawings above. **A community is made up of populations that interact with each other. Sample answer: The rabbits and hawk are part of a community.**

3. Define an ecosystem. Give an example of an ecosystem from the drawings above. **An ecosystem is made up of the populations in a community and their nonliving surroundings. Sample answer: The deer, rabbit, and plant populations that live in the meadow and the lake, air, and rocks are part of an ecosystem.**

Name _____ Date _____ Class _____

**Content Mastery**

## Principles of Ecology, *continued*

Section 2.2 *Nutrition and Energy Flow*

### Complete the Diagrams

The diagram below shows the organisms in a food chain. Draw arrows between the organisms to complete the food chain.

The diagram below shows the organisms in a food web. Draw arrows between the organisms to complete the food web.

---

Name _____ Date _____ Class _____

**Content Mastery**

## Principles of Ecology, *continued*

### Review the Vocabulary

| |
|---|
| abiotic factors (ahy bi YAH tihk)    autotroph |
| biosphere (BI o sfeer)    biotic factors (bi YAH tihk) |
| commensalism (kuh MEN suh liz um)    community |
| decomposer    ecology (ih KAH luh jee) |
| ecosystem (EE khy sihs tum)    food chain |
| food web    habitat |
| heterotroph (HET uh ruh trohfs)    mutualism (MYEW chuh lih zum) |
| niche (NIHCH)    parasitism (PAYR uh sih zum) |
| population    scavengers |
| symbiosis (sihm bee OH sus)    trophic level (TROH fihk) |

Fill in the blank in each sentence below with the correct word from the list above. You will not use all the words.

1. An organism's **habitat** is the place where it lives out its life.

2. Vultures are **scavengers** because they eat animals that are already dead.

3. The role a species has in its environment is called its **niche** .

4. The study of interactions among organisms and their environments is called **ecology** .

5. A **population** is a group of organisms of one species that mate with one another and live in the same place at the same time.

6. An **autotroph** uses the energy from the sun or energy stored in chemical compounds to make its own food.

7. The portion of Earth that supports life is called the **biosphere** .

8. A **community** is a group of populations that interact with one another.

9. An organism that feeds on other organisms is called a **heterotroph** .

10. A relationship between two organisms in which one organism benefits while the other organism is harmed is called **parasitism** .

11. A **decomposer** breaks down and absorbs nutrients from dead organisms.

12. The nonliving parts of an organism's environment are **abiotic factors** .

---

Name _____ Date _____ Class _____

**Content Mastery**

## Chapter 3 Communities and Biomes

### Get the Big Picture

Use the picture below to answer the questions that follow.

**Succession in a Plant Community**

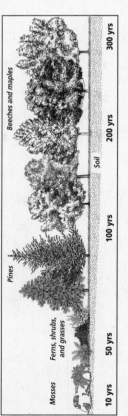

Mosses | Ferns, shrubs, and grasses | Pines | Beeches and maples

Soil

10 yrs | 50 yrs | 100 yrs | 200 yrs | 300 yrs

1. What type of plants were the first to grow in this community?
**mosses**

2. What types of plants were the first to grow in soil?
**ferns, shrubs, and grasses**

3. What types of plants were the last to grow in this community?
**beeches and maples**

4. Why did it take many years for trees to grow in this community?
**Answers may include: Trees need a certain amount of soil to grow.**
**There was not enough soil for the trees to grow earlier.**

CONTENT MASTERY                                    CHAPTER 3   BIOLOGY: The Dynamics of Life   **13**

---

Name _____ Date _____ Class _____

**Content Mastery**

## Chapter 3 Communities and Biomes, *continued*

*Section 3.1 Communities*

### Study the Pictures

**A. Burned Forest**

Grasses
Flowers

**B. New Island**

Mosses
Lichens

Ferns

Look at the pictures and read what is in the boxes. Then use the pictures and definitions to answer the questions.

> **Primary Succession**
>
> This happens when organisms start to live in a new place.

> **Secondary Succession**
>
> This happens when organisms start to live again in a place that had been destroyed by a flood, fire, or other natural disaster.

1. Which picture shows primary succession? Explain your answer.
**Picture B; it shows ferns, mosses, and lichens growing where no plants have**
**grown before.**

2. Which picture shows secondary succession? Explain your answer.
**Picture A; it shows flowers and grasses growing in a place where growing things**
**had been destroyed by a forest fire.**

3. True or false? Primary succession happens after a grassland is destroyed by a flood.
**false**

**14**   CHAPTER 3   BIOLOGY: The Dynamics of Life                                    CONTENT MASTERY

Name _____ Date _____ Class _____

**Content Mastery**

## Chapter 3 — Communities and Biomes, *continued*

**Section 3.2 Biomes**

### Study the Picture

Use the picture below to answer the questions that follow.

**Photic zone** — Plankton, Shrimps, Crabs, Jellyfishes, Snails, Fishes

**Aphotic zone** — Sharks, Worms, Squids, Whales, Fishes

4. What are four kinds of organisms that live in the photic zone?
   **Answers may include any four of the following: plankton, jellyfishes, fishes, shrimps, snails, and crabs.**

5. What are three kinds of organisms that live in the aphotic zone?
   **Answers may include any three of the following: worms, squids, whales, fishes, and sharks.**

6. Suppose that the photic zone becomes polluted, and many organisms living there die. What might happen to the organisms in the aphotic zone? Explain your answer.
   **Organisms in the aphotic zone might die, too, because they survive by eating organisms that live in or near the photic zone.**

---

Name _____ Date _____ Class _____

**Content Mastery**

## Chapter 3 — Communities and Biomes, *continued*

### Review the Vocabulary

Match the Chapter 3 vocabulary words in the box with the definitions below. You will not use all the words.

| | | |
|---|---|---|
| biome | climax community | primary succession | limiting factor |
| permafrost | secondary succession | intertidal zone | plankton |

1. Something that stops or slows down the growth of a population **limiting factor**

2. Happens after a community has been destroyed **secondary succession**

3. A stable or mature community **climax community**

4. A large group of ecosystems that have the same type of climax community **biome**

5. Ground that is always frozen **permafrost**

Draw a line to match each vocabulary word with its description.

a. grassland
b. succession
c. tropical rain forest
d. tundra
e. aphotic zone
f. desert
g. estuary
h. taiga
i. temperate forest
j. photic zone

6. Changes in a community over time
7. Driest biome
8. Biome in which cereal grains are grown
9. Part of the ocean where sunlight penetrates
10. Most of its trees are conifers
11. Body of water in which salt water and fresh water mix
12. Has warm weather and plenty of rainfall
13. Has no trees
14. Part of the ocean where sunlight does not penetrate
15. Most of its trees lose their leaves every year

## Chapter 4 Population Biology

**Content Mastery**

### Get the Big Picture

Find the red and blue headings in Chapter 4 of your textbook. Use the red headings to fill in the rectangles in the idea map below. Use the blue headings to fill in the ovals. Some of the rectangles and ovals have been filled in for you.

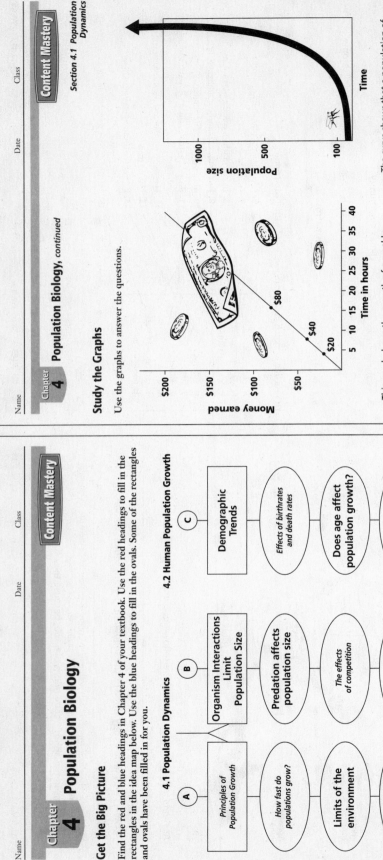

**4.1 Population Dynamics**

A — *Principles of Population Growth*
- *How fast do populations grow?*
- *Limits of the environment*
- *Patterns of population growth*
- *Environmental limits to population growth*

B — **Organism Interactions Limit Population Size**
- *Predation affects population size*
- *The effects of competition*
- *The effects of crowding and stress*

**4.2 Human Population Growth**

C — **Demographic Trends**
- *Effects of birthrates and death rates*
- *Does age affect population growth?*
- *Mobility has an effect on population size*

Each statement below goes with one of the headings in the rectangles above. Write the letter of each heading on the line in front of the statement that goes with it.

**C** ___ Scientists, called demographers, study the growth trends of populations.

**A** ___ A limited food supply can slow down population growth.

**B** ___ Many populations are controlled by prey-predator relationships.

CONTENT MASTERY                    CHAPTER 4   BIOLOGY: The Dynamics of Life      **17**

---

## Chapter 4 Population Biology, *continued*

**Content Mastery**

*Section 4.1 Population Dynamics*

### Study the Graphs

Use the graphs to answer the questions.

This graph shows the growth of a weekly paycheck. Five dollars is earned for every hour that is worked. This growth is called linear **growth**. This type of growth makes a straight line on a graph.

The curve shows that a population of house flies grows more rapidly over time. This growth is called exponential growth. This type of growth makes a J-shaped curve on a graph.

1. Which graph shows a steady rate of growth?
   **the graph for paycheck growth**

2. Which graph shows growth at an increasing rate?
   **the graph for housefly population growth**

3. If you graphed the population growth of household cockroaches, would the graph show a straight line or J-shaped curve? Explain your answer.
   **Sample answer: The graph would show a J-shaped curve. Like the houseflies, the**
   **population of cockroaches would probably grow at a faster and faster rate.**

**18**   CHAPTER 4   BIOLOGY: The Dynamics of Life

---

Name _____ Date _____ Class _____

**Content Mastery**

**Chapter 4  Population Biology,** *continued*

**Section 4.2 Human Population Growth**

## Study the Table

Use the table to answer the questions that follow.

| Birthrates and Death Rates Around the World (mid-1996) | | | |
|---|---|---|---|
| | Birthrates (per 1000 people) | Death Rates (per 1000 people) | Growth Rate (per 1000 people) |
| **Rapidly Growing Countries** | | | |
| Jordan | 39 | 4 | 33 |
| Iraq | 43 | 7 | 36 |
| Uganda | 46 | 21 | 25 |
| **Slowly Growing Countries** | | | |
| Poland | 12 | 10 | 2 |
| Italy | 10 | 10 | 0 |
| Ireland | 13 | 9 | 4 |

The numbers in this table are based on numbers of births and deaths for every 1000 people in each country. The death rate is subtracted from the birthrate to find the growth rate.

**1.** What was the birthrate of Uganda?
**46 per 1000 people**

**2.** What was the death rate of Iraq?
**7 per 1000 people**

**3.** What was the population growth rate of Ireland?
**4 per 1000 people**

**4.** Which country had the fastest growing population?
**Iraq**

**5.** Why did Italy have a growth rate of zero?
**Italy's birthrate was the same as its death rate.**

---

Name _____ Date _____ Class _____

**Content Mastery**

**Chapter 4  Population Biology,** *continued*

## Review the Vocabulary

Use the Chapter 4 vocabulary words in the box to fill in the puzzle.

| emigration | age structure |
|---|---|
| demography | carrying capacity |

Crossword puzzle answers:
- 1 across: **a g e s t r u c t u r e**
- 2 down: **c a r r y i n g**
- 2 down (d/e): **d e m o g r a p h y**
- Down (c): **c a p a c i t y**
- **e m i g r a t i o n**

**Across**

**1.** proportions of a population that are at different age levels

**2.** study of population growth characteristics

**Down**

**3.** number of organisms of one species that an environment can support

**4.** movement of individuals out of a population

Use the vocabulary words in the box to complete the sentences.

| density-dependent factors | density-independent factors |
|---|---|
| exponential growth | immigration |

**5.** Limiting factors that affect populations more as the populations grow are called **density-dependent factors** .

**6.** A growth rate that increases with time results in **exponential growth** .

**7.** Limiting factors that affect populations the same way regardless of their size are called **density-independent factors** .

**8.** **Immigration** is the movement of individuals into a population.

## Page 21 (left panel)

Name _____  Date _____  Class _____

**Content Mastery**

### Chapter 5  Biological Diversity and Conservation

**Get the Big Picture**

Read the paragraphs about biodiversity. Then answer the questions that follow.

> Biodiversity is the variety of life in a certain area. The greater the number of species in an area, the greater is the area's biodiversity.

> Biodiversity provides people with a variety of foods, medicines, and useful products such as clothing and furniture.

> People threaten biodiversity when they destroy the habitats of plants and animals. Building houses and roads, burning forests for farmland, and polluting the environment can destroy habitats.

> People can preserve biodiversity by creating national parks where plants and animals are protected and by keeping endangered animals in zoos.

1. What is biodiversity?
   **Biodiversity is the variety of life in a certain area.**

2. Is there greater biodiversity in a desert or in a tropical rain forest? Explain your answer.
   **There is greater biodiversity in a tropical rain forest than in a desert because there are more kinds of species in a tropical rain forest.**

3. How do national parks help preserve biodiversity?
   **Plants and animals are protected in national parks.**

4. Why is biodiversity important to people?
   **Biodiversity provides people with foods, medicines, and useful products such as clothing and furniture.**

5. How might building houses and roads threaten biodiversity?
   **Building houses and roads may destroy the habitats of plants and animals.**

CONTENT MASTERY                    CHAPTER 5   BIOLOGY: The Dynamics of Life     **21**

## Page 22 (right panel)

Name _____  Date _____  Class _____

**Content Mastery**

### Chapter 5  Biological Diversity and Conservation, *continued*

**Section 5.1  Vanishing Species**

**Study the Picture**

In the picture below, draw a circle around the air pollution. Draw a square around the water pollution. Draw a triangle around the land pollution.

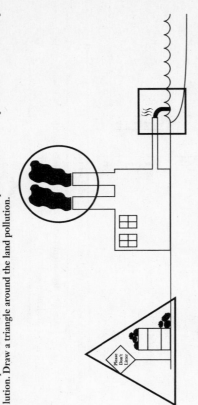

In the table below, list some of the problems caused by air, water, and land pollution.

| Air Pollution | Water Pollution | Land Pollution |
|---|---|---|
| acid precipitation | excess fertilizers | trash |
| CFCs | silt from exposed soil | landfills |
| burning fossil fuels | detergents | pesticides |
| | heavy metals | |
| | industrial chemicals | |
| | abandoned drift nets | |

Answer the following question.

How can pollution cause a species to disappear?
**Pollution can cause the organisms of a species to become sick and die in large numbers, until none are left.**

**22**   CHAPTER 5   BIOLOGY: The Dynamics of Life                    CONTENT MASTERY

---

Copyright © Glencoe/McGraw-Hill, a division of The McGraw-Hill Companies, Inc.

**Content Mastery**

Chapter **5** | **Biological Diversity and Conservation,** *continued*

**Section 5.2 Conservation of Biodiversity**

Study the diagram. Then answer the questions that follow.

A large population of black-footed ferrets lived in Wyoming. The ferrets fed on prairie dogs.

Farmers killed the prairie dogs.

The ferret population decreased.

The remaining ferrets were captured, taken care of, and allowed to reproduce in captivity.

The captured ferrets were released to the land where they used to live.

Farmers no longer killed prairie dogs. The ferret population increased.

1. What caused the ferret population to decrease?
**Farmers killed the prairie dogs, which were the ferrets' food. Ferrets that didn't get enough food died.**

2. Why were the remaining ferrets captured?
**The remaining ferrets were captured so they could be taken care of, allowed to reproduce, and then returned to the land where they used to live.**

3. After the captured ferrets were released, why did the ferret population increase?
**Farmers no longer were killing the prairie dogs, so the ferrets had enough food to eat.**

---

**Content Mastery**

Chapter **5** | **Biological Diversity and Conservation,** *continued*

## Review the Vocabulary

| | | |
|---|---|---|
| acid precipitation | endangered species | habitat fragmentation |
| biodiversity | exotic species | ozone layer |
| captivity | extinction | reintroduction programs |
| conservation biology | habitat corridors | threatened species |
| edge effect | habitat degradation | sustainable use |

The Chapter 5 vocabulary words are listed above. Review the definitions of these words. Then fill in each blank in the sentences below with the correct word from the list. You will not use all the words.

1. A(n) _____**threatened species**_____ is a species that is declining rapidly in number.

2. The variety of life in an area is called _____**biodiversity**_____.

3. _____**Acid precipitation**_____ is rain, snow, sleet, or fog that has a low pH value.

4. Animals in zoos are in _____**captivity**_____.

5. The damage to a habitat by pollution is called _____**habitat degradation**_____.

6. _____**Extinction**_____ is the disappearance of a species when its last member dies.

7. _____**Reintroduction programs**_____ release organisms into an area where they once lived.

8. A(n) _____**endangered species**_____ is a species whose numbers are so low that it is in danger of becoming extinct.

9. The _____**ozone layer**_____ protects organisms on Earth from ultraviolet radiation.

10. _____**Habitat corridors**_____ are strips of land that allow organisms to migrate from one area to another.

11. A(n) _____**exotic species**_____ is a species that has been brought to an area where it normally does not live.

12. _____**Habitat fragmentation**_____ is the separation of a wilderness area from other wilderness areas.

---

## First Panel

Name _____ Date _____ Class _____

**BioDigest 2   Ecology**

### Get the Big Picture

Read the paragraphs in the box. Then answer the questions.

> The plants in a forest are autotrophs. They use sunlight to make their own food. The animals in the forest are heterotrophs. They eat plants and other animals for food. For example, the squirrels eat nuts and seeds. The birds eat seeds and insects. The rabbits and insects eat leaves. The raccoons eat fish, frogs, insects, nuts, and fruit. The foxes eat insects, squirrels, rabbits, young raccoons, and birds.
>
> A heterotroph can be a herbivore, a carnivore, or an omnivore. A herbivore eats only plants. A carnivore eats only animals. An omnivore eats plants and animals. A forest has all three kinds of heterotrophs.

1. Describe one kind of food chain in a forest. **Answers will vary. One possible food chain:**
   **plant → insect → bird → fox**

2. What is the autotroph in the food chain you described? **the plant**

3. What is a heterotroph in the food chain you described? **Answers will vary. All of the animals**
   **in the food chain are heterotrophs.**

4. What is the difference between an omnivore and a carnivore? **An omnivore eats plants and**
   **animals; a carnivore eats only animals.**

5. What kind of heterotroph is a fox? **carnivore**

6. What kind of heterotroph is a raccoon? **omnivore**

7. What kind of heterotroph is a rabbit? **herbivore**

8. What are some nonliving things that the plants and animals in the forest need to survive?
   **Possible answers: water, air, sunlight, and shelter.**

9. What might happen to the rabbit population if all the foxes were removed from the forest? Explain your answer. **The rabbit population would probably increase because they would no**
   **longer be killed by foxes. Then, if the rabbit population became so large that the**
   **rabbits ran out of food, they would starve and the population would decrease.**

10. If a fire destroyed the forest, what would happen to the area where the forest used to be?
    **Answers may vary. Students should show an understanding that succession would**
    **take place, resulting in another forest after a period of many years.**

CONTENT MASTERY                    BIODIGEST 2   BIOLOGY: The Dynamics of Life   **25**

---

## Second Panel

Name _____ Date _____ Class _____

**BioDigest 2   Ecology,** *continued*

### Label the Cycle

Read the paragraph in the box. Then look at the water cycle in the picture. On the lines provided, write where condensation and evaporation are shown in the cycle.

> Water cycles through an ecosystem by the processes of evaporation and condensation. Evaporation of water occurs when liquid water changes into water vapor. Condensation of water occurs when water vapor changes into liquid water.

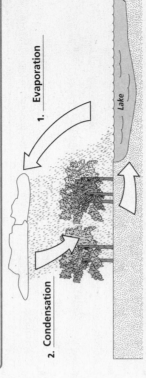

2. **Condensation**

1. **Evaporation**

Lake

### Study the Cycle

Study the carbon cycle below. Then answer the questions.

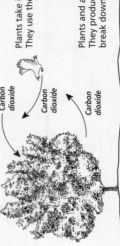

Carbon dioxide

Carbon dioxide

Carbon dioxide

Plants take in carbon dioxide gas. They use the carbon to make food.

Plants and animals release carbon dioxide gas. They produce carbon dioxide when their cells break down food for energy.

1. Why do plants and animals release carbon dioxide?
   **Carbon dioxide is produced when their cells break down food for energy.**

2. What happens to the carbon dioxide that is released by plants and animals?
   **The carbon dioxide goes into the air; some is taken in by plants.**

3. Why do plants need carbon dioxide?
   **Plants need carbon dioxide to make food.**

**26**   BIODIGEST 2   BIOLOGY: The Dynamics of Life                    CONTENT MASTERY

---

## Left page (27)

Copyright © Glencoe/McGraw-Hill, a division of The McGraw-Hill Companies, Inc.

Name _____ Date _____ Class _____

**Content Mastery**

**BioDigest 2** **Ecology,** *continued*

### Study the Diagram

The diagram shows three groups of organisms found in a community — producers, herbivores, and carnivores. The rectangles compare the biomasses of the three groups. Biomass is the total weight of all the organisms that belong to one of the groups of organisms in a community. The larger the rectangle in the diagram, the larger is the biomass of that group of organisms. Study the diagram. Then answer the questions.

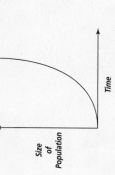

Carnivores are animals that eat other animals.

**Carnivores**

Herbivores are animals that eat only plants.

**Herbivores**

**Producers**

Producers are organisms that make their own food.

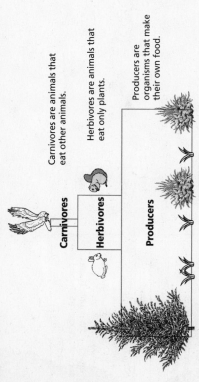

**Biomasses of Different Types of Organisms**

1. Why is a rabbit considered to be a herbivore?
   **Rabbits eat only plants.**

2. What is a producer?
   **A producer is an organism that makes its own food.**

3. To which group of organisms does a hawk belong?
   **carnivores**

4. Which group of organisms in a community has the smallest biomass?
   **carnivores**

5. Which group of organisms in a community has the largest biomass?
   **producers**

6. Why do you think the biomass of the herbivores is greater than the biomass of the carnivores?
   **There are more herbivores than carnivores in a community.**

CONTENT MASTERY

BIODIGEST 2   BIOLOGY: The Dynamics of Life   **27**

---

## Right page (28)

Name _____ Date _____ Class _____

**Content Mastery**

**BioDigest 2** **Ecology,** *continued*

### Study the Graph

Look at the graph. Then answer the questions.

Size of Population ↑ (curve) → Time

1. What kind of population growth is shown in the graph? **exponential growth**

2. What kinds of conditions would be necessary for a population to exhibit the kind of growth shown in the graph? **The population would show exponential growth if it had no predators and if it could meet all its needs.**

3. Why aren't populations able to grow indefinitely? **At some point, biotic and abiotic factors in the environment, such as available food and space, limit the sizes of populations.**

### Number the Steps

Farmland that is not planted for many years may eventually change into a forest. The sequence of changes that occurs in a community over time is called succession. Number the steps below from 1 to 5 to show how an abandoned farm changes into a forest.

**4** ____ 4. Tree saplings block out more of the sun, causing the flowers, grasses, and bushes to die.

**1** ____ 5. Weeds grow on the barren land.

**5** ____ 6. Tree saplings grow into a forest of trees.

**2** ____ 7. Flowers, grasses, and small bushes grow and produce shade.

**3** ____ 8. Tree seeds are protected by the shade and grow into saplings.

**28**   BIODIGEST 2   BIOLOGY: The Dynamics of Life

CONTENT MASTERY

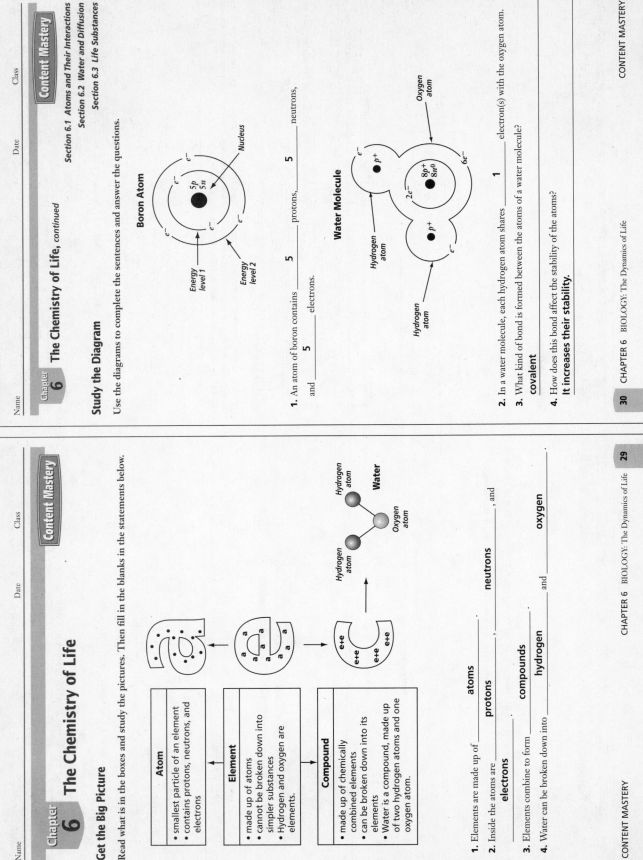

## Page 29

Name _____ Date _____ Class _____

**Content Mastery**

**Chapter 6 — The Chemistry of Life**

**Get the Big Picture**

Read what is in the boxes and study the pictures. Then fill in the blanks in the statements below.

**Atom**
- smallest particle of an element
- contains protons, neutrons, and electrons

**Element**
- made up of atoms
- cannot be broken down into simpler substances
- Hydrogen and oxygen are elements.

**Compound**
- made up of chemically combined elements
- can be broken down into its elements
- Water is a compound, made up of two hydrogen atoms and one oxygen atom.

Hydrogen atom
Oxygen atom
Hydrogen atom
**Water**

1. Elements are made up of _____ **atoms** _____.

2. Inside the atoms are _____ **protons** _____, _____ **neutrons** _____, and _____ **electrons** _____.

3. Elements combine to form _____ **compounds** _____.

4. Water can be broken down into _____ **hydrogen** _____ and _____ **oxygen** _____.

CONTENT MASTERY         CHAPTER 6   BIOLOGY: The Dynamics of Life   **29**

## Page 30

Name _____ Date _____ Class _____

**Content Mastery**

**Chapter 6 — The Chemistry of Life,** *continued*

Section 6.1 *Atoms and Their Interactions*
Section 6.2 *Water and Diffusion*
Section 6.3 *Life Substances*

**Study the Diagram**

Use the diagrams to complete the sentences and answer the questions.

**Boron Atom**

Energy level 1
Energy level 2
Nucleus
5p 5n

**Water Molecule**

Hydrogen atom
Hydrogen atom
Hydrogen atom
Oxygen atom
8p+ 8n0
2e−
6e−

1. An atom of boron contains _____ **5** _____ protons, _____ **5** _____ neutrons, and _____ **5** _____ electrons.

2. In a water molecule, each hydrogen atom shares _____ **1** _____ electron(s) with the oxygen atom.

3. What kind of bond is formed between the atoms of a water molecule?
   **covalent**

4. How does this bond affect the stability of the atoms?
   **It increases their stability.**

**30**   CHAPTER 6   BIOLOGY: The Dynamics of Life         CONTENT MASTERY

Name _____  Date _____  Class _____

**Content Mastery**

**Chapter 6**  **The Chemistry of Life,** *continued*

## Study the Diagram

Order each step from 1 to 3 to show how diffusion occurs. Then complete the sentences.

Water molecule — Cell — **2**

Water molecule — Cell — **3**

Water molecule — Cell — **1**

5. During diffusion, particles move from an area of **higher** concentration to an area of **lower** concentration.

6. Diffusion occurs because particles are always **moving** randomly.

Use the diagram to answer the questions below.

H—☐—OH + H—☐—OH → H—☐—☐—OH
→ H₂O

7. Does the above reaction show condensation or hydrolysis?
**condensation**

8. Is the reaction used to make a polymer or to break apart a polymer?
**make a polymer**

---

Name _____  Date _____  Class _____

**Content Mastery**

**Chapter 6**  **The Chemistry of Life,** *continued*

## Review the Vocabulary

Some of the Chapter 6 vocabulary words are listed below. Review the definitions of these words. Then use the clues to complete the puzzle. The letters in the dark boxes will make up three words that tell you what you are studying in Chapter 6.

atom
base
carbohydrate
diffusion
enzyme
hydrogen bond
metabolism
nucleic acid
nucleotide
polar molecule
polymer
protein
solution

Crossword answers:
1. nucleotide
2. carbohydrate
3. base
4. metabolism
5. solution
6. diffusion
7. atom
8. polar molecule
9. hydrogen bond
10. protein
11. polymer
12. nucleic acid
13. enzyme

1. subunit of nucleic acids
2. compound used by cells to store and release energy
3. substance that forms hydroxide ions in water
4. all the chemical reactions that occur in an organism
5. mixture in which a substance dissolves into another substance
6. movement of particles from an area of higher concentration to an area of lower concentration
7. smallest particle of an element that has the characteristics of that element
8. molecule with a positive end and a negative end
9. weak bond formed between water molecules, due to their polarity
10. polymer made of amino acids that is essential to all life
11. large molecule made of many smaller molecules bonded together
12. large molecule that stores information in cells
13. protein that changes the rate of a chemical reaction

## Content Mastery

# Chapter 7  A View of the Cell, *continued*

Section 7.1 **The Discovery of Cells**
Section 7.2 **The Plasma Membrane**
Section 7.3 **Eukaryotic Cell Structure**

### Study the Reading

Read the paragraph in the box and study the figure. Then answer the questions that follow.

> The first microscope was made about 300 years ago. When light rays pass through certain shapes of glass, the rays bend and change direction. Pairs of convex lenses—round pieces of glass shaped like ovals—are used in microscopes. These lenses make very tiny objects such as cells appear larger. As light passes through the first lens, the light rays bend and then cross, as you can see in the diagram. By the time the crossed light rays reach the second lens, the object is magnified—it appears bigger. If you could see the object after the light passed through the first lens, the object would seem to be upside down. When the light reaches the second lens, it bends again so that you perceive the object as right side up.

**Light Microscope**

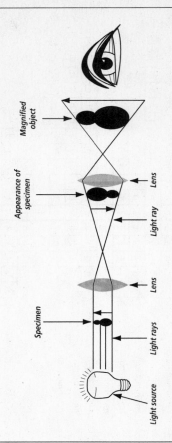

Light source

Specimen

Light rays

Lens

Lens  Light ray  Lens

Appearance of specimen

Magnified object

**1.** A microscope is made up of two or more glass lenses. What do the lenses do to the light that passes through them? What does this do to the object being looked at?
**The lenses bend the light; the object appears to be larger.**

**2.** Why is it important to have the second lens in the microscope?
**If the second lens were not there, the image of the object would appear upside down.**

CONTENT MASTERY

---

## Content Mastery

# Chapter 7  A View of the Cell

### Get the Big Picture

Read the paragraphs in the box and study the pictures. Then answer the questions that follow.

> Cells are the smallest units of life. They come in many sizes and shapes. Cells can be found as single cells or joined together in groups as in skin cells. Prokaryotic cells were the first cells to evolve. They had very simple internal parts. Later, more complex cells, called eukaryotic cells, evolved. Eukaryotic cells have more internal parts, called organelles. Prokaryotic cells do not have organelles.
>
> Organelles are surrounded by membranes. These organelles do different jobs for the cell such as digest food or make energy. The nucleus is a major organelle that acts like a brain. It has all the information necessary to run the cell and to make new cells. Plants and animals are made up of many kinds of eukaryotic cells that live and work together. These different kind of cells help adapt the plants and animals to living in a wide variety of environments.

**A**

Cell membrane
Ribosome
Nuclear membrane
Nucleus
Smooth endoplasmic reticulum
Vesicle
Golgi apparatus
Mitochondrion
Lysosome
Rough endoplasmic reticulum

**B**

Cell wall
Cell membrane
Chromosomes
Ribosomes
Mesosomes
Storage granule

**1.** Which cell in the picture is a prokaryotic cell? Explain your answer.
**Cell B; it is simpler inside and has no organelles.**

**2.** Which of the two types of cells do scientists think was the first to evolve? Why do they think this?
**The prokaryotic cell; it is simpler in form and has no nucleus.**

CONTENT MASTERY

**Chapter 7**  A View of the Cell, *continued*

## Study the Diagram

When scientists examined the eukaryotic cell under the microscope, they discovered a small, self-contained package filled with individual parts called organelles. Some organelles make proteins; others store food. Still other organelles make and store energy. The cell is surrounded by a plasma membrane, which allows materials to enter and leave the cell, maintaining homeostasis.

**The Eukaryotic Cell**

Rough endoplasmic reticulum

Golgi apparatus

Smooth endoplasmic reticulum

Lysosome

Nucleolus

Phospholipids

Surface protein

Plasma membrane

Phospholipids

Transport protein

Nucleus

Mitochondrion

3. The Golgi apparatus receives and distributes proteins for the cell. Describe what the Golgi apparatus looks like. **Answers will vary. Students may say that it looks like flattened sacs that are closely spaced.**

4. How many nuclei do you see in the cell? **one**

5. Look at the close-up of the plasma membrane. What is it made of? **The plasma membrane is made up of two layers of phospholipids with proteins embedded on its surface or within the membrane.**

---

**Chapter 7**  A View of the Cell, *continued*

## Review the Vocabulary

| | | |
|---|---|---|
| cell | electron microscope | nucleolus |
| cell theory | endoplasmic reticulum | nucleus |
| cell wall | eukaryote (yew KER ee oht) | organelle |
| chlorophyll | flagella | phospholipid |
| chloroplast | fluid mosaic model | plasma membrane |
| chromatin | Golgi apparatus (GALW jee) | plastid |
| cilia | homeostasis | prokaryote (pro KER ee oht) |
| compound light | lysome | ribosome |
| microscope | microfilament | selective permeability |
| cytoplasm | microtubule | transport protein |
| cytoskeleton | mitochondria | vacuole |

Review the Chapter 7 vocabulary words listed above. Match the words with the definitions below.

1. Cell having a nucleus and other membrane-bound organelles ___**eukaryote**___

2. Short, hairlike projections on a cell's surface that are composed of microtubules ___**cilia**___

3. Fluid-filled space within the cytoplasm; temporarily stores food ___**vacuole**___

4. Building block of both unicellular and multicellular organisms ___**cell**___

5. Contains the cell's DNA and manages cell functions ___**nucleus**___

6. Green pigment that traps light energy from the sun ___**chlorophyll**___

7. The process of maintaining the cell's environment ___**homeostasis**___

8. Organelles in which food molecules are broken down to produce ATP ___**mitochondria**___

9. Creates selective permeability of plasma membrane ___**transport protein**___

10. Rigid structure outside the plasma membrane of plant cell ___**cell wall**___

11. Membrane sacs that receive and package proteins ___**Golgi apparatus**___

12. Serves as a boundary between the cell and its external environment ___**plasma membrane**___

13. Cell lacking a nucleus or other membrane-bound organelles ___**prokaryote**___

---

**Content Mastery**

Name _____   Date _____   Class _____

## Chapter 8  Cellular Transport and the Cell Cycle

### Get the Big Picture

Study the picture and answer the questions that follow.

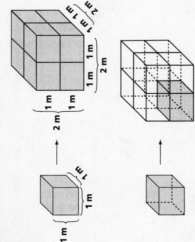

When a cube is doubled in size, the outside area, called the surface area, grows by four times the size. The inside area, called the volume, grows by eight times.

1. Suppose you double the length, height, and width of a cube. By how many times does the surface area of the cube increase?
   **four**

2. Suppose you double the length, height, and width of a cube. By how many times does the volume of the cube increase? Hint: count the number of little cubes inside the big cube.
   **eight**

3. Think about what you have just learned about what happens to the surface area and volume of a cube when it doubles in size. What will happen to the surface area and volume of a cell if it doubles in size? The volume will increase by eight.
   **The surface area of the cell will increase by four. The volume will increase by eight.**

4. How would this increase in cell size affect the cell's ability to get nutrients and get rid of wastes?
   **It would take longer for the cell to get the nutrients it needs and to get rid of its wastes, possibly causing starvation or poisoning.**

5. What does a cell do to make sure that it does not grow too big?
   **It divides.**

---

**Content Mastery**

Name _____   Date _____   Class _____

## Chapter 8  Cellular Transport and the Cell Cycle, *continued*

*Section 8.1 Cellular Transport*

### Study the Diagrams

Study the diagrams of the cells. Then circle the word that best completes each sentence.

*Cell with water molecules and dissolved particles*

*Cell after being placed in an isotonic solution*

*Cell after being placed in a hypotonic solution*

*Cell after being placed in a hypertonic solution*

• *Water molecule*   ○ *Dissolved particle*

When the cell is placed in an isotonic solution, water molecules move into and out of the cell at the same rate.

When the cell is placed in a hypotonic solution, more water molecules enter than leave the cell.

When the cell is placed in a hypertonic solution, more water molecules leave the cell than enter the cell.

1. Placing a cell in a hypertonic solution causes the cell to (swell, **shrink**, stay the same).

2. Placing a cell in an isotonic solution causes the cell to (swell, shrink, **stay the same**).

3. Placing a cell in a hypotonic solution causes the cell to (**swell**, shrink, stay the same).

Name _____ Date _____ Class _____

**Chapter 8**

# Cellular Transport and the Cell Cycle, *continued*

Content Mastery

## Review the Vocabulary

Use the Chapter 8 vocabulary words in the box below to fill in the puzzle. You will not use all of the words.

| centromere |
| cancer |
| gene |
| centrioles |
| spindle |
| chromosomes |
| mitosis |

**ACROSS**
1. joins two sister chromatids
3. process of nuclear division

**DOWN**
1. structures that contain DNA
2. small, dark, cylindrical structures made of microtubules
4. result of uncontrolled cell division

Use the vocabulary words in the box below to fill in the blanks in the statements. You will not use all of the words.

| isotonic solution | hypotonic solution | endocytosis | active transport |
| hypertonic solution | osmosis | exocytosis | passive transport |

5. In a __**hypotonic solution**__, the concentration of dissolved substances is lower than the concentration inside a cell.

6. __**Osmosis**__ is the diffusion of water through a selectively permeable membrane.

7. __**Exocytosis**__ is the expulsion of materials from a vacuole of a cell.

CONTENT MASTERY

CHAPTER 8  BIOLOGY: The Dynamics of Life  **39**

---

Name _____ Date _____ Class _____

**Chapter 8**

# Cellular Transport and the Cell Cycle, *continued*

Content Mastery

### Section 8.2 Cell Growth and Reproduction
### Section 8.3 Control of the Cell Cycle

## Study the Diagrams

Study the diagrams of the cell cycle and answer the questions that follow.

**Cell Cycle**

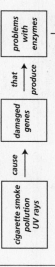

Interphase  Prophase  Metaphase  Anaphase  Telophase

1. Chromosomes move to the middle of the spindle during which phase? __**metaphase**__

2. What are sister chromatids? When do they separate? __**Sister chromatids are the two halves of a replicated chromosome that separate during anaphase.**__

3. During which phase do the chromosomes first become visible? __**prophase**__

4. In multicellular organisms, the cell cycle produces groups of cells that perform the same function. What are these groups of cells called? __**tissues**__

Study the diagram showing the causes and results of an abnormal cell cycle. Then answer the questions that follow.

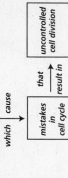

5. What happens when there are problems with the enzymes that control the cell cycle? __**Mistakes occur in the cell cycle.**__

6. Name three environmental factors that can damage the genes that produce those enzymes. __**cigarette smoke, pollution, and UV rays**__

7. What can result from an abnormal cell cycle? __**uncontrolled cell division and cancer**__

**40**  CHAPTER 8  BIOLOGY: The Dynamics of Life

CONTENT MASTERY

---

---

Name _____   Date _____   Class _____

# Chapter 9   Energy in a Cell

## Get the Big Picture

Study the picture. Then answer the questions that follow.

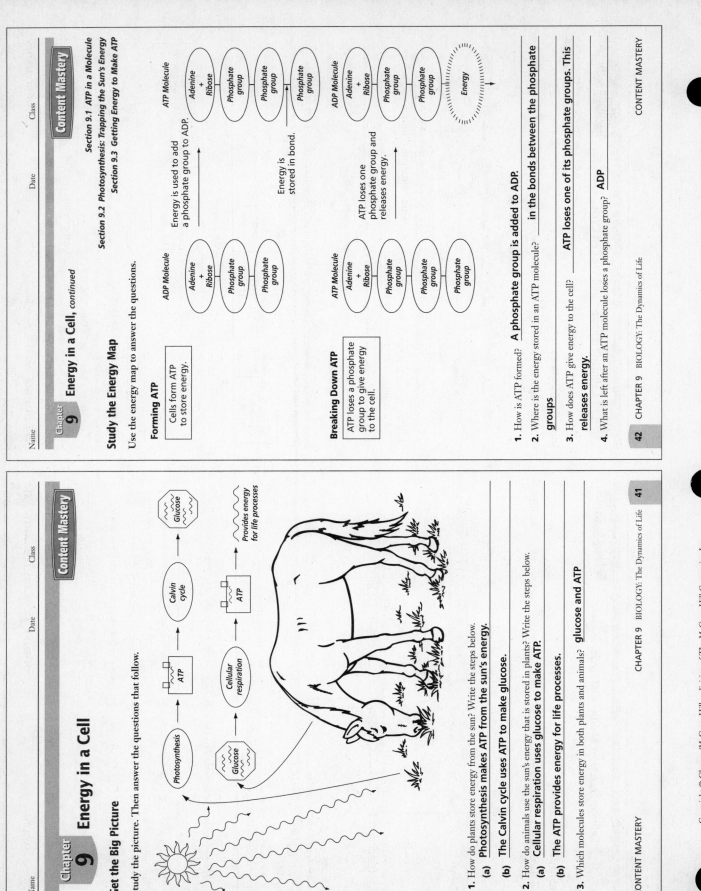

1. How do plants store energy from the sun? Write the steps below.
   (a) **Photosynthesis makes ATP from the sun's energy.**
   (b) **The Calvin cycle uses ATP to make glucose.**

2. How do animals use the sun's energy that is stored in plants? Write the steps below.
   (a) **Cellular respiration uses glucose to make ATP.**
   (b) **The ATP provides energy for life processes.**

3. Which molecules store energy in both plants and animals?   **glucose and ATP**

CONTENT MASTERY                    CHAPTER 9   BIOLOGY: The Dynamics of Life   41

---

Name _____   Date _____   Class _____

# Chapter 9   Energy in a Cell, *continued*

Section 9.1 *ATP in a Molecule*
Section 9.2 *Photosynthesis: Trapping the Sun's Energy*
Section 9.3 *Getting Energy to Make ATP*

## Study the Energy Map

Use the energy map to answer the questions.

### Forming ATP

Cells form ATP to store energy.

Energy is used to add a phosphate group to ADP.

Energy is stored in bond.

### Breaking Down ATP

ATP loses a phosphate group to give energy to the cell.

ATP loses one phosphate group and releases energy.

1. How is ATP formed?   **A phosphate group is added to ADP.**

2. Where is the energy stored in an ATP molecule?   **in the bonds between the phosphate groups**

3. How does ATP give energy to the cell?   **ATP loses one of its phosphate groups. This releases energy.**

4. What is left after an ATP molecule loses a phosphate group?   **ADP**

42   CHAPTER 9   BIOLOGY: The Dynamics of Life                    CONTENT MASTERY

Name _____ Date _____ Class _____

## Chapter 9  Energy in a Cell, *continued*

Content Mastery

### Study the Diagram

Use the diagram to answer the question.

Sunlight hits green chlorophyll molecules.

The chlorophylls' electrons absorb the sun's energy.

The electrons move to other molecules.

As the electrons move, they release energy to form ATP molecules.

5. Describe the steps that plants use to store the sun's energy. Remember to number the steps.
(1) Sunlight hits chlorophyll molecules. (2) Chlorophylls' electrons absorb the energy. (3) Electrons move to other molecules. (4) Electrons release energy to form ATP molecules.

### Study the Energy Map

Use the energy map to answer the questions.

**Energy Processes**

**Photosynthesis**
- Light energy
- Light-dependent reactions
- Calvin cycle
- Stored energy

**Cellular Respiration**
- Sugar molecules → Glycolysis → Citric acid cycle → Electron transport chain → Released energy

6. a. What happens to energy during photosynthesis? Energy is stored.
   b. What happens to energy during cellular respiration? Energy is released.

7. What process does your body use to get the energy it needs for running or for riding a bike? aerobic respiration

---

Name _____ Date _____ Class _____

## Chapter 9  Energy in a Cell, *continued*

Content Mastery

### Review the Vocabulary

Use the Chapter 9 Vocabulary words in the box below. Review the definitions of these words. Then draw a line to match each word in the box with its definition.

a. light-independent reactions
b. photolysis
c. chlorophyll
d. adenosine triphosphate
e. adenosine diphosphate
f. electron transport chain
g. photosynthesis
h. cellular respiration

1. Breaks down sugar molecules to produce ATP
2. Green pigment that absorbs sunlight
3. Splitting of water during photosynthesis to resupply electrons to chlorophyll
4. Series of proteins that pass electrons
5. Energy-storing molecule that has two phosphate groups
6. Part of photosynthesis that does not require sunlight and takes place in the stroma
7. Biological process that traps energy from the sun to make carbohydrates
8. Energy-storing molecule that has three phosphate groups

Look at each Chapter 9 vocabulary word in the box below. If the word goes with photosynthesis, write it in the table under *Photosynthesis*. If the word goes with aerobic respiration, write it under *Aerobic Respiration*. If the word goes with anaerobic processes, write it under *Anaerobic Processes*. A word may go under more than one heading.

citric acid cycle   light-dependent reactions   glycolysis   electron transport chain
lactic acid fermentation   alcoholic fermentation   Calvin cycle

| Photosynthesis | Aerobic Respiration | Anaerobic Processes |
| --- | --- | --- |
| light-dependent reactions | citric acid cycle | glycolysis |
| Calvin cycle | glycolysis | lactic acid fermentation |
| electron transport chain | electron transport chain | alcoholic fermentation |

**BioDigest**
**3**   The Life of a Cell

**Content Mastery**

## Get the Big Picture

Find the red and blue headings in BioDigest 3. Use the blue headings to fill in the rectangles in the idea map below. Use the red headings to fill in the ovals. One rectangle and one oval have been filled in for you.

### The Life of a Cell

- (A) **The Chemistry of Life**
  - **Element and Atoms** (oval)
  - **Organic Compounds** (oval)
- (B) **Eukaryotes and Prokaryotes**
- (C) **Cell Organelles**
  - *Plasma Membrane* (oval)
  - **Control of Cell Functions** (oval)
  - **Assembly, Transport, and Storage** (oval)
  - **Energy Transformers** (oval)
  - **Support and Locomotion** (oval)
- (D) **Diffusion and Osmosis**
- (E) **Mitosis**
- (F) **Energy in a Cell**

Each statement below goes with one of the headings in the rectangles above. Write the letter of each heading on the line in front of the statement it goes with.

**B**   The presence or lack of membrane-bound structures within cells is used to classify cells.

**C**   The functions of a cell are controlled by the nucleus.

**F**   Cells use ATP as the most common source of energy.

**A**   The smallest component of an element is an atom.

**E**   A cell divides when it reaches a size that its plasma membrane cannot transport enough nutrients and wastes to maintain cell growth.

---

**BioDigest**
**3**   The Life of a Cell, *continued*

**Content Mastery**

## Study the Reading

Every substance is an element or a combination of elements. Elements include oxygen, which has the atomic symbol O; carbon, C; hydrogen, H; aluminum, Al; and nitrogen, N. The smallest component of an element is an atom. Compounds are combinations of elements. Molecules are atoms that have joined together. Organic compounds contain carbon. The four main types of organic compounds that make up living things are carbohydrates, lipids, proteins, and nucleic acids. Carbohydrates are compounds that contain carbon, hydrogen, and oxygen.

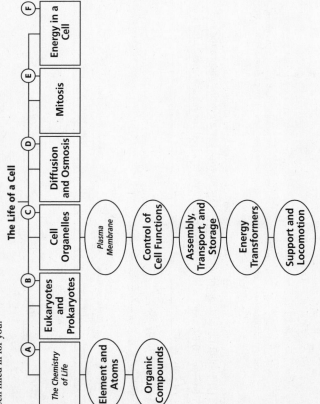

Na      H–O–H      O–N–O

*sodium*      *water*      *nitrogen monoxide*

*glucose*

1. Which of the four substances shown is an element?
   **sodium**

2. What two elements make up water?
   **oxygen and hydrogen**

3. Which substance is an organic compound?
   **glucose**

4. Which substance is a carbohydrate?
   **glucose**

*glycine*   +   *lysine*   →   *a dipeptide*   +   *water*

5. The diagram above shows the formation of an organic compound called a dipeptide. In the reaction, two amino acids, glycine and lysine, are joined together by a peptide bond forming the dipeptide and water. Circle the atoms in glycine and lysine that form water when the peptide bond is formed.

Name _____ Date _____ Class _____

**Content Mastery**

**BioDigest 3**

## The Life of a Cell, *continued*

### Study the Pictures

**I** *Rate of water molecules moving across membrane*

Water molecule

Dissolved particle

Selectively permeable membrane

A  B

**II**

A  B

**III**  *Glycine*

A  B

| The concentration of dissolved particles on each side of the membrane is equal. | The concentration of dissolved particles on side A is less than the concentration on side B. | The concentration of dissolved particles on side A is more than the concentration on side B. |

Characteristics of isotonic, hypotonic, and hypertonic solutions

• The concentration of a dissolved material in an **isotonic** solution is the same as the concentration of the dissolved material in a cell.
• The concentration of a dissolved material in a **hypotonic** solution is less than the concentration of the dissolved material within a cell.
• The concentration of a dissolved material in a **hypertonic** solution is more than the concentration of the dissolved material within a cell.

1. In which picture is the rate of water molecules moving from side A to B greater than the rate of water moving from side B to A?
**II**

2. If picture II represents a cell placed in a hypertonic solution, does side A or side B represent the interior of the cell?
**A**

3. Describe what will happen to animal cells placed in a hypotonic solution. Explain why this will happen.
**The cells will swell and perhaps burst as water molecules enter the cell by osmosis.**

4. Describe what will happen to animal cells placed in a hypertonic solution.
**The cells will shrivel as water molecules leave the cell by osmosis.**

CONTENT MASTERY

BIODIGEST 3  BIOLOGY: The Dynamics of Life

47

---

Name _____ Date _____ Class _____

**Content Mastery**

**BioDigest 3**

## The Life of a Cell, *continued*

### Study the Pictures

The pictures show the five stages of mitosis in sequence. Write the letter of the description and the letter of the name of the stage below each picture.

1. _d, B_   2. _c, D_   3. _a, C_   4. _b, A_   5. _e, E_

**Description**

a. Chromosomes move to equator of the cell.
b. Chromosomes separate and move to opposite poles of the cell.
c. Duplicated chromosomes condense and mitotic spindle forms on the opposite poles of the cell.
d. Intense metabolic activity takes place prior to mitosis.
e. Two daughter cells each with a complete set of chromosomes form as cytoplasm divides.

**Stage**

A. anaphase
B. interphase
C. metaphase
D. prophase
E. telophase

### Study the Reading

Cells store energy in molecules of adenosine triphosphate (ATP). As plant cells produce sucrose from glucose and fructose, energy is released from the breakdown of ATP to adenosine diphosphate (ADP) and inorganic phosphate ($P_i$).

Use the word list to complete the diagram on the right.

ATP
energy
fructose
sucrose

$$ATP \longrightarrow energy + ADP + P_i$$

$$glucose + fructose \longrightarrow sucrose + water$$

48  BIODIGEST 3  BIOLOGY: The Dynamics of Life

CONTENT MASTERY

---

**Content Mastery**

# Chapter 10 Mendel and Meiosis

## Get the Big Picture

Study the diagram and read the explanations. Then answer the questions below.

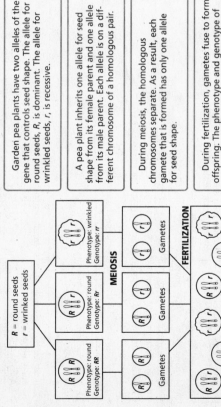

R = round seeds
r = wrinkled seeds

Phenotype: round
Genotype: RR

Phenotype: round
Genotype: Rr

Phenotype: wrinkled
Genotype: r

**MEIOSIS**

Gametes

**FERTILIZATION**

Gametes

**Offspring**

Garden pea plants have two alleles of the gene that controls seed shape. The allele for round seeds, R, is dominant. The allele for wrinkled seeds, r, is recessive.

A pea plant inherits one allele for seed shape from its female parent and one allele from its male parent. Each allele is on a different chromosome of a homologous pair.

During meiosis, the homologous chromosomes separate. As a result, each gamete that is formed has only one allele for seed shape.

During fertilization, gametes fuse to form offspring. The phenotype and genotype of an offspring depend on which alleles were in the gametes that produced the offspring.

1. How is the phenotype of a pea plant different from its genotype?
**The phenotype is the appearance of the plant. The genotype is the plant's combination of alleles.**

2. Why does a pea plant with the genotype Rr have round seeds, not wrinkled seeds?
**The allele for round seeds, R, is dominant to the allele for wrinkled seeds, r.**

3. Why does a pea plant with the genotype Rr produce some gametes that have the allele for round seeds, R, and other gametes that have the allele for wrinkled seeds, r?
**The pea plant's two alleles separate during meiosis.**

4. Two gametes fused and formed an offspring that had wrinkled seeds. What kind of allele for seed shape did each gamete have?
**Each gamete had an allele for wrinkled seeds, r.**

---

**Content Mastery**

# Chapter 10 Mendel and Meiosis, continued

### Section 10.1 Mendel's Laws of Heredity

## Study the Diagram

The diagram below shows one of the crosses Mendel made while studying garden pea plants. Identify the genotypes of the plants. Use the letter T to represent the allele for tallness and the letter t to represent the allele for shortness. Write one allele in each box.

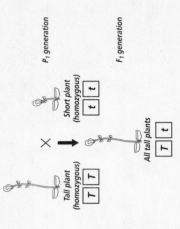

$P_1$ generation

Tall plant
(homozygous)

| T | T |

×

Short plant
(homozygous)

| t | t |

$F_1$ generation

All tall plants

| T | t |

Use the diagram above to answer the following questions.

1. Why were all the plants in the $F_1$ generation tall?
**The allele for tallness is dominant to the allele for shortness.**

2. Mendel continued his experiment by allowing the $F_1$ plants to self-pollinate. Make a Punnett square to find the expected genotypes of the offspring.

|     | T   | t   |
| --- | --- | --- |
| **T** | TT  | Tt  |
| **t** | Tt  | tt  |

3. What fraction of the offspring of the $F_1$ generation would you expect to be tall? What fraction would you expect to be short?
**Three-fourths of the offspring would be expected to be tall. One-fourth would be expected to be short.**

**Content Mastery**

## Chapter 10 — Mendel and Meiosis, *continued*

### Section 10.2 Meiosis

**Study the Diagram**

Meiosis I: Prophase I, Metaphase I, Anaphase I, Telophase I

Meiosis II: Prophase II, Metaphase II, Anaphase II, Telophase II

**Use the diagram to answer the questions.**

1. Meiosis I begins with one cell. By the end of meiosis II, how many cells are formed?
**four**

2. During which phase(s) does crossing over occur? Why is crossing over important?
**Crossing over occurs during prophase I. Crossing over is important because it leads**
**to greater variation among organisms.**

3. Compare how homologous chromosomes line up during metaphase I and metaphase II.
**During metaphase I, homologous chromosomes line up in pairs in the middle of the**
**spindle. During metaphase II, homologous chromosomes line up randomly in the**
**middle of the spindle.**

4. Why is it important that meiosis produces gametes that have only half the number of chromosomes of the parent cell?
**If the number of chromosomes were not reduced, the offspring would have twice**
**the number of chromosomes as the parents.**

---

## Chapter 10 — Mendel and Meiosis, *continued*

### Review the Vocabulary

Review the definitions of the Chapter 10 vocabulary words in the box below. Then match each word with its definition by writing the letter of the word on the line provided.

| | |
|---|---|
| a. genetics | |
| b. fertilization | |
| c. heredity | |
| d. phenotype | |
| e. nondisjunction | |
| f. genotype | |

**b** 1. when male and female gametes unite
**e** 2. homologous chromosomes not separating properly
**c** 3. passing on of traits to offspring
**a** 4. study of heredity
**d** 5. the appearance of an organism
**f** 6. the genetic makeup of an organism

Use the Chapter 10 vocabulary words in the box below to fill in the blanks in the sentences. You will not use all the words.

| | |
|---|---|
| diploid (DIH ployd) | genetic recombination |
| haploid (HAP loyd) | gametes (GAM eets) |
| heterozygous | dominant |
| sexual reproduction | pollination |

homologous (huh MAHL uh gus)
crossing over
meiosis (mi OH sus)
zygote (ZI goht)

7. A cell with two of each kind of chromosome is called **diploid** .

8. Sperm or egg cells are **gametes** .

9. A cell with one of each kind of chromosome is a(n) **haploid** cell.

10. **Homologous** chromosomes have genes for the same traits in the same order on both chromosomes.

11. Specialized body cells make gametes in a process that involves **meiosis** .

12. A(n) **zygote** is the cell created when a sperm fertilizes an egg.

13. **Sexual reproduction** involves the production and subsequent fusion of gametes.

14. When nonsister chromatids exchange genes, the process is called **crossing over** .

15. The reassortment of genetic information, which results in variation among organisms, is called **genetic recombination** .

---

## Left page

### Chapter 11  DNA and Genes

## Get the Big Picture

**Study the picture. Then answer the questions.**

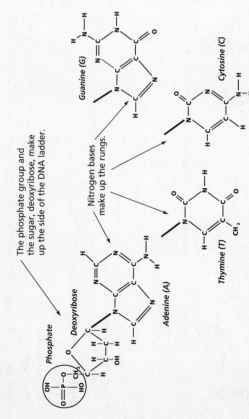

The phosphate group and the sugar, deoxyribose, make up the side of the DNA ladder.

Phosphate

Deoxyribose

Nitrogen bases make up the rungs.

Adenine (A)

Guanine (G)

Thymine (T)

Cytosine (C)

A DNA molecule is similar in shape to a ladder.

1. How many types of nitrogen bases does DNA have? **four**
   Name them. **adenine, thymine, cytosine, guanine**

2. What are the sides of the DNA ladder made of?
   **a phosphate group and a sugar**

3. What are the steps of the DNA ladder made of?
   **pairs of nitrogen bases**

4. What kind of bonds hold the chains of building blocks together?
   **hydrogen bonds**

CONTENT MASTERY          CHAPTER 11  BIOLOGY: The Dynamics of Life  **53**

---

## Right page

### Chapter 11  DNA and Genes, *continued*

*Section 11.1 DNA: The Molecule of Heredity*

## Study the Diagram

When the DNA ladder replicates, or copies itself, the ladder breaks apart. You can think of the ladder breaking apart as a zipper unzipping. When the two sides of the ladder are apart, free nucleotides attach to the nucleotides already on the sides of the ladder, and two copies of the DNA are formed. The copies are the same as the original because adenine (A) usually pairs with thymine (T). Cytosine (C) usually pairs with guanine (G).

The diagram below shows an unzipped strand of DNA. Write the letters (A, T, C, or G) of the bases that will pair with the bases on the strand. Some of the bases have been paired for you.

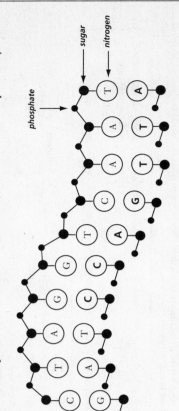

phosphate

sugar

nitrogen

T — A
A — T
A — T
C — G
T — A
G — C
G — C
A — T
T — A
C — G

1. **True or false?** Nucleotide bases already attached to proteins form the copied side of the DNA ladder.
   **false**

2. **True or false?** The process of DNA replication results in a copy of the original strand of DNA.
   **true**

3. **True or false?** Sugar and phosphates provide the energy for DNA replication.
   **false**

4. **True or false?** The final result of DNA replication is two copies of the original DNA strand.
   **true**

**54**  CHAPTER 11  BIOLOGY: The Dynamics of Life          CONTENT MASTERY

Name _____ Date _____ Class _____

**Content Mastery**

## Chapter 11 DNA and Genes, *continued*

**Section 11.2 *From DNA to Protein***
**Section 11.3 *Genetic Changes***

### Study the Diagram

The mRNA strand shown below is in the process of synthesizing, or making, proteins from amino acids. tRNA molecules bring the amino acids to the mRNA strand. Circle the tRNA molecule that will attach to the codon shown on the mRNA strand. Remember, cytosine (C) pairs with guanine (G), and adenine (A) pairs with uracil (U).

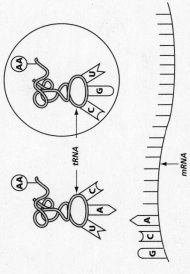

**Now look at the diagram again and answer the questions.**

**1.** How did you know which tRNA molecule would attach to the codon shown?
**The base pairs matched.**

**2.** Suppose one of the bases on the mRNA was changed. Would the same tRNA molecule would attach to the strand? Explain your answer.
**No. If one of the bases on the mRNA strand was changed, it would not match the bases on the same tRNA molecule, so that molecule would not attach.**

**3.** What would happen to the mRNA strand if an incorrect amino acid was inserted?
**The protein shape could change, altering the molecule's entire structure.**

---

Name _____ Date _____ Class _____

**Content Mastery**

## Chapter 11 DNA and Genes, *continued*

### Review the Vocabulary

Review the Chapter 11 vocabulary words in the box below. Then write **true** or **false** after each statement.

| double helix | nitrogen | DNA replication |
|---|---|---|

**1.** DNA replication produces an exact copy of a DNA molecule. ____ **true**

**2.** A double helix is shaped like a straight ladder. ____ **false**

**3.** DNA has only three different nitrogen bases. ____ **false**

Use the vocabulary words in the box below. Review the definitions of these words. Then draw a line to match each word in the box with its definition.

**a.** transcription
**b.** translation
**c.** transfer RNA
**d.** ribosomal (ri buh SOH muh) RNA
**e.** messenger RNA
**f.** codon (KOH dahn)

**4.** This is the set of three nitrogen bases used to make amino acids.

**5.** This happens when a sequence of bases in mRNA is used to make a sequence of amino acids.

**6.** This brings amino acids to ribosomes.

**7.** This carries the copied DNA code out to the cytoplasm.

**8.** This happens when DNA unzips and makes an RNA copy of itself.

**9.** This is the part of the RNA that makes up ribosomes.

Use the vocabulary words in the box below to fill in the blanks in the statements. You will not use all the words.

| frameshift mutation | nondisjunction |
| (FRAYME shihft • mew TAY shun) | point mutation |
| chromosomal mutation | mutation |
| mutagen (MYEWT uh jun) | |

**10.** A ___ **point mutation** ___ is a change in a single base pair in DNA.

**11.** Broken chromosomes are one cause of ___ **chromosomal mutation** ___.

**12.** ___ **Nondisjunction** ___ happens when homologous chromosomes fail to separate properly.

**13.** A ___ **mutagen** ___ is any agent that can cause a change in DNA.

Name _____ Date _____ Class _____

**Content Mastery**

## Chapter 12 Patterns of Heredity and Human Genetics

### Get the Big Picture

Find the red and blue headings in Chapter 12 of your textbook. Use the red headings to fill in the rectangles in the idea map below. Use the blue headings to fill in the ovals. Some of the rectangles and ovals have been filled in for you.

**12.1 Mendelian Inheritance of Human Traits**

- A Making a Pedigree
  - Pedigrees illustrate inheritance
  - *Analyzing a pedigree*
- B *Simple Recessive Heredity*
  - Cystic fibrosis
  - Tay-Sachs disease
  - *Phenylketonuria*
- C Simple Dominant Heredity
  - *Simple dominant traits*
  - Huntington's disease

**12.2 When Heredity Follows Different Rules**

- A Complex Patterns of Inheritance
  - *Incomplete dominance: appearance of a third phenotype*
  - Codominance: Expression of both alleles
  - Multiple phenotypes from multiple alleles
  - Sex determination
  - *Sex-linked inheritance*
  - Polygenic inheritance
- B Environmental Influences
  - Influence of internal environment
  - *Influence of external environment*

Each statement below goes with one of the headings in the rectangles above. Write the letter of each heading on the line in front of the statement it goes with.

**A** _____ Scientists use pedigrees to find the genetic makeup of a related group of organisms.

**D** _____ Many inheritance patterns are more complex than those studied by Mendel.

**B** _____ Most genetic disorders are caused by recessive alleles.

**E** _____ Both internal and external factors affect how a gene shows up.

CONTENT MASTERY                    CHAPTER 12    BIOLOGY: The Dynamics of Life    **57**

---

Name _____ Date _____ Class _____

**Content Mastery**

## Chapter 12 Patterns of Heredity and Human Genetics, *continued*

**Section 12.1 Mendelian Inheritance of Human Traits**

### Analyze the Pedigree

Below is a pedigree for a group of dogs. Some of the dogs in this group are tall, and some are short. Some are tall but carry the recessive short trait.

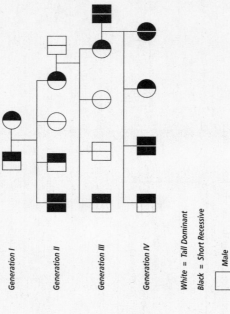

Generation I

Generation II

Generation III

Generation IV

White = Tall Dominant

Black = Short Recessive

□ Male

○ Female

1. How many generations are shown in the pedigree?
   **four**

2. How many offspring did the parents in the first generation have?
   **four**

3. What does the square in generation I stand for? Why is it half shaded?
   **The square stands for a tall male dog. It is half shaded because the dog carries the recessive short trait.**

4. Which dog was the first in the family to be short?
   **the first male in generation II**

5. A female dog from generation III has four puppies. How many of these offspring carry the short trait? How many of the offspring are short?
   **Four carry the short trait. Two are short.**

**58**    CHAPTER 12    BIOLOGY: The Dynamics of Life    CONTENT MASTERY

Name _____ Date _____ Class _____

**Content Mastery**

## Chapter 12 Patterns of Heredity and Human Genetics, *continued*

**Section 12.2 When Heredity Follows Different Rules**

**Section 12.3 Complex Inheritance of Human Traits**

### Study the Diagram

This diagram shows the mating of a human male (XY) and a human female (XX). Use the diagram to answer the questions.

1. What do the letters X and Y stand for? **the sex chromosomes**

2. Which chromosome is found only in the male? **the Y chromosome**

3. True or false? A person having two X chromosomes is female. **true**

4. In the mating shown in the diagram, which statement is **true**? Circle the letter.
   a. All the offspring are female.
   b. All the offspring are male.
   **c.** One-half the offspring are female.
   d. Three of the four offspring are female.

5. What happens to offspring with an extra sex chromosome, such as XXX or XXY? **Some of these individuals exhibit mental retardation. Others, although leading active lives, will be unable to have children.**

---

Name _____ Date _____ Class _____

**Content Mastery**

## Chapter 12 Patterns of Heredity and Human Genetics, *continued*

### Review the Vocabulary

| | |
|---|---|
| autosomes | multiple alleles |
| carrier | pedigree |
| codominant alleles (koh DAH muh nunt • uh LEELZ) | polygenic inheritance |
| fetus | sex chromosomes |
| incomplete dominance | sex-linked trait |

The Chapter 12 vocabulary words are listed above. Review the definitions of these words. Then fill in each blank in the statements below with the correct word from the list. You will not use all the words.

1. A(n) __**pedigree**__ shows an individual's family tree.

2. Some genes are located on sex chromosomes. A(n) __**sex-linked trait**__ is a trait controlled by these genes.

3. In humans, the 22 pairs of matching homologous chromosomes are called __**autosomes**__.

4. Traits controlled by more than two alleles are said to have __**multiple alleles**__.

5. An individual with a recessive allele for an undesirable trait is called a(n) __**carrier**__.

6. In __**incomplete dominance**__, the phenotype of the heterozygote is intermediate between those of the two homozygotes.

7. __**Sex chromosomes**__ are chromosomes that determine the sex of an individual.

8. __**Codominant alleles**__ cause the phenotypes of both homozygotes to be produced in the heterozygote.

Name _____ Date _____ Class _____

**Content Mastery**

## Chapter 13 Genetic Technology

### Get the Big Picture

Study the paragraphs in the boxes and answer the questions.

> Scientists have learned how to move genes from one organism to another. This process is called **genetic engineering**. Genetic engineering can be used to give an organism new traits. For example, certain bacteria have been developed with the ability to clean up oil spills. They can break down oil into harmless substances. Scientists also use genetically engineered bacteria to improve agriculture and to treat human disease.

1. In genetic engineering, what is moved from one organism to another one?
   **genes**

2. Give two examples of how genetic engineering can help humans.
   **Answers may include any two of the following: Genetics engineering can clean up oil spills, improve agriculture, and treat human diseases.**

> The human genome is made up of all the genes on the 46 human chromosomes. Scientists are now mapping the human genome. They intend to use this map to detect, treat, and cure genetic disorders. DNA fingerprinting is another use of this technology. Every person's DNA is unique. Therefore, DNA from blood, skin, or hair found at a crime scene may be compared with the DNA of a crime suspect. This evidence could give clues about the guilt or innocence of a suspect.

3. What is the human genome made of?
   **all the genes on the 46 human chromosomes**

4. Why is the mapping of the human genome important?
   **This information can be used to detect, treat, and cure genetic disorders. It can also be used for DNA fingerprinting.**

---

Name _____ Date _____ Class _____

**Content Mastery**

## Chapter 13 Genetic Technology, continued

Section 13.1 *Applied Genetics*
Section 13.2 *Recombinant DNA Technology*

### Complete the Idea Map

Find the red heading *Applications of DNA Technology* in Chapter 13 of your textbook. Then find the blue headings and fill in the rectangles in the idea map below. They describe ways that DNA technology can be used. Next, write an example of each use in the circle below it. Two rectangles and one circle have been filled in for you.

**Applications of DNA Technology**

- Recombinant bacteria in agriculture
  - Soybeans that increase production of nitrates
- Recombinant bacteria in industry
  - Bacteria that break down pollutants
- Transgenic bacteria in medicine
  - *Bacteria used to produce insulin*
- Transgenic plants
  - Plants that produce insecticides
- Transgenic animals
  - Livestock that produce more milk

Use the idea map to answer the questions.

1. True or false? Some bacteria are used in industry to break down pollutants. **true**

2. True or false? Bacteria are all harmful organisms that should be eliminated. **false**

3. True or false? Some plants produce their own insecticides that keep pests away. **true**

4. What is genetic technology?
   **Using various methods to increase the frequency of desired alleles in a population.**

## Left Page (63)

Name _____ Date _____ Class _____

**Content Mastery**

**Chapter 13  Genetic Technology,** *continued*

**Section 13.3  The Human Genome**

### Complete the Idea Map

Find the red heading *Applications of the Human Genome Project* in Chapter 13 of your textbook. Then find the blue headings and fill in the rectangles in the idea map that describe ways that the Human Genome Project can be used. Next, write an example of each use in the circle below it. One rectangle and one circle have been filled in for you.

**Applications of the Human Genome Project**

- **Diagnosis of genetic disorders**
  - *Detect genetic disorders before birth*
- **Gene therapy**
  - Treat patients suffering from cystic fibrosis
- **DNA fingerprinting**
  - Convict or acquit crime suspects

Use the idea map to answer the questions.

**1. True or false?** Parents who want to know if their children may be genetically inclined towards certain disorders can have their children DNA fingerprinted before birth.

**false**

**2. True or false?** People suspected of particular types of crimes may have their DNA examined for evidence.

**true**

**3. True or false?** Some genetic disorders may be treated with proper detection and diagnosis.

**true**

CONTENT MASTERY

CHAPTER 13  BIOLOGY: The Dynamics of Life  **63**

## Right Page (64)

Name _____ Date _____ Class _____

**Content Mastery**

**Chapter 13  Genetic Technology,** *continued*

### Review the Vocabulary

Use the Chapter 13 vocabulary words to complete the crossword puzzle. One vocabulary word has been filled in for you.

test cross
clones
gene splicing
gene therapy
genetic engineering
human genome
linkage map
plasmid
recombinant DNA
restriction enzyme
transgenic organism
vector

**Across**

3. organisms that are genetically identical
5. the thousands of genes that make up the 46 human chromosomes
6. DNA made by connecting pieces of DNA from different sources
8. small ring of DNA
9. A mechanical or biological _____ is used to transfer DNA.
10. A test _____ involves an individual of unknown genotype and an individual of known genotype.
11. An organism that has been changed by genetic engineering is a(n) _____ organism.

**Down**

1. therapy that can be used to correct genetic disorders
2. enzymes used to cut DNA molecules
4. map showing the location of genes on a chromosome
5. engineering used to move genes from one organism to another
7. Gene _____ is used to reconnect pieces of DNA.

**64**  CHAPTER 13  BIOLOGY: The Dynamics of Life

---

CONTENT MASTERY  ANSWER KEY  BIOLOGY: The Dynamics of Life  **T229**

Content Mastery

## BioDigest 4 Genetics

### Get the Big Picture

Read the paragraphs in the boxes. Then answer the questions.

From the smallest, simplest bacterium to you, all organisms have DNA. DNA is a chemical that stores the blueprints for each individual organism. DNA determines what each organism looks like and how it functions.

DNA is passed from parent to offspring. For example, ducks pass the information required to grow into ducklings to their young in DNA molecules. Your parents passed all the information needed for you to grow into a human adult to you in DNA molecules. The information about the color of your eyes is contained in DNA you received from your parents. This process is called heredity.

1. What is DNA and why is it important?

**DNA is a chemical that all living things contain. It stores the information that deter-**
**mines what organisms look like and how they function.**

2. Explain why ducks produce ducklings and not piglets when they reproduce.

**Offspring inherit the information about what kind of an organism they will**
**become from their parents. Ducks pass the information for becoming an adult duck**
**to their offspring.**

3. List three traits that you probably inherited from your parents. Explain why you think you inherited these things from your parents.

**Answers will vary. Students may suggest aspects of their appearance, personality,**
**or talents that they have. Students should explain that the information for these**
**traits is contained in the DNA they inherited from their parents.**

CONTENT MASTERY

BIODIGEST 4 BIOLOGY: The Dynamics of Life **65**

---

Content Mastery

## BioDigest 4 Genetics, continued

### Study the Diagram

Study the diagram. Then answer the questions.

1. The diagram above shows the shape of a DNA molecule. How would you describe the shape of this molecule? Accept any of the following answers: **double helix, spiral staircase, twisted ladder, or and other answer that suggests the shape of the molecule shown.**

2. If the DNA molecule were compared to a spiral staircase, which parts would make up the rails of the staircase? **phosphate groups and sugars**

3. If the DNA molecule were compared to a spiral staircase, which parts would make up the steps of the staircase? **the base pairs**

4. Which bases tend to pair together? **Adenine pairs with thymine. Guanine pairs with cytosine.**

**66** BIODIGEST 4 BIOLOGY: The Dynamics of Life CONTENT MASTERY

Name _____ Date _____ Class _____

**Content Mastery**

## Study the Diagram

**Read the paragraph in the box and study the diagram. Then answer the questions.**

> How does DNA convey its information? It converts its information into chemical messengers, called messenger RNA (mRNA), which are then translated into proteins. These proteins affect the appearance and the internal workings of an organism.

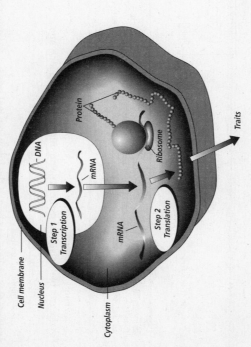

1. List two steps that are needed to convert information in DNA to proteins.
   **DNA converts its information into messenger RNA, which is then translated into proteins.**

2. Where does transcription take place in a cell?
   **in the nucleus**

3. Where does translation take place in a cell?
   **in the cytoplasm**

4. If your eyes are brown and your brother's eyes are blue, what can you conclude about your and your brother's DNA for eye color and proteins?
   **The DNA and the proteins that affect eye color in you and your brother are different. Your DNA makes proteins that make your eyes brown. Your brother's DNA makes proteins that make his eyes blue.**

---

Name _____ Date _____ Class _____

**Content Mastery**

## Study the Table

**Study the table. Then answer the questions.**

### Dominant vs. Recessive

| Trait | | | | F₁ Offspring |
|---|---|---|---|---|
| Flower color | Purple | × | White | = Purple (purple flower) |
| Pea color | Yellow | × | Green | = Yellow (yellow pea) |
| Pea texture | Round | × | Wrinkled | = Round (round pea) |
| Pod color | Green | × | Yellow | = Green (green pea pod) |
| Pod texture | Round | × | Constricted | = Round (round pea pod) |
| Flower height | Tall | × | Short | = Tall (tall pea plant) |

1. Look at the crosses shown in the table above. Do the offspring favor the pea plant with the dominant trait or the recessive trait?   **the dominant trait**

2. What happens to the alleles for the recessive traits in the offspring? Are they still represented in the offspring's DNA?
   **Yes, the alleles are still in the DNA, but the recessive traits are masked by the dominant traits.**

3. How could you demonstrate whether the purple-flowering offspring have the allele for white flowers?
   **You could cross a purple-flowering offspring with a white-flowering pea plant. If any of the offspring from this cross have white flowers, then the purple-flowering plant has an allele for white flowers.**

4. If you crossed two tall offspring, how many pea plants would be short?   **about 25%**

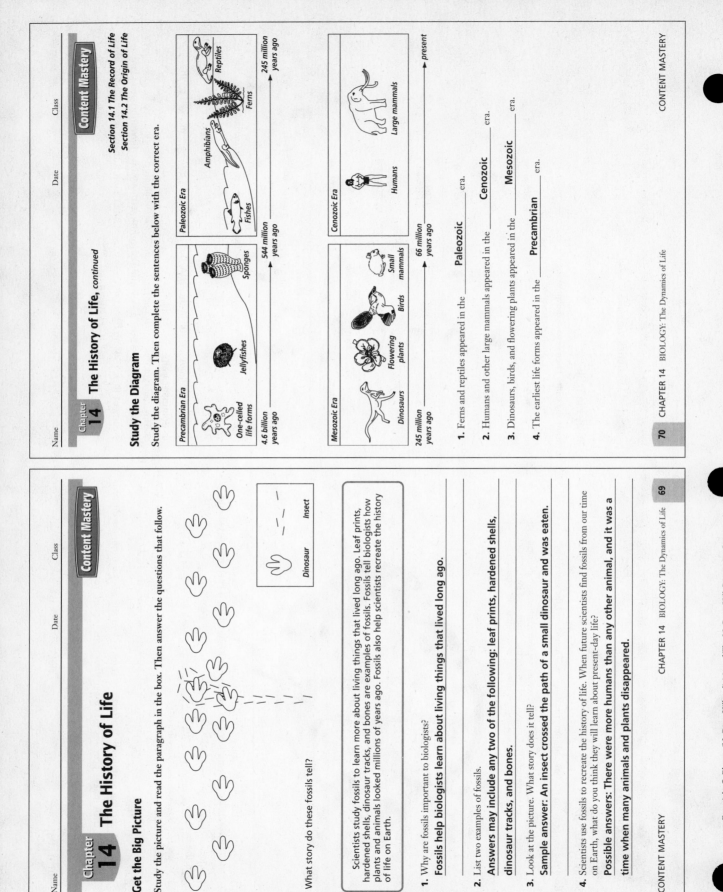

## Page 69 (Left)

Name _____ Date _____ Class _____

**Content Mastery**

### Chapter 14 — The History of Life

## Get the Big Picture

Study the picture and read the paragraph in the box. Then answer the questions that follow.

Dinosaur | Insect

What story do these fossils tell?

> Scientists study fossils to learn more about living things that lived long ago. Leaf prints, hardened shells, dinosaur tracks, and bones are examples of fossils. Fossils tell biologists how plants and animals looked millions of years ago. Fossils also help scientists recreate the history of life on Earth.

**1.** Why are fossils important to biologists?
**Fossils help biologists learn about living things that lived long ago.**

**2.** List two examples of fossils.
**Answers may include any two of the following: leaf prints, hardened shells, dinosaur tracks, and bones.**

**3.** Look at the picture. What story does it tell?
**Sample answer: An insect crossed the path of a small dinosaur and was eaten.**

**4.** Scientists use fossils to recreate the history of life. When future scientists find fossils from our time on Earth, what do you think they will learn about present-day life?
**Possible answers: There were more humans than any other animal, and it was a time when many animals and plants disappeared.**

CONTENT MASTERY

CHAPTER 14   BIOLOGY: The Dynamics of Life   **69**

Copyright © Glencoe/McGraw-Hill, a division of The McGraw-Hill Companies, Inc.

## Page 70 (Right)

Name _____ Date _____ Class _____

**Content Mastery**

### Chapter 14 — The History of Life, *continued*

Section 14.1 The Record of Life
Section 14.2 The Origin of Life

## Study the Diagram

Study the diagram. Then complete the sentences below with the correct era.

*Precambrian Era*
One-celled life forms | Jellyfishes | Sponges
4.6 billion years ago → 544 million years ago

*Paleozoic Era*
Fishes | Amphibians | Ferns | Reptiles
→ 245 million years ago

*Mesozoic Era*
Dinosaurs | Flowering plants | Birds | Small mammals
245 million years ago → 66 million years ago

*Cenozoic Era*
Humans | Large mammals
→ present

**1.** Ferns and reptiles appeared in the ____**Paleozoic**____ era.

**2.** Humans and other large mammals appeared in the ____**Cenozoic**____ era.

**3.** Dinosaurs, birds, and flowering plants appeared in the ____**Mesozoic**____ era.

**4.** The earliest life forms appeared in the ____**Precambrian**____ era.

**70**   CHAPTER 14   BIOLOGY: The Dynamics of Life

CONTENT MASTERY

Name _____ Date _____ Class _____

**Content Mastery**

**Chapter 14** **The History of Life,** *continued*

Study the diagram below. Then answer the questions that follow.

Energy from the sun and lightning strikes molecules in the sea.

Molecules combine to form simple organic molecules.

Larger molecules continue to form, making simple amino acids.

Amino acids are the building blocks of life. Early protocells were probably made of groups of amino acids.

5. Where did the energy to make organic molecules come from?
**from the sun and lightning**

6. What type of larger organic molecules formed? Why are these larger molecules important?
**The larger molecules were amino acids. Amino acids are important because they
are the building blocks of life.**

7. What do scientists believe was formed from groups of amino acids?
**early protocells**

---

Name _____ Date _____ Class _____

**Content Mastery**

**Chapter 14** **The History of Life,** *continued*

**Review the Vocabulary**

archaebacteria (ar kee bac TIHR ee uh)        plate tectonics
biogenesis (bi oh JEN uh sus)                 protocell
fossil                                        spontaneous generation

The Chapter 14 vocabulary words are listed above. Review the definitions of these words. Then fill in the puzzle. You will not use all the words for the puzzle.

**Across**

2. unicellular life forms that live with little sunlight or oxygen
4. evidence of an organism that lived long ago

**Down**

1. structure that carries out some life activities such as growth or division
3. idea that living things come only from other living things

**Fill in each blank with the correct vocabulary word.**

5. The idea that life can come from something nonliving is called   **spontaneous generation**

6. The theory of _____ **plate tectonics** _____ explains how continents move.

---

Name _____ Date _____ Class _____

**Content Mastery**

## Chapter 15   The Theory of Evolution

### Get the Big Picture

Find the blue headings in Section 15.1 of your textbook. Use a blue heading to fill in the rectangles in the organizer below. One rectangle has been filled in for you.

**Charles Darwin and Natural Selection**

(A) *Fossils shape ideas about evolution*

(B) **Darwin on HMS Beagle**

(C) **Darwin in the Galápagos**

(D) **Darwin continues his studies**

(E) **Darwin explains natural selection**

(F) **Interpreting evidence after Darwin**

Each statement below goes with one of the headings in the rectangles above. Write the letter of each heading on the line in front of the statement it goes with.

**C**   1. Darwin saw many life forms on the Galápagos Islands. He was convinced that species change over time.

**E**   2. Darwin's theory of evolution by natural selection explains how populations change over time.

**A**   3. Fossil records made scientists wonder if plant and animal species changed over time.

**B**   4. In 1831, Darwin became a naturalist on a ship called HMS *Beagle*.

**D**   5. Back in England, Darwin did more research. He learned that some plants and animals have traits that help them survive.

**F**   6. Some people consider the fossil evidence for natural selection to be inconclusive because the fossil record is incomplete.

CONTENT MASTERY      CHAPTER 15   BIOLOGY: The Dynamics of Life    73

---

Name _____ Date _____ Class _____

**Content Mastery**

## Chapter 15   The Theory of Evolution, *continued*

**Section 15.1 Natural Selection and the Evidence for Evolution**

**Section 15.2 Mechanisms of Evolution**

### Study the Diagrams

Study the diagrams. Then answer the questions that follow.

1.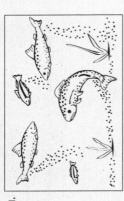

In nature, many animals overproduce offspring.

2.

Members of a population have a variety of traits. These fishes differ in size and speed.

3.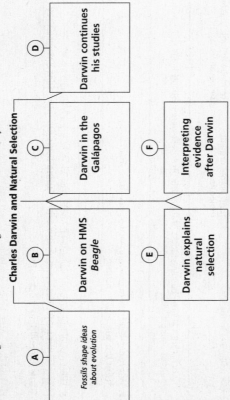

Fishes that are slow and small usually get eaten by predators. Faster, larger fishes can get away from predators.

4.

Offspring of surviving fishes make up a larger part of the new population.

1. Why is a fast fish more likely to survive than a slow fish?
**A fast fish is more likely to escape from predators.**

2. **True or false?** Natural selection happens when traits that help an organism survive are passed from generation to generation.
**true**

74    CHAPTER 15   BIOLOGY: The Dynamics of Life      CONTENT MASTERY

Name _____  Date _____  Class _____

**Content Mastery**

## Chapter 15  The Theory of Evolution, *continued*

Study the diagrams. Then answer the questions that follow.

**Flower Population**

*First Generation*

TT  Tt  tt  TT  Tt  tt

*Second Generation*

TT  Tt  TT  Tt  tt  tt

3. Two genotypes—gene types—are present in the first generation population. One is *TT*. What is the other?
**tt**

> **Allelic frequency** tells how often an allele occurs in a population. In the first generation, 8 out of 16 alleles are the *T* allele. The *T* allele is present one-half of the time, so the allelic frequency for the *T* allele is 50%. The allelic frequency for the *t* allele is also 50%.

4. What is the allelic frequency for each allele in the second generation?
a. *T*  __50%__
b. *t*  __50%__

CHAPTER 15  BIOLOGY: The Dynamics of Life

---

Name _____  Date _____  Class _____

**Content Mastery**

## Chapter 15  The Theory of Evolution, *continued*

### Review the Vocabulary

> adaptive radiation
> allelic frequency
> analogous structure
> artificial selection
> camouflage (KAM uh flahj)
> directional selection
> disruptive selection
> embryo
> gene pool
> genetic drift
> genetic equilibrium
> homologous structure
> mimicry
> natural selection
> punctuated equilibrium
> reproductive isolation
> speciation (spee shee AY shun)
> stabilizing selection
> vestigial structure (veh SYTIHJ ee yul)

Review the definitions of the Chapter 15 vocabulary words listed in the box. Then read the statements below. If the statement is true, write <u>true</u>. If a statement is false, replace the underlined word with another vocabulary word that will make the statement true. You will not use all the words.

1. <u>Natural selection</u> is breeding living things to select for certain traits.
**Artificial selection**

2. <u>Mimicry</u> enables an animal or a plant to blend with its surroundings.
**Camouflage**

3. <u>Homologous structures</u> are similar structures found in groups of related organisms.
**true**

4. <u>Genetic equilibrium</u> happens when allelic frequencies stay the same from generation to generation.
**true**

5. The <u>allelic frequency</u> is the entire collection of genes in a population.
**gene pool**

Use the vocabulary words in the box below. Review the definitions of these words. Then draw a line to match each word in the box with its definition.

a. divergent evolution
b. geographic isolation
c. convergent evolution
d. polyploid
e. gradualism

6. When a physical barrier divides a population into groups
7. Any organism that has multiple sets of chromosomes
8. The idea that species form by gradual change over time
9. When two or more similar species become more unlike each other over time
10. When distantly related life forms develop similar traits

CONTENT MASTERY

---

## Chapter 16 Primate Evolution

### Get the Big Picture

Study the picture. Then answer the questions that follow.

Opposable thumbs help primates grasp objects.

The primate's large brain helps it remember, think, and communicate.

Keen vision in primates helps them watch for predators and spot food sources.

Primates have flexible joints for easy movement.

Primate feet are adapted for grasping.

1. What traits help some primates live in trees?
**opposable thumbs, flexible joints, and feet made for grasping**

2. What traits do humans share with other primates?
**opposable thumbs, keen vision, larger brains, and flexible joints**

3. What are some ways in which humans use their opposable thumbs?
**Sample answer: to hold tools, write, and build things**

CONTENT MASTERY          CHAPTER 16   BIOLOGY: The Dynamics of Life   **77**

---

## Chapter 16 Primate Evolution, *continued*

Section 16.1 *Primate Adaption and Evolution*
Section 16.2 *Human Ancestry*

### Study the Idea Map

Use the idea map to answer the questions that follow.

**Primates**

**Anthropoids**
• Large brains
• Complex skeleton

**Prosimians**
• Live in trees
• Mostly active at night
• No larger than house cat
• Eat insects, seeds, fruits

**New World Monkeys**
• Central and South America
• Live in trees
• Can grab things with their tails

**Old World Monkeys**
• Africa and Asia
• Live in trees or on the ground
• Some live in cold regions.
• Use tails for balance

**Hominoids**
• Do not have tails
• Largest primate brains
• Can use simple tools
• Includes humans and apes

1. Suppose you found a small primate climbing in a tree at night. What type of primate would it most likely be? Explain. **It would most likely be a prosimian because they are small, live in trees, and are mostly active at night.**

2. How could you tell whether an anthropoid was a hominoid or an Old World monkey? **An Old World monkey would have a tail; a hominoid would not.**

3. True or false? New World monkeys are an important part of the African rain forest ecosystem. **false**

**78**   CHAPTER 16   BIOLOGY: The Dynamics of Life          CONTENT MASTERY

**Content Mastery**

## Chapter 16   Primate Evolution, *continued*

Study the diagram. Then answer the questions that follow.

### Evolution of *Homo Sapiens*

| | Skills |
|---|---|
| *Australopithecus afarensis* <br> 4 million years ago  →  *Australopithecus africanus* <br> 3 million years ago | • Australopithecines climbed trees. <br> • They could also walk upright on the ground. |
| *Homo habilis* <br> 1.5–2 million years ago  →  *Homo erectus* <br> 1.6 million years ago | • *Homo habilis* used simple tools. <br> • *Homo erectus* used larger tools. |
| *Neanderthal* <br> 35 000–100 000 years ago  →  *Cro-Magnons* <br> 35 000–40 000 years ago  →  *Homo sapiens* <br> 100 000 years ago | • Neanderthals seem to have had culture and spoken language. <br> • Cro-Magnons were talented artists and toolmakers. <br> • *Homo sapiens* built cities and used technology. |

**4.** Which primate species was the first to use simple tools?

*Homo habilis*

**5.** Which primate species spent some of their time in trees?

*Australopithecus afarensis and Australopithecus africanus*

**6.** The *Homo sapiens* skull is much larger than the *Australopithecus* skull. What can you say about these two groups, using skull size as evidence?

*Homo sapiens have larger brains than australopithecines had.*

---

**Content Mastery**

## Chapter 16   Primate Evolution, *continued*

### Review the Vocabulary

> anthropoid (AN thruh poyd) <br> australopithecine (ah stray loh pihth uh sine) <br> bipedal <br> Cro-Magnon <br> hominid (hoh MIHN ud) <br> Neanderthals (nee AN dur tawl) <br> opposable thumb <br> prehensile tail (pree HEN sul) <br> primate

Use some of the Chapter 16 vocabulary words listed above to fill in the puzzle.

Crossword puzzle answers:
- 1 across / down: a u s t r a l o p i t h e c i n e
- (down) a n t h r o p o i d
- 2 down: o p p o s a b l e
- 3 across: p r i m a t e
- 4 across: b i p e d a l
- 5 across: p r e h e n s i l e

**Across**

**1.** early hominid that lived in Africa

**3.** group of mammals that includes lemurs, monkeys, apes, and humans

**4.** ability to walk upright on two legs

**5.** type of tail that can grasp tree branches

**Down**

**1.** subgroup of primates that includes monkeys, apes, and humans

**2.** type of thumb that can be used to grasp objects

Use the rest of the vocabulary words to finish the words in the sentences.

**6.** _Neanderthals_ lived from 35 000 to 100 000 years ago.

**7.** _Hominids_ are humanlike primates that walk on two legs.

**8.** Cro- _Magnon_ people lived in Europe 35 000 to 40 000 years ago.

**Content Mastery**

**Chapter 17 Organizing Life's Diversity**

### Get the Big Picture

Read the paragraph in the box and study the picture. Then answer the questions that follow.

The classification of organisms into groups is based on similarities and differences of the organisms' traits. Organisms that are placed in the same group have more traits in common than those in different groups. All the organisms on Earth belong to one of six kingdoms. Each kingdom is divided into two or more smaller groups (each called a phylum). Those groups are divided into two or more smaller groups (each called a class), and so on. Each smaller group includes a smaller number of different types of organisms.

1. What are the seven kinds of groups that make up the above classification system?
**kingdom, phylum, class, order, family, genus, species**

2. In the above classification system, two or more families make up a(n) **order** _____

3. Do you think there are more species or more families of organisms on Earth? Explain.
**Species; each family is made up of two or more genera, and each genus is made up**
**of two or more species.**

4. What is the basis for classifying organisms into groups? **similarities and differences of the organisms' traits**

---

**Content Mastery**

**Chapter 17 Organizing Life's Diversity,** continued

Section 17.1
Classification

### Study the Diagram

Study the diagram, which shows the classification of the northern raccoon and the pet guinea pig. Then use the diagram to answer the questions that follow.

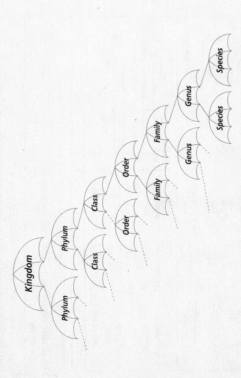

1. To which of the same groups do the raccoon and the guinea pig belong?
**kingdom Animalia, phylum Chordata, and class Mammalia**

2. What two orders are included in class Mammalia? **order Carnivora and order Rodentia**

3. What is the scientific name of the northern raccoon? The pet guinea pig?
**northern raccoon: Procyon lotor, pet guinea pig: Cavia porcellus**

4. How is the common name *guinea pig* misleading? **A guinea pig isn't a pig.**

Name _____ Date _____ Class _____

**Content Mastery**

**Chapter 17 Organizing Life's Diversity,** *continued*

Section 17.2 *The Six Kingdoms*

## Study the Drawings

Use the drawings to answer the questions that follow.

### The Six Kingdoms

**Archaebacteria**
• one-celled
• some make their own food, others consume food
• found in extreme environments

**Eubacteria**
• one-celled
• some make their own food, others consume food
• found in many kinds of environments

**Protists**
• one-celled or many-celled
• some make their own food, others consume food
• found only in moist environments

**Fungi**
• one-celled or many-celled
• consume food
• stay in one place

**Plants**
• many-celled
• make their own food
• stay in one place

**Animals**
• many-celled
• consume food
• most can move from place to place

1. Name the six kingdoms.
**eubacteria, archaebacteria, protists, fungi, plants, animals**

2. In which kingdom(s) are all of the organisms many-celled?
**plant kingdom and animal kingdom**

3. Compare how a mushroom and a fern get the food they need.
**A mushroom consumes food. A fern makes its own food.**

4. How are eubacteria and archaebacteria different?
**Archaebacteria are found in extreme environments. Eubacteria are found in many kinds of environments.**

CHAPTER 17 BIOLOGY: The Dynamics of Life **83**

---

Name _____ Date _____ Class _____

**Content Mastery**

**Chapter 17 Organizing Life's Diversity,** *continued*

## Review the Vocabulary

Use the Chapter 17 vocabulary words listed in the box to fill in the blanks in the sentences. You will not use all the words.

> binomial nomenclature   phylogeny (fi LAW juh nee)
> cladistics   protists
> division   taxonomy
> eubacteria

1. The naming system called **binomial nomenclature** gives each species a two-word name.

2. **Cladistics** is a classification system based on the derived traits of organisms.

3. **Eubacteria** are prokaryotes.

4. **Taxonomy** is the branch of biology that groups and names living things.

5. **Phylogeny** is the history of the evolution of a species.

Draw a line to match each vocabulary word in the box with its definition.

a. family
b. order
c. genus (JEE nus)
d. phylum (FI lum)
e. class
f. kingdom

6. Group of related orders
7. Group of related genera
8. Group of related species
9. Group of related families
10. Group of related phyla
11. Group of related classes

CONTENT MASTERY

---

**Name** _____  **Date** _____  **Class** _____

## BioDigest 5 — Change Through Time

**Content Mastery**

### Get the Big Picture

Find the red and blue headings in Biodigest 5. Use the blue headings to fill in the rectangles in the idea map below. Use the red headings to fill in the ovals. One rectangle and one oval have been filled in for you.

**Change Through Time**

- (A) Geologic Time Scale
- (B) Origin of Life Theories
- (B) Evidence of Evolution
- (D) Mechanics of Evolution
- (E) Primate Evolution
- (F) Organizing Life's Diversity

Ovals:
- The Precambrian Era
- The Paleozoic Era
- The Mesozoic Era
- The Cenozoic Era
- Modern Ideas About the Origin of Life
- Fossils
- Additional Evidence
- Three Patterns of Evolution
- Human Ancestry
- Six Kingdoms of Classification
- Criteria for Classification

Each statement below goes with one of the headings in the rectangles above. Write the letter of each heading on the line in front of the statement it goes with.

___C___  Possible shared ancestry between different organisms may be indicated by similar anatomical structures.

___A___  The most recent era of the Geologic Time Scale is the Cenozoic era.

___B___  The first true cells may have evolved from protocells, which were formed from clusters of organic molecules.

___D___  If a change in the genetic equilibrium of a population takes place, evolution occurs.

___E___  Fossils indicate that possible human ancestors walked on two legs and climbed trees.

___F___  Biologists use criteria such as body structure, breeding behavior, geographic distribution, and biochemical similarities to explain relationships among organisms.

CONTENT MASTERY        BIODIGEST 5  BIOLOGY: The Dynamics of Life   **85**

---

**Name** _____  **Date** _____  **Class** _____

## BioDigest 5 — Change Through Time, continued

**Content Mastery**

### Study the Pictures

Evolution by natural selection can be summarized in four statements.

- Variation exists within populations.
- Some variations are more advantageous for survival and reproduction than others.
- Organisms produce more offspring than can survive.
- Over time, offspring of survivors will make up a larger portion of the population.

Write the statement from the box that best matches each of the situations shown.

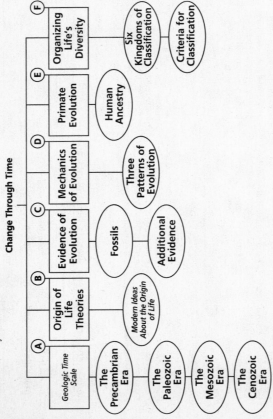

Snowshoe rabbits produce many offspring.

**1.** Organisms produce more offspring than can survive.

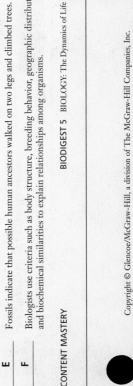

The back feet of some snowshoe rabbits are larger than the back feet of other snowshoe rabbits.

**2.** Variation exists within populations.

Snowshoe rabbits with large back feet can run across snow faster than those with small back feet and escape predators, such as wolves, more often.

**3.** Some variations are more advantageous for survival and reproduction than others.

More snowshoe rabbits with larger feet survive in the population and reproduce.

**4.** Over time, offspring of survivors will make up a larger portion of the population.

86   BIODIGEST 5  BIOLOGY: The Dynamics of Life       CONTENT MASTERY

**BioDigest 5**

## Change Through Time, *continued*

**Content Mastery**

### Study the Graphs

Each graph compares the normal distribution of a characteristic in the original population with the distribution of the characteristic in a population altered by natural selection.

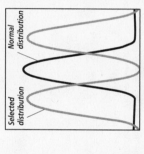

**Graph A**

More individuals in the altered population have the average value of the characteristic than in the original population.

**Graph B**

The distribution of the characteristic in the altered population differs from the distribution of the characteristic in the original population.

**Graph C**

Two altered populations appear—each having a distribution of a characteristic distinct from the characteristic of the original population.

In the space at the left, write the letter of the graph that illustrates the type of natural selection described.

**B**    **5.** Directional selection:    natural selection that results in a regular change in a population in one direction

**C**    **6.** Disruptive selection:    natural selection that results in two separate populations that have distinct characteristics

**A**    **7.** Stabilizing selection:    natural selection that favors the average individuals in a population

In the space at the left, write the letter of the graph that illustrates each of the following situations.

**C**    **8.** A large valley is flooded and a population of lizards is divided into two smaller populations that can no longer interbreed.

**B**    **9.** A population of penicillin-resistant bacteria develops from a population of bacteria (some of which were resistant to penicillin), which was treated with penicillin.

**A**    **10.** In a large population of grass plants, variation in the height of grass decreases over time.

---

**BioDigest 5**

## Change Through Time, *continued*

**Content Mastery**

### Study the Table

The table shows the phylogenetic classification of six organisms.

| Taxon | Name | | | | | |
|---|---|---|---|---|---|---|
| Kingdom | Animalia | | | | | |
| Phylum | Mollusca | Chordata | | | | |
| Class | Gastropoda | Osteichthyes | Aves | | Mammalia | |
| Order | Stylommatophora | Cypriniformes | Anseriformes | Sphenisciformes | Carnivora | |
| Family | Helicidae | Cyprinidae | Anatidae | Spheniscidae | Ursidae | |
| Genus | Helix | Carassius | Aix | Aptenodytes | Ursus | |
| Species | Aspersa | Auratus | Spona | Forsteri | Americanus | Arctos |
| Common name | brown garden snail | goldfish | wood duck | emperor penguin | American black bear | brown bear |

In the space at the left, write the letter of the word or phrase that best completes each statement.

**b**    **11.** The largest taxon, or classification group, is

     **a.** class.    **b.** kingdom.    **c.** phylum.    **d.** species.

**a**    **12.** All of the organisms in the table are

     **a.** animals.    **b.** autotrophs.    **c.** vertebrates.    **d.** warm-blooded.

**d**    **13.** The two most closely related organisms are the

     **a.** brown garden snail and goldfish.
     **b.** emperor penguin and goldfish.
     **c.** American black bear and wood duck.
     **d.** American black bear and brown bear.

**c**    **14.** The binomial nomenclature name of the brown garden snail is

     **a.** *Gastropoda belicidae.*    **b.** *Gastropoda belix.*
     **c.** *Helix aspera.*    **d.** *Mollusca gastropoda.*

**d**    **15.** The number of taxa that the wood duck and emperor penguin have in common is

     **a.** zero.    **b.** one.    **c.** two.    **d.** three.

## Study the Cycle

Viruses use a host cell to make new viruses, then destroy the cell. This process is called the lytic cycle. Here are the steps of the lytic cycle.

1. The virus attaches to the cell.
2. DNA from the virus enters the cell.
3. The cell makes new viral DNA and proteins.
4. New viruses are assembled from the proteins and DNA.
5. The cell breaks open and the viruses are released.

The steps of the lytic cycle are shown in the diagram below. Use the list above to number the steps.

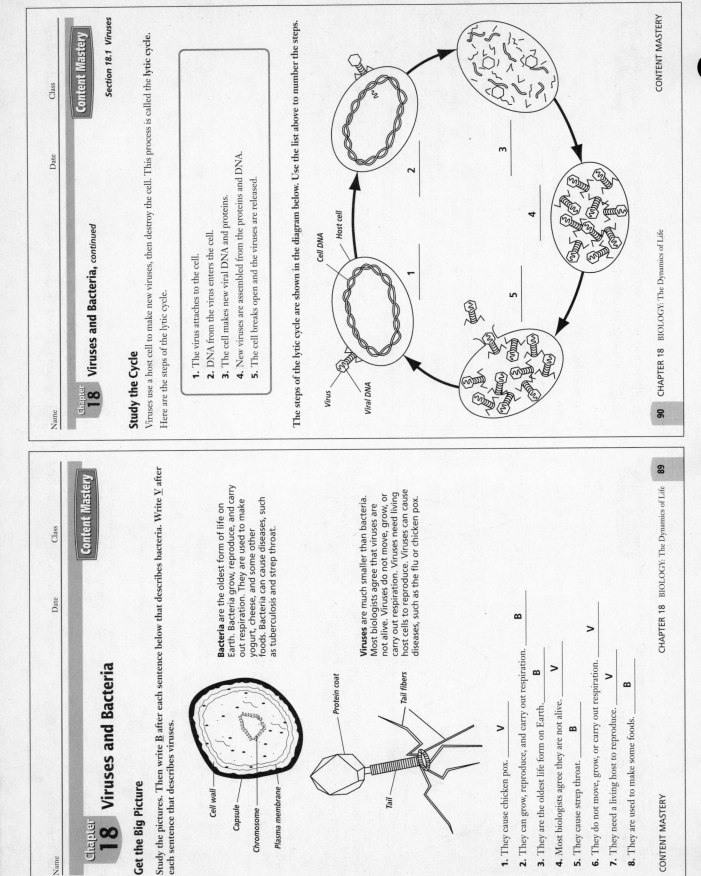

Cell DNA

Host cell

2

3

4

1

5

Virus

Viral DNA

---

## Get the Big Picture

Study the pictures. Then write **B** after each sentence below that describes bacteria. Write **V** after each sentence that describes viruses.

**Bacteria** are the oldest form of life on Earth. Bacteria grow, reproduce, and carry out respiration. They are used to make yogurt, cheese, and some other foods. Bacteria can cause diseases, such as tuberculosis and strep throat.

**Viruses** are much smaller than bacteria. Most biologists agree that viruses are not alive. Viruses do not move, grow, or carry out respiration. Viruses need living host cells to reproduce. Viruses can cause diseases, such as the flu or chicken pox.

Cell wall

Capsule

Chromosome

Plasma membrane

Protein coat

Tail fibers

Tail

1. They cause chicken pox. __V__
2. They can grow, reproduce, and carry out respiration. __B__
3. They are the oldest life form on Earth. __B__
4. Most biologists agree they are not alive. __V__
5. They cause strep throat. __B__
6. They do not move, grow, or carry out respiration. __V__
7. They need a living host to reproduce. __V__
8. They are used to make some foods. __B__

Name _____  Date _____  Class _____

**Content Mastery**

## Chapter 18 Viruses and Bacteria, *continued*

**Section 18.2 *Archaebacteria and Eubacteria***

### Study the Shapes

Bacteria are the smallest and simplest living things. They come in three basic shapes: spheres, rods, and spirals. The figures below show the three shapes. Write the name of the shape below each figure.

1. __spheres__

2. __spirals__

3. __rods__

Bacteria usually live in groups. The names of bacteria often tell how the bacteria are grouped. If the name starts with *Diplo-*, the bacteria live in pairs. If the name starts with *Staphylo-*, they live in clusters like grapes. If the name starts with *Strepto-*, they live in chains. The figures below show these three groups. Write the prefix of the name of the bacteria below each figure.

4. __Diplo-__

5. __Staphylo-__

6. __Strepto-__

CHAPTER 18   BIOLOGY: The Dynamics of Life   91

---

Name _____  Date _____  Class _____

**Content Mastery**

## Chapter 18 Viruses and Bacteria, *continued*

### Review the Vocabulary

Use the Chapter 18 vocabulary words in the box to fill in the puzzle.

| | |
|---|---|
| virus (VI rus) | bacteriophage (bak TEER ee yuh fayj) | retrovirus |
| provirus | toxin | endospore |

**Across**

3. virus that infects only bacteria
5. poison produced by some bacteria
6. virus whose DNA has been inserted into the host cell's chromosome

**Down**

1. virus that has RNA
2. tiny, nonliving particle
4. bacterium with a tough outer covering

Crossword answers:
- 1 (down): r e t r o v i r u s
- 2 (down): v i r u s
- 3 (across): b a c t e r i o p h a g e
- 4 (down): e n d o s p o r e
- 5 (across): t o x i n
- 6 (across): p r o v i r u s

Look at each vocabulary word in the box below. If the word is related to bacteria, write it in the table under *Bacteria*. If the word is related to viruses, write it in the table under *Viruses*.

| | |
|---|---|
| lytic cycle (LI tihk) | lysogenic cycle (li suh JEN ihk) |
| capsid | reverse transcriptase |
| obligate aerobe | binary fission |
| conjugation | obligate anaerobe |
| nitrogen fixation | |

| Bacteria | Viruses |
|---|---|
| obligate aerobe | lytic cycle |
| obligate anaerobe | lysogenic cycle |
| binary fission | capsid |
| conjugation | reverse transcriptase |
| nitrogen fixation | |

92   CHAPTER 18   BIOLOGY: The Dynamics of Life

---

**Content Mastery**

## Chapter 19 Protists

### Get the Big Picture

Read the paragraphs in the boxes and study the picture. Then answer the questions that follow.

Protists are all around us. There are more than 200 000 species in the kingdom Protista. Protists come in many different shapes, sizes, and colors. Some protists have traits like animals. Protozoans are animal-like protists. Other protists have traits like plants. Algae are plantlike protists. Still other protists have traits like fungi. Slime molds, water molds, and downy mildews are examples of funguslike protists.

Protists are important to nearly all ecosystems. Some protists produce large amounts of oxygen. Other protists form the first link in aquatic food chains. Protists live in almost every moist habitat on Earth.

1. What are protozoans?
**Protozoans are animal-like protists.**

2. Why are protists important to other living things on Earth? Give two reasons.
**Responses may include two of the following: Protists produce oxygen, provide food, and are part of most ecosystems on Earth.**

3. True or false? Protists live mostly in dry habitats. **false**

---

**Content Mastery**

## Chapter 19 Protists, *continued*

Section 19.1 *The World of Protists*

### Study the Diagram

Use the diagram to answer the questions that follow.

*Pseudopodia*

*Pseudopodia*

*Food vacuole forming*

*Food vacuole*

**A.** An amoeba senses food nearby. It extends pseudopodia toward the food.

**B.** The amoeba captures the food and forms a food vacuole around it.

**C.** Digestive enzymes in the food vacuole break down the food.

1. What does an amoeba use its pseudopodia for?
**An amoeba uses its pseudopodia to capture food.**

2. Where does an amoeba digest its food?
**An amoeba digests food in the food vacuole.**

Name _____ Date _____ Class _____

**Content Mastery**

## Protists, *continued*

Section 19.2  *Algae: Plantlike Protists*
Section 19.3  *Slime Molds, Water
Molds, and Downy Mildews*

### Study the Idea Maps

Use the idea map to answer the questions that follow.

**Plantlike Protists: Algae**

- Major producers of oxygen
- Major food source in water ecosystems

**Six Phyla of Algae**

**Unicellular**
- Euglenoids
- Diatoms
- Dinoflagellates
- Green algae

**Multicellular**
- Red algae
- Brown algae
- Green algae

1. Why are plantlike protists important to all living things?
**Plantlike protists produce oxygen and provide food for other living things.**

2. How many cells does a dinoflagellate have? **one**

Use the idea map to answer the questions that follow.

**Funguslike Protists**

Break down organic materials
to obtain energy.

**Three Phyla
of Funguslike Protists**

**Plasmodial Slime Molds**
- Live in moist, cool places
- Move and ingest food like amoebas
- Form a mass that has many nuclei but no cell walls or membranes

**Cellular Slime Molds**
- Live in moist, cool places
- Move and ingest food like amoebas
- Form a mass of amoeboid cells before reproducing

**Water Molds and Downy Mildews**
- Live in water or moist, cool places
- Grow and feed like fungi
- Some are plant parasites.

3. How are slime molds and cellular slime molds different?
**The mass formed by cellular slime molds is made up of cells. The mass formed by
plasmodial slime molds is not made up of cells.**

4. How are some funguslike protists harmful to plants?
**Some water molds and downy mildews are plant parasites.**

---

Name _____ Date _____ Class _____

**Content Mastery**

## Protists, *continued*

### Review the Vocabulary

Use the Chapter 19 vocabulary words in the box below to fill in the blanks in the sentences. You will not use all the words.

| |
|---|
| algae (AL jee) |
| flagellate (FLAJ uh lut) |
| pseudopodia (sew duh POH dee uh) |
| sporozoan (spor uh ZOH un) |
| ciliate |
| plasmodium (plaz MOH dee um) |
| protozoan (proh tuh ZOH un) |

1. An animal-like protist is called a(n) _____**protozoan**_____.

2. An animal-like protist that has flagella is called a(n) _____**flagellate**_____.

3. A(n) _____**sporozoan**_____ is a protist that produces spores.

4. Some protists use _____**pseudopodia**_____ to move and to capture food.

5. A(n) _____**ciliate**_____ is a protist that has cilia.

Use the vocabulary words in the box below. Review the definitions of these words. Then draw a line to match each word in the box with its definition.

| |
|---|
| **a.** alternation of generations |
| **b.** colony (KAH luh nee) |
| **c.** gametophyte (guh MEE tuh fite) |
| **d.** sporophyte (SPOR uh fite) |
| **e.** thallus (THAL us) |

1. Haploid form of algae that produces sex cells
2. Algal body without roots, stems, or leaves
3. Group of cells that live together
4. Diploid form of algae that produces spores
5. Life cycle of algae that have a haploid stage followed by a diploid stage

## Get the Big Picture

Study the diagram. Then answer the questions that follow.

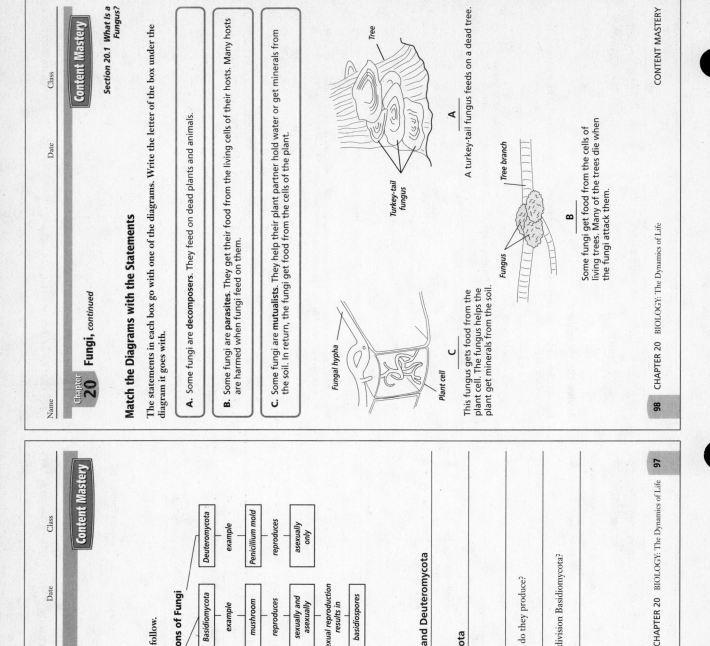

**Four Major Divisions of Fungi**

| Zygomycota | Ascomycota | Basidiomycota | Deuteromycota |
|---|---|---|---|
| example | example | example | example |
| bread mold | yeast | mushroom | Penicillium mold |
| reproduces | reproduces | reproduces | reproduces |
| sexually and asexually | sexually and asexually | sexually and asexually | asexually only |
| sexual reproduction results in | sexual reproduction results in | sexual reproduction results in | |
| zygospores | ascospores | basidiospores | |

1. What are the four major divisions of fungi?
**Zygomycota, Ascomycota, Basidiomycota, and Deuteromycota**

2. In which divisions do the fungi reproduce sexually?
**Zygomycota, Ascomycota, and Basidiomycota**

3. How does the *Penicillium* mold reproduce?
**asexually**

4. When yeasts reproduce sexually, what kind of spore do they produce?
**ascospore**

5. What is an example of a fungus that belongs to the division Basidiomycota?
**mushroom**

---

## Match the Diagrams with the Statements

The statements in each box go with one of the diagrams. Write the letter of the box under the diagram it goes with.

**A.** Some fungi are **decomposers**. They feed on dead plants and animals.

**B.** Some fungi are **parasites**. They get their food from the living cells of their hosts. Many hosts are harmed when fungi feed on them.

**C.** Some fungi are **mutualists**. They help their plant partner hold water or get minerals from the soil. In return, the fungi get food from the cells of the plant.

Tree

Turkey-tail fungus

**A**

A turkey-tail fungus feeds on a dead tree.

Fungal hypha

Plant cell

**C**

This fungus gets food from the plant cell. The fungus helps the plant get minerals from the soil.

Tree branch

Fungus

**B**

Some fungi get food from the cells of living trees. Many of the trees die when the fungi attack them.

---

## Chapter 20   Fungi, continued

**Section 20.2 The Diversity of Fungi**

### Match the Steps

The drawing below shows the steps in the life cycle of a mushroom. Write the numbers from the drawing next to the matching life-cycle steps that follow.

**1.** Mushrooms release spores called basidiospores.

**2.** Basidiospores grow threadlike hyphae.

**3.** Hyphae with different mating types join.

*Basidiospores*

*Basidium*

*Basidiospore*

*– Mating type*

*+ Mating type*

*Button*

*Gills*

*Stipe*

*Cap*

**4.** Compact masses of hyphae form buttons.

**5.** Buttons develop into mushrooms.

**6.** Mushrooms grow and mature.

___6___ Mushrooms grow a stipe and cap with gills.

___1___ Mushrooms release basidiospores.

___5___ Buttons become mushrooms.

___2___ Basidiospores grow threadlike hyphae in the ground.

___3___ Two mating types of hyphae join.

___4___ Buttons form.

---

## Chapter 20   Fungi, continued

### Review the Vocabulary

Use the Chapter 20 vocabulary words in the box to fill in the puzzle. You will not use all the words.

| | |
|---|---|
| mycorrhiza (my kuh RHY zuh) | hypha (HI fuh) |
| conidiophore (kuh NIH dee uh for) | sporangium (spuh RAN jee um) |
| haustoria (haw STOR ee uh) | mycelium (mi SEE lee um) |

1. Sac or case where spores are produced   **spo** r **an** g **ium**

2. Mutualistic relationship between a fungus and a plant   **my** c **orr** h **iza**

3. Hyphae that grow into host cells without killing them   **haus** t **oria**

4. Network of filaments   **m** y **celium**

5. Basic structural unit of fungi   **hy** p **ha**

Use the vocabulary words in the box below. Review the definitions of these words. Then draw a line to match each word in the box with its definition.

| | |
|---|---|
| **a.** ascospore | |
| **b.** ascus | |
| **c.** basidia (buh SIH dee uh) | |
| **d.** basidiospore | |
| **e.** conidium (kuh NIH dee um) | |

6. Small sac in which sexual spores develop

7. Spore produced by basidia

8. Asexual spore in a chain of spores

9. Club-shaped hyphae

10. Spore produced in an ascus

Read the statements below. If the statement is true, write T on the line. If the statement is false, write F.

___T___  **11.** A stolon (STOH lun) is a hypha that grows across a food source.

___F___  **12.** A zygospore (ZI goh spor) is a fungal structure with a haploid nucleus.

___F___  **13.** A rhizoid (RI zoyd) is a fungus that has a symbiotic relationship with green algae.

___F___  **14.** Lichens (LI kunz) are club-shaped hyphae.

___T___  **15.** A gametangium (gam uh TAN jee um) is a fungal structure with a haploid nucleus.

**BioDigest 6**

**Content Mastery**

## Viruses, Bacteria, Protists, and Fungi, *continued*

### Study the Diagram

Read the paragraph in the box and study the diagram. Then answer the questions that follow.

> Sometimes when a virus infects a host cell, it does not destroy the cell to make new viruses. Instead, the virus's DNA is inserted into the DNA of the host cell. When the host cell reproduces, the virus's DNA is copied along with the cell's DNA. This method of viral replication is called the **lysogenic cycle**.

1. Which numbered step in the diagram shows that the virus's DNA has been copied along with the DNA of the host cell?

   **3**

2. In which step is the virus infecting the host cell?

   **1**

3. Which step shows that the virus's DNA has just been inserted into the DNA of the host cell?

   **2**

### Label the Diagram

Label the main parts of the bacterium. Use these labels: *cytoplasm, cell wall, chromosome, plasma membrane*.

1. **cell wall**

2. **plasma membrane**

3. **cytoplasm**

4. **chromosome**

*Bacterium*

---

**BioDigest 6**

**Content Mastery**

## Viruses, Bacteria, Protists, and Fungi

### Get the Big Picture

After you have read the Biodigest, look at the pictures below. Then answer the questions that follow.

**A. Virus**   **B. Bacterium**   **C. Protist**   **D. Fungus**

1. Which pictures show eukaryotes?

   **C, D**

2. Which picture shows a prokaryote?

   **B**

3. Which picture does not show a living organism?

   **A**

4. Identify the shape of the bacterium in picture B.

   **rod shaped**

5. Which organism is animal-like?

   **C**

6. Which organism is multicellular?

   **D**

7. Identify the protist shown in picture C.

   **amoeba**

8. Identify the fungus shown in picture D.

   **mushroom**

## Left page (103)

Name      Date      Class

**Content Mastery**

**BioDigest 6   Viruses, Bacteria, Protists, and Fungi,** *continued*

### Matching

Match the pictures of the different kinds of protists with their descriptions below. Write the number of the correct description below each picture.

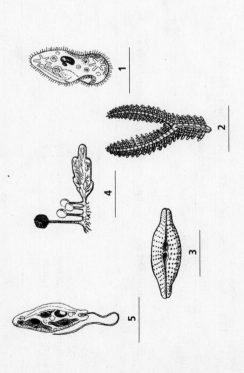

1    2    4    3    5

1. Paramecia are unicellular animal-like protists that use tiny hairlike cilia to move and collect food.

2. Red algae are multicellular plantlike protists that can grow in deep ocean water where there is little sunlight.

3. Diatoms are unicellular plantlike protists that have shells made of two pieces.

4. Slime molds are funguslike protists that obtain food by decomposing dead plants and animals.

5. Euglena are unicellular protists that use whiplike flagella to move. They usually make their own food and sometimes obtain food by feeding on other organisms.

CONTENT MASTERY      BIODIGEST 6   BIOLOGY: The Dynamics of Life   **103**

## Right page (104)

Name      Date      Class

**Content Mastery**

**BioDigest 6   Viruses, Bacteria, Protists, and Fungi,** *continued*

### Study the Diagram

Study the diagram that shows how fungi obtain food. Then use the diagram to complete the sentences and answer the questions that follow.

**1.** The structural units of a fungus are hyphae. The cell walls of hyphae are made of chitin.

Large food molecule

Small food molecule

Enzyme

**2.** The hyphae release enzymes into a food source.

**3.** The enzymes break down large food molecules into small food molecules.

**4.** The small food molecules move into the hyphae.

1. **Hyphae** release enzymes.

2. The enzymes break down **large food molecules** into small food molecules.

3. The small food molecules move into the **hyphae** .

4. Hyphae are the structural units of a **fungus** .

5. **Chitin** makes up the cell walls of hyphae.

6. Why is it necessary for a fungus to release enzymes that break down large food molecules? **The large food molecules are too large to move into the hyphae.**

7. Why can a fungus with many hyphae absorb more food than a fungus with few hyphae? **The fungus with many hyphae releases more enzymes and has more surface area to absorb food molecules.**

**104**   BIODIGEST 6   BIOLOGY: The Dynamics of Life      CONTENT MASTERY

## Chapter 21 What Is a Plant?

### Get the Big Picture

Read the paragraph in the box. Then answer the questions that follow.

> Plants were some of the earliest living things on land. When they moved to land, plants faced challenges to get water, food, and energy. Some plants, like giant redwood trees, formed deep roots. These roots helped the trees get water and food from deep below the surface of Earth. Other plants, like some desert cacti, formed shallow roots like bicycle spokes. These roots help desert plants capture water near the ground over a great distance. Most plants have leaves that capture energy from the sun. The leaves of many plants are covered with a waxy coating called a cuticle that helps them hold water. Plants have adapted to many types of land environments.

1. How does each plant structure below help plants live on land?

a. Roots: **help plants get water and food from below the surface of Earth**

b. Leaves: **help plants capture energy from the sun**

c. Waxy coating: **helps plants hold water**

2. Why are the roots of many desert plants very shallow?
**Shallow roots help desert plants capture water near the ground over a great distance.**

3. What trait of plants helps prevent water loss from their leaves?
**a waxy coating or cuticle**

---

## Chapter 21 What Is a Plant?, *continued*

### Study the Diagram

Use the diagram to answer the questions.

*Leaves: broad, flat organs that trap sunlight for photosynthesis.*

*Cuticle: waxy coating on fruits, leaves, and stems. It helps plants hold water.*

1. What is a cuticle?
**A cuticle is a waxy coating found on fruits, leaves, and stems.**

2. What is the purpose of a plant's cuticle?
**The cuticle helps the plant hold water.**

3. What is the purpose of leaves?
**Leaves trap sunlight for photosynthesis.**

Name _____ Date _____ Class _____

**Content Mastery**

## Chapter 21 What Is a Plant?, *continued*

### Study the Idea Map

Use the idea map to answer the questions.

**Plants**

Plants are divided into two groups based on whether or not a plant produces seeds.

- There are seven divisions of non-seed plants.
- These plants release hard-walled reproductive cells called spores.
- Non-seed plants may be either vascular or nonvascular.

- There are five divisions of seed plants.
- Seed plants release seeds.
- Seeds are made up of an embryonic plant and a food supply covered by a hard protective seed coat.
- All seed plants are vascular.

**4.** How are plants divided into two groups?

**Plants are divided into two groups based on whether or not seeds are produced by**

**the plant.**

_____

_____

**5.** How do non-seed plants and seed plants reproduce?

**Non-seed plants release hard-walled reproductive cells called spores. Seed plants**

**release seeds, which are made up of an embryonic plant and a food supply covered**

**by a hard protective seed coat.**

_____

_____

**6.** True or false? Non-seed plants are always nonvascular plants.

**false**

_____

**Section 21.2  Survey of the Plant Kingdom**

---

Name _____ Date _____ Class _____

**Content Mastery**

## Chapter 21 What Is a Plant?, *continued*

### Review the Vocabulary

Use the Chapter 21 vocabulary words in the box to label the parts of the plant.

| cuticle (KYEW tih kul) | seed |
| leaf | stem |
| root | |

**seed**

**leaf**

**stem**

cuticle

root

Look at the vocabulary statements below. If the statement is true, write T on the line. If the statement is false, write F.

**F** **1.** Nonvascular plants possess vascular tissues.

**T** **2.** A frond is the leaf found on ferns that vary in length from 1 cm to 500 cm.

**T** **3.** Tubelike, elongated cells through which water, food, and other materials are transported make up **vascular tissues.**

**F** **4.** Cuticles are scaly structures that support male or female reproductive structures.

**T** **5.** Plants that possess vascular tissues are known as **vascular plants.**

---

**Chapter 22** The Diversity of Plants

## Get the Big Picture

**Nonvascular plants** lack vascular tissue and reproduce by releasing spores. They usually live in moist, cool environments. There are three divisions of nonvascular plants: mosses, liverworts, and hornworts.

The **non-seed vascular plants** require a continuous film of water through which sperm swim to the egg. These plants have vascular tissues that transport water and nutrients throughout the plant. Vascular tissues also provide the structural support that enables vascular plants to grow taller than nonvascular plants.

**Seed plants** include vascular plants that produce naked seeds, as well as plants that produce flowers and have seeds enclosed in a fruit. Fertilization in most seed plants does not require a continuous film of water.

Label the pictures below. Use these choices: nonvascular plant, non-seed vascular plant, seed plant that produce naked seeds, seed plant that produces fruit.

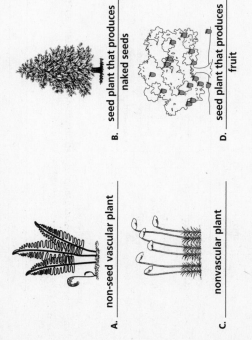

A. ____ non-seed vascular plant

B. ____ seed plant that produces naked seeds

C. ____ nonvascular plant

D. ____ seed plant that produces fruit

Each statement below goes with one of the pictures. Write the letter of each picture on the line in front of the statement it goes with.

**A** ____ These plants were prominent members of Earth's ancient forests.

**D** ____ These plants are divided into two classes: monocotyledons and dicotyledons.

**C** ____ The gametophyte generation is dominant.

**B** ____ This group is sometimes referred to as gymnosperms, meaning "naked seed."

---

**Chapter 22** The Diversity of Plants, *continued*

Section 22.1  *Nonvascular Plants*
Section 22.2  *Non-seed Vascular Plants*

## Study the Diagram

*Male gametophyte*

1.

3.
*Sperm*

4.

2.
*Female gametophyte with eggs*

**Strobilus of the Sporophyte**

**Sporophyte**

### Life Cycle of a Lycophyte

Each statement below goes with one of the stages of the lycophyte life cycle shown in the diagram. Write the number from the diagram on the line in front of the statement it goes with.

**3** ____ Sperm swim to the eggs, and fertilization takes place.

**1** ____ Sperm are produced in the antheridium.

**2** ____ Eggs are produced in the archegonium.

**4** ____ New sporophyte develops from the fertilized egg.

Answer the questions.

1. True or false? Nonvascular plants do not need water for reproduction.
**false**

2. True or false? All non-seed vascular plants have a gametophyte stage.
**true**

3. True or false? Nonvascular plants reproduce by releasing spores.
**true**

4. True or false? Fertilization in non-seed vascular plants requires a continuous surface film of water through which sperm swim to the egg.
**true**

Name _____  Date _____  Class _____

**Content Mastery**

## Chapter 22  The Diversity of Plants, *continued*

### Section 22.3  Seed Plants

**Study the Diagram**

**A. Spruce tree**

**B. Maple tree**

Each statement below goes with one of the pictures. Write the letter of the picture on the line in front of the statement it goes with.

__A__  This tree is a conifer.

__A__  This tree is often found where the warm growing season is short, so keeping leaves year-round gives it a head start on growth.

__B__  This tree is a deciduous tree.

__B__  This tree loses all of its leaves at once.

__A__  Although individual leaves drop off as they age or are damaged, this tree never loses all its leaves at once.

**Answer the following questions.**

1. True or false? Dicotyledons make up the majority of flowering plants.
   **true**

2. True or false? There are only two living species of Ginkgophytes.
   **false**

3. True or false? Most annuals are herbaceous, which means their stems are green and do not contain woody tissue.
   **true**

4. True or false? Biennials have a life span that lasts half a year.
   **false**

5. True or false? Anthophytes are the only division of plants that produce fruits.
   **true**

CONTENT MASTERY          CHAPTER 22   BIOLOGY: The Dynamics of Life   **111**

---

Name _____  Date _____  Class _____

**Content Mastery**

## Chapter 22  The Diversity of Plants, *continued*

**Review the Vocabulary**

| |
|---|
| archegonium          frond (FRAWND) |
| antheridium          monocotyledon |
| cotyledon (kah tuh LEE dun)   perennial |
| deciduous plant (dih SIH juh wus)   prothallus |
| dicotyledon          rhizome (RI zohm) |
| fruit          sorus (SOR us) |

Use the Chapter 22 vocabulary words listed above to fill in the blanks in the statements.

1. A fern leaf is called a **frond**.

2. A(n) **monocotyledon** has one seed leaf, leaves with parallel veins, and flower parts in multiples of three.

3. A plant that lives for several years is called a(n) **perennial**. It produces flowers and seeds periodically, usually once a year.

4. A(n) **dicotyledon** has two seed leaves, leaves with branched veins, and flower parts in multiples of four or five.

5. A(n) **deciduous plant** loses all its leaves at one time.

6. The part of the seed plant embryo that functions to store food is the **cotyledon**.

7. The thick underground stem in ferns is the **rhizome**.

8. A(n) **antheridium** is a male reproductive structure in which sperm are produced.

9. The spores released from a strobilus then grow to form a gametophyte, called a(n) **prothallus**.

10. A group of sporangia on the back of a fern frond is called a(n) **sorus**.

11. A(n) **fruit** is the ripened ovary of a flower.

12. The female reproductive structure in which eggs are produced is called a(n) **archegonium**.

**112**  CHAPTER 22   BIOLOGY: The Dynamics of Life          CONTENT MASTERY

**Content Mastery**

# Plant Structure and Function

## Get the Big Picture

Read the following summary paragraphs and fill in the blanks using the word lists given for each section.

| collenchyma |
| dermal tissue |
| ground tissue |
| parenchyma |
| phloem |
| sclerenchyma |
| vascular tissue |
| xylem |

Most plant tissues are composed of three types of cells. (1) **Parenchyma** cells are thin-walled cells that can carry on photosynthesis and store food. (2) **Collenchyma** cells, with unevenly thickened cell walls, provide structure for growing tissue. (3) **Sclerenchyma** cells, with their thick walls, provide structural support. (4) **Dermal tissue** is the protective covering of a plant. (5) **Vascular tissue** transports materials. (6) **Xylem** moves water and minerals up the stems. (7) **Phloem** transports sugars and organic compounds throughout the plant. (8) **Ground tissue** is found between the dermal tissue and the vascular tissue and often functions in food production and storage.

| leaves | roots | stems |

(9) **Leaves** have chloroplasts and perform photosynthesis.
(10) **Roots** grow downward into the soil as cells elongate. (11) **Stems** support leaves and upright growth and transport water and food from one part of the plant to another.

| auxins |
| cytokinins |
| ethylene |
| gibberellins |
| nastic responses |
| tropisms |

Three major plant hormones that affect plant growth and development by promoting cell division and cell elongation are (12) **auxins** , (13) **cytokinins** , and (14) **gibberellins** . Another hormone called (15) **ethylene** speeds up the ripening of fruit. (16) **Tropisms** are plants' responses to external stimuli that result in a growth response. (17) **Nastic responses** are not dependent on the direction of the stimulus but are often the result of changes in cell pressure.

---

**Content Mastery**

# Plant Structure and Function, *continued*

Section 23.1  *Plant Cells and Tissues*
Section 23.2  *Roots, Stems, and Leaves*

## Study the Diagrams

Use the diagram of the tree trunk to answer the questions.

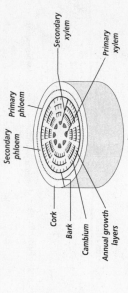

Cork
Bark
Cambium
Annual growth layers
Secondary phloem
Primary phloem
Secondary xylem
Primary xylem

1. What tissue makes up the annual growth rings in a tree? **xylem**

2. Vascular cambium produces new xylem and phloem. The newest growth is closest to the cambium. Which is older, primary phloem or secondary phloem? **primary phloem**

3. The inner part of bark is made of phloem. The outer layer of bark is made of **cork** .

Use the diagram of the leaf to answer the questions.

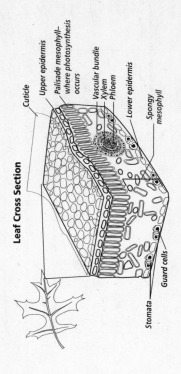

**Leaf Cross Section**

Cuticle
Upper epidermis
Palisade mesophyll—where photosynthesis occurs
Vascular bundle
Xylem
Phloem
Lower epidermis
Spongy mesophyll
Guard cells
Stomata

4. True or false? Only a stem has xylem and phloem. **false**

5. As well as being coated with a waxy cuticle, leaves prevent water loss by controlling the size of the stomata. This is done by surrounding cells called **guard cells** .

6. In which leaf cells does most photosynthesis take place? **palisade mesophyll**

Name _____ Date _____ Class _____

Section 23.2 *Roots, Stems, and Leaves*
Section 23.3 *Plant Responses*

## Study the Diagram

Use the diagram of the root to answer the questions.

Mineral ions and water molecules enter root hair cells and travel through the cells of the cortex by osmosis (A). Water may also flow between the cells of the cortex.

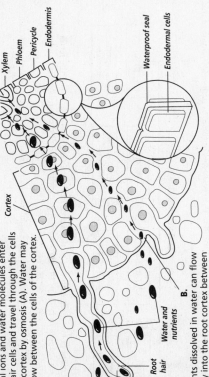

Xylem
Phloem
Pericycle
Endodermis

Cortex

Waterproof seal
Endodermal cells

A.
B.
Root hair
Water and nutrients

Nutrients dissolved in water can flow directly into the root cortex between the parenchyma cells (B), then through the cells of the endodermis.

1. True or false? Water and minerals can be absorbed by root hairs.
   **true**

2. True or false? Water and minerals travel through the cortex to the cells of the phloem.
   **false**

3. True or false? The endodermis forms a seal that controls the flow of water.
   **true**

Answer the following questions about plant responses.

4. True or false? Gibberellins cause plants to grow taller.
   **true**

5. True or false? The growth of a plant toward light is called phototropism.
   **true**

6. True or false? The sudden closing of a Venus's flytrap is an example of a nastic movement.
   **true**

CONTENT MASTERY CHAPTER 23 BIOLOGY: The Dynamics of Life 115

---

Name _____ Date _____ Class _____

## Review the Vocabulary

| | |
|---|---|
| cortex | petiole (PET ee ohl) |
| epidermis | phloem (FLOH em) |
| guard cells | transpiration |
| parenchyma (puh RENG kuh muh) | tropism (TROH pih zum) |
| pericycle | xylem (ZI lum) |

Review the Chapter 23 vocabulary words listed in the box. Then write the correct word on the line after each definition below.

1. Tissue that transports water and minerals from roots to the rest of the plant **xylem**

2. Thin-walled cells often used for storage **parenchyma**

3. Cells in leaf epidermis that control the opening and closing of stomatal pores **guard cells**

4. Leaf part that joins the leaf to the stem **petiole**

5. A plant's response to an external stimuli that causes a growth response **tropism**

6. Outermost layer of cells in plants **epidermis**

7. Plant tissue that helps form lateral roots **pericycle**

8. Tissue found in plant stems and roots between the epidermis and vascular core **cortex**

9. Evaporation of water from the stomata of leaves **transpiration**

10. Tissue that transports sugar from the leaves to all parts of the plant **phloem**

116 CHAPTER 23 BIOLOGY: The Dynamics of Life CONTENT MASTERY

---

**Content Mastery**

## Chapter 24  Reproduction in Plants, *continued*

Section 24.1 *Life Cycles of Mosses, Ferns, and Conifers*

### Study the Diagram

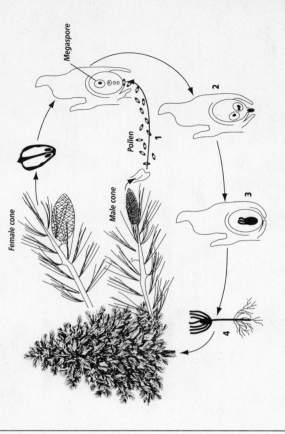

Each statement below goes with one of the stages of the pine life cycle shown in the diagram. Write the number from the diagram on the line in front of the statement it goes with.

___2___  Male gametophytes form a pollen tube that grows into the ovule, and the sperm fertilize the eggs.

___1___  Pollen grains—the male gametophytes—are carried by the wind to the female cones.

___3___  Inside the seed coat, the food is stored for the developing embryo.

___4___  When the seed germinates, a new seedling is formed.

---

**Content Mastery**

## Chapter 24  Reproduction in Plants

### Get the Big Picture

Use the information from Section 24.1 to fill in the rectangles in the idea map below. Some of the rectangles have been filled in for you.

**Life Cycles of**

- (A) **mosses** — *whose dominant stage is the* — **gametophyte**
- (B) **ferns** — *whose dominant stage is the* — **sporophyte**
- (C) **conifers** — *whose dominant stage is the* — **sporophyte**

Use the information from Section 24.2 to fill in the rectangles in the idea map below. Some of the rectangles have been filled in for you.

**Organs of a Flower**

- (D) **sepal** — *protects flower buds*
- (E) **petals** — *often have nectar at base*
- (F) **stamen** — *male reproductive structure*
- (G) **pistil** — *female reproductive structure*

Each statement below goes with one of the words in the rectangles above. Write the letter of the rectangle on the line in front of the statement it goes with. Not all the words in rectangles will be used.

___A___  Protonema develops into a small green filament of cells that develop into either a male or female gametophyte.

___F___  Anther is at the top of this structure.

___B___  Fronds grow from the underground stem called the rhizome.

___G___  The bottom of this structure enlarges to form an ovary.

Name _____  Date _____  Class _____

**Content Mastery**

## Chapter 24 Reproduction in Plants, *continued*

Section 24.2 **Flowers and Flowering**
Section 24.3 **The Life Cycle of a Flowering Plant**

### Study the Diagram

Use the diagram to answer the questions.

**Students may draw any flower as long as it has a pistil and no stamens.**

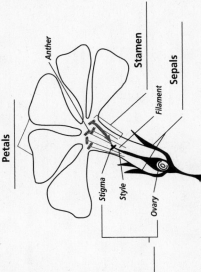

Petals

Anther

Stigma

Style

Filament

Ovary

Stamen

Sepals

Pistil

1. Label the diagram with the following parts of a flower.
Stamen—male part of the flower; pollen is made in the anther
Pistil—female part of the flower; the ovary will become the fruit
Petals—often brightly colored to attract insects and birds
Sepals—protect the flower bud

2. Complete flowers have all four parts, but some flowers are incomplete. Some plants have separate male and female flowers. Draw an incomplete female flower next to the complete flower in the diagram.

3. Some plants produce fruits and seeds that are attractive to animals. How does it help a plant to have an animal eat its fruits? **After the animal eats the fruit, the seeds pass through its digestive system and are deposited in the animal's waste. This can disperse the seeds miles away from the plant.**

4. True or false? Seeds require water to germinate. **true**

CONTENT MASTERY                    CHAPTER 24  BIOLOGY: The Dynamics of Life     119

---

Name _____  Date _____  Class _____

**Content Mastery**

## Chapter 24 Reproduction in Plants, *continued*

### Review the Vocabulary

| anther | ovary |
|--------|-------|
| dormancy | petal |
| endosperm | photoperiodism |
| germination | short-day plant |
| long-day plant | stamen |
| micropyle (MI kruh pile) | |

Review the Chapter 24 vocabulary words listed in the box. Then write the correct word on the line after each definition below.

1. Plant's response to the difference in day and night length __**photoperiodism**__

2. Flower parts that are usually brightly colored and leaflike __**petals**__

3. Process by which a seed begins to develop into a new plant __**germination**__

4. Period of seed inactivity __**dormancy**__

5. Tiny opening in the ovule through which sperm enter __**micropyle**__

6. Plant that flowers when exposed to a long night __**short-day plant**__

7. Food-storage tissue used by developing anthophyte embryo __**endosperm**__

8. Female reproductive organ formed at lower end of pistil __**ovary**__

9. Consists of an anther and a filament __**stamen**__

10. Plant that flowers when the nights are short __**long-day plant**__

11. Male reproductive structure that contains pollen grains __**anther**__

120    CHAPTER 24  BIOLOGY: The Dynamics of Life                    CONTENT MASTERY

---

CONTENT MASTERY          ANSWER KEY  BIOLOGY: The Dynamics of Life     **T257**

---

Name _____ Date _____ Class _____

**Content Mastery**

## BioDigest 7 Plants

### Get the Big Picture

Review all of the headings and photos in the BioDigest. Then look at the following pictures and answer the questions.

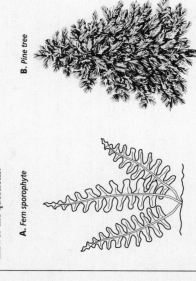

A. Fern sporophyte

B. Pine tree

C. Dogwood flowers

1. Which picture shows a non-seed plant?
   **A**

2. Which picture shows a flowering plant?
   **C**

3. Which picture shows a plant adapted for cold?
   **B**

4. Which picture shows a plant that produces fruits?
   **C**

5. Vascular tissues let plants grow tall. Which pictures show plants with vascular tissue?
   **A, B, C**

6. Some insects are attracted to plants with brightly colored flowers or fragrances. Which picture shows a plant that is pollinated by insects?
   **C**

---

Name _____ Date _____ Class _____

**Content Mastery**

## BioDigest 7 Plants, *continued*

### Study the Picture

Study the picture of the vascular plant. Then answer the questions.

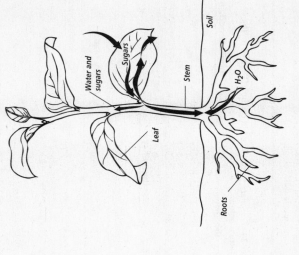

1. Where does the plant produce energy in the form of sugars?
   **in its leaves**

2. What part of the plant takes in water?
   **the roots**

3. Vascular tissues move sugars and water throughout the plant and provide some support. Which part of the plant provides support and allows the plant to grow taller?
   **the stems**

**BioDigest 7**    **Plants,** *continued*     **Content Mastery**

## Study the Diagrams

Read the paragraphs in the box and study the diagrams. Then answer the questions.

> Plants are very interesting organisms. One of the most interesting aspects of plant life is that most of them have two different forms or stages they go through during their lifetime. The gametophyte stage or generation is where the sperm and eggs are formed. The number of chromosomes in these gametes are half the normal number for the plant species. This is called a haploid (n) condition. In nonvascular plants, the gametophyte is the larger, more visible form of the plant.
>
> In vascular plants, the situation is reversed. The sporophyte generation is the larger form. It has the full number of chromosomes and is diploid (2n). The sporophyte generation produces spores. In ferns, the spores are dispersed by wind. When it is wet and warm enough, the gametophyte generation grows and the cycle starts again. The process of one plant stage following another is called the alternation of generations.

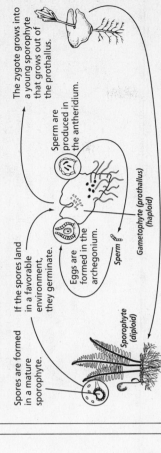

The zygote grows into a young sporophyte that grows out of the prothallus.

Sperm are produced in the antheridium.

Eggs are formed in the archegonium.

*Sperm*

*Gametophyte (prothallus) (haploid)*

Spores are formed in a mature sporophyte.

If the spores land in a favorable environment, they germinate.

*Sporophyte (diploid)*

1. Which form of a plant produces spores?   **the sporophyte**

    Which form produces gametes?   **the gametophyte**

2. In nonvascular plants, which generation is the largest?
    **the gametophyte generation**

3. Give two examples of gametes.
    **eggs and sperm**

4. Which generation is haploid and which is diploid?
    **The gametophyte generation is haploid, and the sporophyte generation is diploid.**

---

**BioDigest 7**    **Plants,** *continued*     **Content Mastery**

## Study the Picture

Study the picture of the flower. Then fill in the blanks in the statements. The pistil is the female reproductive part of the flower. The stamen is the male reproductive part of the flower.

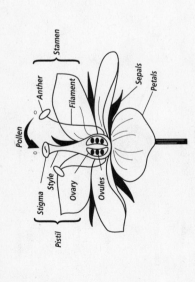

*Anther*

*Pollen*

*Stamen*

*Filament*

*Stigma*

*Style*

*Ovary*

*Ovules*

*Pistil*

*Sepals*

*Petals*

1. Flowering plants attract animal pollinators with nectar, perfumes, or brightly colored
    **petals** .

2. Pollen from the **stamen or anther** rubs off onto the animal as it drinks the nectar.

3. Egg cells develop at the base of the pistil inside the **ovule or ovary** .

4. Pollen sticks to the **stigma** and forms a pollen tube to reach the egg.

## Matching

Fruits provide flowering plants with different ways to disperse their seeds. Draw a line to match each fruit in the box with its method of dispersal.

> a. The fruit of a coconut floats.
> b. The fruit of a maple is wing-shaped.
> c. The fruit of a grape vine is edible.
> d. Some fruits, like burrs, have hooks.

5. The seed falls out while the fruit is eaten.
6. The fruit is carried by the wind.
7. The fruit sticks to the fur of animals.
8. The fruit is carried by ocean currents.

## Chapter 25 — What Is an Animal?

### Get the Big Picture

Read the paragraph in the box. Then study the picture and answer the questions.

> There are so many kinds of animals that it is nearly impossible to describe just what an animal is. All animals, however, have some things in common. All animals have some kind of shape. Scientists often identify animals by their shape and symmetry—the balance in their body proportions. All animals go through a developmental stage when they go from a single cell to an adult. They also have a life cycle they pass through as they grow. All animals have some way to reproduce. Most animals interact with their environment in some way. And all animals must reproduce if their species is going to survive.

### Some Characteristics of Animals

**Shape or Symmetry**

None — Sponge

Radial — Sea star

Bilateral — Human

**Development**

One cell — Gastrula — Animals

**Protection and Support**

Crab exoskeleton

Cat endoskeleton

1. What do all adult animals develop from?
   **a single cell**

2. A sea urchin is related to a sea star. What kind of symmetry do you think a sea urchin would have?
   **radial symmetry**

3. What kind of skeleton do you have? Explain.
   **An endoskeleton; it is on the inside of my body.**

---

## Chapter 25 — What Is an Animal?, *continued*

**Section 25.1 Typical Animal Characteristics**

### Study the Diagram

Use the diagram to answer the questions.

Soon after fertilization, the cell begins to divide. Each new cell divides over and over again until a hollow ball called a blastula is formed.

One side of the blastula begins to fold inward, making an inner pouch. At this point, the embryo is called a gastrula. The outside of the gastrula eventually becomes the animal's outer covering. The inside develops into the lining of the digestive system. In some animals, the opening of the gastrula becomes the mouth. In other animals, the mouth develops elsewhere.

1. What is a blastula? How does it form?
   **A blastula is a hollow ball of cells. It is formed during the division of cells after fertilization.**

2. What is a gastrula? How does it form?
   **A blastula becomes a gastrula after one side of it folds in to make a pouch.**

3. Why is it important to determine whether an animal is a protostome or a deuterostome?
   **Scientists hypothesize that protostomes appeared before deuterostomes in evolution. Determining whether an animal is a protostome or dueterostome can help biologists identify its group more accurately.**

Name _____ Date _____ Class _____

**Content Mastery**

## Chapter 25  What Is an Animal?, continued

Section 25.2 Body Plans
and Adaptations

### Study the Diagram

Read the paragraph in the box. Then study the diagram and answer the questions.

> One way scientists can identify an animal is by the presence and type of body cavity. Two types of body cavities are a **pseudocoelom** and a **coelom** (SEE lome). Simple animals, such as flatworms, have no body cavity. More complex animals, such as roundworms, have a pseudocoelom, a body cavity filled with fluid that provides support. In more complex animals with a coelom, the internal organs are suspended within the coelom and are completely surrounded by the **mesoderm**.

Mesoderm  Endoderm  Digestive tract
Ectoderm

**A COELOM ATE**
without ← animal
body cavity

**Flatworms**

Mesoderm  Endoderm  Digestive tract
Ectoderm  Coelom

**PSEUDO COELOM ATE**
false ← animal
body cavity

**Roundworms**

Mesoderm  Endoderm
Ectoderm  Coelom  Digestive tract

**COELOM ATE**
← animal
body cavity

**Segmented Worms**

1. What type of animals have no body cavity? Give an example of this type of animal.
**The acoelomates; flatworms are acoelomates.**

2. What type of animal is a roundworm? How do you know?
**A pseudocoelomate; roundworms have a pseudocoelom filled with fluid that is used for bracing muscles against.**

3. Why is an earthworm a coelomate?
**Earthworms are segmented worms. They have a coelom.**

4. What does the coelom do?
**provides support for the animal; provides space for development of internal organs**

---

Name _____ Date _____ Class _____

**Content Mastery**

## Chapter 25  What Is an Animal?, continued

### Review the Vocabulary

Circle the Chapter 25 vocabulary word in brackets that best matches each description.

1. A sponge is an example of a(n) _____ organism.
[sessile (SES sile)/ dorsal / ventral / anterior]

2. hollow ball made up of a single layer of cells
[gastrula (GAS truh luh) / deuterostome (DEW tuh roh stohm) / (blastula)/ coelom]

3. layer of cells on the outer surface of the gastrula
[(ectoderm)/ endoderm / mesoderm / exoskeleton]

4. An earthworm is an example of a(n) _____.
[acoelomate / pseudocoelom /(protostome)/ gastrula]

5. Most sponges have this type of symmetry (SIH muh tree).
[radial / bilateral /(asymmetry)/ ventral]

6. Hydras have this type of symmetry.
[(radial)/ bilateral / asymmetry / dorsal]

7. An organism that can be divided down its length into halves that are mirror images of each other is said to have _____ symmetry.
[radial /(bilateral)/ ventral/ dorsal]

8. head end of a flatworm
[posterior / dorsal / ventral /(anterior)]

9. an animal that has three cell layers with a digestive tract but no body cavity
[pseudocoelomate / coelomate /(acoelomate (uh SEE luh mayt))/ protostome]

10. Humans, insects, and fishes have this type of body cavity.
[(coelom (SEE lum))/ pseudocoelom (sew duh SEE lum) / acoelom / gastrula]

11. An internal skeleton is called a(n)
[exoskeleton /(endoskeleton)/ blastula / protostome (PROH tuh stohm)]

Name _____ Date _____ Class _____

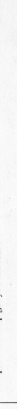

### Content Mastery

## Chapter 26
# Sponges, Cnidarians, Flatworms, and Roundworms

### Get the Big Picture

Read the paragraphs in the boxes. Then answer the questions.

> Organisms similar to the sponges, cnidarians, flatworms, and roundworms of today were Earth's earliest animals. Scientists sometimes study these animals to find out how animal bodies have evolved. Sponges have a simple body. They have an irregular shape with only one body opening. Most sponges live in the ocean. The body of a cnidarian also has only one body opening. However, their body is shaped like the wheel of a bicycle. The body of the cnidarian is the hub, or center, of the wheel. Their body parts extend outward from the hub like spokes. Most cnidarians also live in the oceans.

> Flatworms have a thin body with only one opening. If you drew a line lengthwise down the center of a flatworm's body, the left half would be the mirror image of the right half. Some flatworms live in the water. Others are parasitic and live in other animals. Roundworms have a round body with a mirror-image form similar to the flatworm. Unlike flatworms, roundworms have two body openings. Most roundworms live in soil or water. Some are parasites.

1. Where can sponges, cnidarians, flatworms, and roundworms all be found?
   **living in water**
   _____

2. To what can you compare the body of a cnidarian?
   **the wheel of a bicycle**
   _____

3. Which three types of animals have only one body opening?
   **sponges, cnidarians, and flatworms**
   _____

4. How is the body of a sponge different from the body of a roundworm?
   **Sponges have an irregularly shaped body with one body opening. Roundworms**
   **have a mirror-image body shape with two body openings.**
   _____

---

Name _____ Date _____ Class _____

### Content Mastery

## Chapter 26
# Sponges, Cnidarians, Flatworms, and Roundworms, continued

Section 26.1  Sponges
Section 26.2  Cnidarians
Section 26.3  Flatworms
Section 26.4  Roundworms

### Interpret the Diagrams

Study the diagrams and read the paragraphs. Then complete the table. Part of the table has been completed to help get you started.

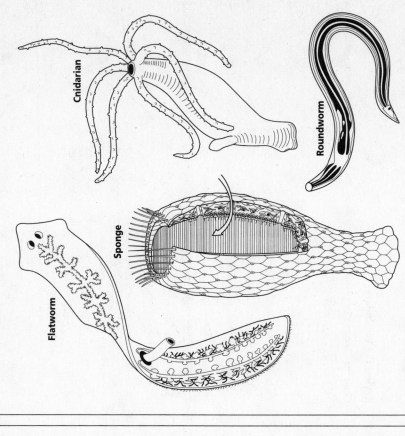

Name _____ Date _____ Class _____

**Content Mastery**

**Chapter 26**

## Sponges, Cnidarians, Flatworms, and Roundworms, *continued*

The animals shown are all simple animals with distinct traits. The **sponge** is the simplest. Sponges have only one body opening. Sponges belong to a group of animals that evolved entirely in the water. They live alone or in colonies.

The **cnidarian** is a soft-bodied animal that lives in water. Cnidarians evolved a wide variety of body shapes. They have one body opening in which they digest their food. Most species of cnidarians use stinging cells to capture their prey. Jellyfishes and hydras are cnidarians.

The **flatworm** has a more complex body than the sponge or the cnidarian, but it still has only one body opening. The two eye spots on a flatworm's head are made up of cells that can tell the difference between light and dark. Some flatworms, such as planarians, are scavengers. Others, such as tapeworms, are parasites. Some flatworms spend their entire lives under rocks in the water, whereas others live on land.

The fourth animal is a **roundworm**. Roundworms have two body openings—one for eating and one for excretion. They often live as parasites in plants, humans, and other animals. Roundworms can live on land or in water.

| Name of Animal | Example | One or Two Openings in Body? | Do They Live on Land or in Water? | Are Any Species Parasites? |
|---|---|---|---|---|
| Sponge | sponge | one | water | no |
| Cnidarian | hydra | one | water | no |
| Flatworm | planarian | one | land and water | yes |
| ...worm | *Ascaris* | two | land and water | yes |

---

Name _____ Date _____ Class _____

**Content Mastery**

**Chapter 26**

## Sponges, Cnidarians, Flatworms, and Roundworms, *continued*

### Review the Vocabulary

a. external fertilization
b. filter feeding
c. gastrovascular cavity (gas troh VAS kyuh lur)
d. hermaphrodite (hur MAF ruh dite)
e. internal fertilization
f. medusa
g. nematocyst (nuh MAT uh sihst)
h. nerve net
i. pharynx (FAYR ingks)
j. polyp (PAH lup)
k. proglottid (proh GLAH tud)
l. scolex (SKOH leks)

Write the letters of the Chapter 26 vocabulary words on the lines after the definitions. One word has been matched with its definition to help you get started.

1. Reproduction in which the eggs are fertilized inside the animal's body ___ **e**
2. Reproduction in which the eggs are fertilized outside the animal's body ___ **a**
3. Conducts nerve impulses in cnidarians ___ **h**
4. Individual, repeating sections of a tapeworm ___ **k**
5. The way in which sponges get their food ___ **b**
6. Tubelike organ used by planarians to suck food into the digestive system ___ **i**
7. Structure used by cnidarians to capture or poison their prey ___ **g**
8. Individual that can produce both eggs and sperm ___ **d**
9. Stage of cnidarian life cycle in which its body is shaped like a tube ___ **j**
10. Cavity in which cnidarian digestion takes place ___ **c**
11. Head of a tapeworm ___ **l**
12. Stage of cnidarian life cycle in which its body is shaped like an umbrella ___ **f**

---

Name                                            Date                    Class

## Get the Big Picture

Read the paragraphs in the boxes and study the pictures. Then answer the questions.

> Did you know that the simple garden snail is a close relative of the squid? Both these animals are **mollusks**, one of the largest groups of animals on Earth. Some mollusks, like the clam and the beautiful sea snails named gastropods, have shells. Most mollusk shells are secreted by the mantle. The mantle cavity may have gills for gas exchange. Mollusks usually have a large hump that holds the intestines. Their mouthparts look like a tongue and are called a **radula**. All mollusks have a free-swimming larval stage. Most adult mollusks have a foot that can be used in a variety of ways, including movement. Most mollusks live in the ocean or in other wet environments. Mollusks will die if they dry out.

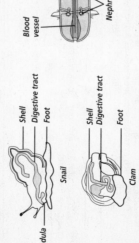

Radula

Shell
Digestive tract
Foot

Snail

Shell
Digestive tract
Foot

Clam

Blood vessel   Nerve cord   Setae   Body segment

Nephridia   Parapodia   Digestive tract

**A Generalized Annelid Worm**

**Two Members of the Mollusk Group**

> **Annelid** worms are found in the ocean and on land. The term annelida means "ringed," and the bodies of these animals have repeating body segments. Some worms have footlike projections on their segments, called **parapodia**, for movement. Others, like the earthworm, have very small hairs called **setae**. Most marine annelids are filter feeders. These annelids live in tubes in the mud and extend feathery arms into the water to capture floating organic food. Annelids need to live in moist environments because they will die if they dry out.

1. How are mollusks and annelids similar?
   **Both live in the ocean an in moist places on land. Both will die if they dry out.**

2. How are mollusks and annelids different?
   **Mollusks may have shells; annelids never do. Annelids have repeating body**
   **segments; mollusks do not.**

---

Name                                            Date                    Class

## Study the Figure

Use the figure to answer the questions.

**B. Mantle**
The mantle is a thin membrane. It protects the snail's organs. It also builds the snail's shell.

**A. Foot**
The snail has one large foot. It uses its foot to move.

**C. Radula**
The radula is located in the snail's mouth. It is a tonguelike organ with teeth. It is used to scrape and cut food.

The snail belongs to the class of mollusks called gastropods.

1. What is the name of the animal in the picture? To what class of mollusks does it belong?
   **Snail; it is a gastropod.**

2. What is the name of the structure labeled *A*?
   **foot**

3. What is the name of the structure labeled *B*? What is its function?
   **Mantle; it is a thin membrane that protects the snail's organs and builds its shell.**

4. What is the name of the structure labeled *C*? For what does the snail use it?
   **Radula; the snail uses it to scrape and cut food.**

**Content Mastery**

*Section 27.2 Segmented Worms*

## Study the Figure

Use the figure to answer the questions.

**A. Segments**
Segments allow the earthworm to move. A group of segments may perform a certain task.

**B. Nephridia**
Nephridia are used to remove waste from each segment.

**C. Gizzard**
The gizzard grinds food into small pieces.

The earthworm belongs to the phylum Annelida.

1. What is the name of the animal in the figure? To what phylum does it belong?
**Earthworm; it is a member of the phylum Annelida.**

2. What is the name of the structures labeled *A*? Why are these structures important?
**Segments; they allow an earthworm to move.**

3. What is the name of the structures labeled *B*? What do these structures do?
**Nephridia; they remove waste from each segment.**

4. What is the name of the structure labeled *C*? For what is this structure used?
**Gizzard; it is used to grind food into small pieces.**

---

**Content Mastery**

## Review the Vocabulary

Use the Chapter 27 vocabulary words to fill in the puzzle.

closed circulatory system
nephridia (ne FRIH dee uh)

gizzard
open circulatory system

mantle
radula (RAJ uh luh)

**ACROSS**

2. Blood moves into open spaces around an animal's organs. This is called an open _____ system.

5. thin membrane that protects a mollusk's organs

6. structures that remove waste from an animal's body

**DOWN**

1. tonguelike organ used to scrape or cut food

3. annelid organ that grinds food

4. The blood in an animal's body stays in the blood vessels. This is called a(n) _____ circulatory system.

## Chapter 28 Arthropods

### Get the Big Picture

Read the paragraphs in the boxes and study the picture. Then answer the questions.

> The arthropods are the largest group of animals in the world. This group includes crabs, spiders, insects, and many extinct fossil forms. Arthropods have many different body shapes and sizes, but they all have:
> 1. paired, jointed legs or appendages
> 2. a hard, armored exoskeleton that protects them and prevents water loss
> 3. segmented bodies
> 4. an open circulatory system with a dorsal heart

> In order to grow, arthropods shed their exoskeletons in a process called **molting**. Arthropods live both in water and on land. Although some arthropods are considered pests, many of them, including shrimp and crabs, can be eaten by humans. Many arthropods eat other arthropods and help keep Earth from being overrun by these successful animals.

**Lobster**

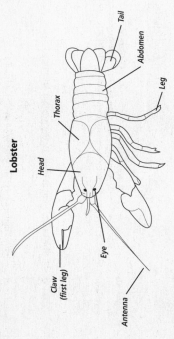

Head, Thorax, Abdomen, Tail, Leg, Eye, Claw (first leg), Antenna

1. Name one characteristic of arthropods.
   **Answers may include any one of the following: jointed legs, exoskeleton, segmented bodies, open circulatory system.**

2. How do arthropods grow?
   **They molt their exoskeletons.**

3. True or false? Arthropods are all herbivores (eat only plants).
   **false**

---

## Chapter 28 Arthropods, *continued*

Section 28.1 *Characteristics of Arthropods*

### Identify the Arthropods

Write the names of the arthropods shown in the figure.

A. __Grasshopper__

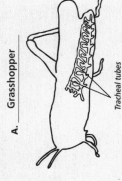

*Tracheal tubes*

Tracheal tubes are inside the body. They carry air close to each cell.

B. __Crab__

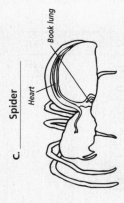

*Gills*

Gills have a large surface area. They expose blood-rich tissue to water. When water passes over the gills, oxygen is taken in. Carbon dioxide is released.

C. __Spider__

*Book lung*

*Heart*

Book lungs are folded membranes. They expose blood-rich tissue to air.

Complete the table.

| Name of Arthropod | Structures Used for Breathing | How Breathing Structures Work |
| --- | --- | --- |
| Grasshopper | tracheal tubes | Air travels through the body in tracheal tubes. The air passes close to the cells. |
| Crab | gills | As water travels over them, gills take in oxygen. They release carbon dioxide into the water. |
| Spider | book lungs | Folded membranes expose blood-rich tissue to air. |

**CONTENT MASTERY**

## Arthropods, *continued*

Section 28.2 *Diversity of Arthropods*

### Sequence the Diagram

The diagram below shows the four stages of metamorphosis of a butterfly. Number the stages to put them in order.

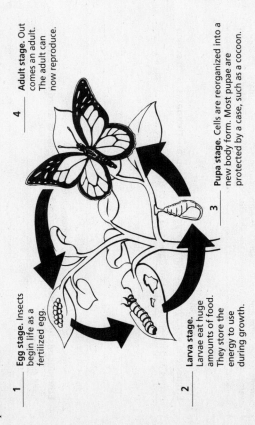

**1** Egg stage. Insects begin life as a fertilized egg.

**4** Adult stage. Out comes an adult. The adult can now reproduce.

**2** Larva stage. Larvae eat huge amounts of food. They store the energy to use during growth.

**3** Pupa stage. Cells are reorganized into a new body form. Most pupae are protected by a case, such as a cocoon.

Complete the table. Part of the table has been filled in for you.

| Stage of Complete Metamorphosis | Description of Each Stage |
| --- | --- |
| Egg | Life begins with a fertilized egg. |
| Larva | The larva eats huge amounts of food. It stores the energy for growth. |
| Pupa | Cells are reorganized into a new body form. This stage takes place in a protective case. |
| Adult | Out comes an adult. The adult can reproduce. |

---

## Arthropods, *continued*

### Review the Vocabulary

| | |
| --- | --- |
| appendage | chelicerae (kuh LIH sur ee) |
| book lungs | mandible (MAN duh bul) |
| compound eyes | pedipalps (PED uh palps) |
| larva | pheromone (FAYR uh mohn) |
| molting | spinnerets (sih nuh RETS) |
| nymph (NIHMF) | spiracles (SPEER uh kulz) |
| pupa | tracheal tube (TRAY kee ul) |
| simple eye | |

Many of the Chapter 28 vocabulary words are listed in the box. Review the definitions of these words. Then fill in each blank in the sentences below with the correct word.

**1.** A(n) **pheromone** is an odor given off by animals.

**2.** The wormlike stage of an insect is the **larva**.

**3.** A(n) **appendage** is a structure that grows out of an animal's body.

**4.** Arachnids use **pedipalps** for holding food and for sensing.

**5.** The biting appendages of arachnids are called **chelicerae**.

**6.** Spiders use **spinnerets** to spin silk into thread.

**7.** Spiders and their relatives use **book lungs** to breathe.

**8.** A(n) **nymph** hatches from an egg during incomplete metamorphosis.

**9.** Many arthropods see with a pair of large **compound eyes**.

**10.** The mouthpart an arthropod uses to hold, chew, suck, or bite food is called a(n) **mandible**.

---

Name _____ Date _____ Class _____

## Chapter 29   Echinoderms and Invertebrate Chordates

### Get the Big Picture

Read the paragraphs in the boxes. Then answer the question that follow.

Echinoderms have characteristics that make them different from other animals. Echinoderms move by hundreds of tiny suction cups on their tube feet. They have hard, spiny skeletons that are covered by a thin layer of skin. They also have a water vascular system. This system controls how they move, eat, respire, and get rid of waste. You can find echinoderms in all the oceans of the world.

Invertebrate chordates are ocean animals that do not have a hard skeleton. These chordates share some characteristics with echinoderms and animals with backbones. For example, echinoderm embryos look similar to embryos of invertebrate chordates. An ancient invertebrate chordate may have been the ancestor of all animals with backbones.

1. How are echinoderms and invertebrate chordates similar?

**Echinoderm embryos look like embryos of invertebrate chordates. Both echinoderms and invertebrate chordates live in oceans.**

_____

_____

_____

2. How are echinoderms and invertebrate chordates different?

**Echinoderms have a hard, spiny skeleton, but invertebrate chordates do not have a hard skeleton.**

_____

_____

---

Name _____ Date _____ Class _____

## Chapter 29   Echinoderms and Invertebrates Chordates, continued

### Study the Diagram

Read the paragraph in the box. Then use the diagram to answer the question that follows.

#### How Do Sea Stars Move?

All sea stars have hundreds of tube feet. Each tube foot has a suction cup on the end. Sea stars use their tube feet to creep along the ocean floor. Sea stars also use their tube feet to pry open the shells of mollusks to get food. The tube feet are part of a sea star's water vascular system. One of the main uses of this system is to create water pressure to move the tube feet.

1. Write numbers to order the steps of water flow from the madreporite to the sea star's tube feet.

**4** _____ Ampullae contract to squeeze water into the tube feet.

**1** _____ Water enters the madreporite.

**3** _____ Water flows from the ring canal into the radial canals.

**2** _____ Water flows from madreporite to the ring canal.

Name _____ Date _____ Class _____

## Study the Diagrams

Read what is in the boxes and study the diagrams below them. Then answer the questions that follow.

> All **chordates** share certain characteristics at some time during their development. They have a dorsal hollow nerve cord, a notochord, gill slits, a tail that extends beyond the anus, and muscles that are found in blocks along the body.

### Typical Chordate Characteristics

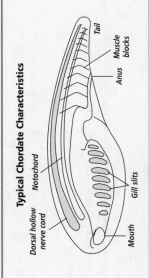

> Sea squirts, or **tunicates**, are considered to be chordates because their larvae have traits that are found in other chordates. The figure below shows the change of a larval tunicate into an adult. The larva is free-swimming, but the adult remains attached to rocks in the sea.

### Tunicate Metamorphosis

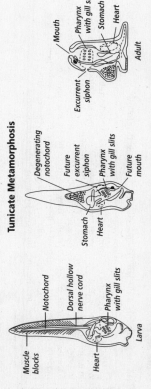

1. What are five characteristics common to all chordates? **a tail that extends beyond the anus, a notochord, gill slits, a dorsal hollow nerve cord, and muscle blocks**

2. What tunicate body traits shown in the diagrams indicate that tunicates are chordates? **a notochord, a dorsal hollow nerve cord, muscle blocks, and gill slits**

---

Name _____ Date _____ Class _____

## Review the Vocabulary

Use the Chapter 29 vocabulary words in the box to fill in the puzzle.

> ampulla (am POOL uh)
> madreporite (MAD ruh por ite)
> notochord (NOH tuh kord)
> pedicellaria (ped uh suh LAYR ee uh)
> ray

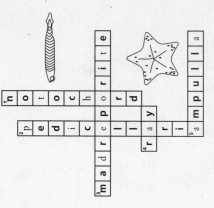

**Across**

3. disk-shaped opening in an echinoderm's body that lets water in and out
4. long, tapering arm of an echinoderm
5. round, muscular structure that squeezes water into or out of tube feet

**Down**

1. long, rodlike structure in all chordates
2. pincerlike appendage on an echinoderm

Find the vocabulary word in the box that matches each definition. Then write the letter of the word on the line in front of the definition.

> a. dorsal hollow nerve cord
> b. gill slits
> c. tube feet
> d. water vascular system

**d**  6. System in echinoderms that helps them move, respire, eat, and get rid of waste

**c**  7. Hollow, thin-walled tubes with a suction cup on the end

**a**  8. Tube of cells surrounding a fluid-filled canal above the notochord

**b**  9. Paired openings located behind the mouth

## BioDigest 8 — Invertebrates

### Get the Big Picture

Read the paragraph in the box. Then answer the questions that follow.

> How are sponges and grasshoppers alike? Both animals are **invertebrates**—animals without backbones. The ancestors of modern invertebrates had simple body plans. They lived in water and got food, oxygen, and other materials from their surroundings. Some modern invertebrates, such as sponges, have simple body plans like their ancestors. Sponges do not have tissues, organs, or organ systems. They live in the ocean and stay in one place. Other modern invertebrates are adapted to live in different environments. Arthropods such as spiders and grasshoppers developed tissues, organs, organ systems, and legs. These invertebrates live on land and can move from one habitat to another.

1. What is the main difference between invertebrates and other animals?
   **Invertebrates do not have backbones.**

2. Describe the ancestors of modern invertebrates.
   **Ancestors of modern invertebrates had simple body plans with no tissues, organs, or organ systems. They lived in water and got food, oxygen, and other materials from their surroundings.**

3. Name a modern invertebrate that is very different from its ancestors. Describe the difference.
   **Grasshoppers and spiders are very different from their ancestors. They have tissues, organs, organ systems, and legs. They live on land, not in water.**

4. Name a modern invertebrate that has a simple body plan like its ancestors. What makes this body plan simple?
   **Sponges have a simple body plan like their ancestors because they have no tissues, organs, or organ systems.**

---

## BioDigest 8 — Invertebrates, *continued*

### Study the Table

Study the table. Then answer the questions that follow.

| Animal | Parts of the Nervous System |
|---|---|
| Sponges | • none |
| Cnidarians | • no brain or control center<br>• simple nervous system<br>• Nerve net carries impulses to and from all parts of the body.<br>• Impulses from the nerve net cause muscles to contract. |
| Flatworms | • ganglion—brainlike structure that receives messages along nerve cords from eyespots and sensory pits<br>• two nerve cords that run the length of the body |
| Arthropods | • brain<br>• at least one ganglion per body segment<br>• double nerve cord that runs along the ventral side of the animal |

1. Which animals have the most complex nervous system?
   **arthropods**

2. Which animals have the least complex nervous system?
   **sponges**

3. Summarize the nervous system of each type of animal.
   Cnidarians: **simple nervous system consisting of a nerve net**

   Flatworms: **brainlike structure and two nerve cords**

   Arthropods: **brain, double nerve cord, and ganglia in body segments**

Name    Date    Class

**Content Mastery**

**BioDigest 8**   **Invertebrates,** *continued*

Study the table. Then answer the questions.

| Animal | Parts of the Digestive System |
| --- | --- |
| Sponges | • no mouth; opening at the top through which water leaves the body<br>• pores through which water and food enter the body<br>• no special cavity or space for digestion |
| Cnidarians | • single body opening through which food enters and wastes leave<br>• gastrovascular cavity—space inside the body where enzymes break down food |
| Flatworms | • single body opening through which food enters and wastes leave<br>• pharynx—muscular tube that begins digesting food outside the body<br>• gastrovascular cavity |
| Arthropods | • mouth—opening through which food enters the body<br>• stomach—organ where enzymes break down food<br>• intestine—tube that absorbs water from food and moves waste toward the anus<br>• anus—opening through which waste leaves the body |

4. Which animals have the most complex digestive system?
**arthropods**

5. Which animals have the least complex digestive system?
**sponges**

6. How are the cnidarian digestive system and the arthropod digestive system similar?
**Both have a space inside the body where enzymes break down food.**

7. How are the cnidarian digestive system and the arthropod digestive system different?
**Cnidarians have a single body opening, and arthropods have two (mouth and anus). Cnidarians do not have a stomach or an intestine.**

CONTENT MASTERY    BIODIGEST 8   BIOLOGY: The Dynamics of Life   147

---

Name    Date    Class

**Content Mastery**

**BioDigest 8**   **Invertebrates,** *continued*

## Complete the Sentences

Read the paragraphs in the box. Then use the words in bold type in the paragraphs to complete the sentences that follow.

> **Invertebrates** are animals without a backbone. How do invertebrates keep their shape without a skeleton?
>
> Many invertebrates, including **cnidarians** such as jellyfishes, live in the ocean. Jellyfishes use properties of the water, such as water pressure and density, to keep their shapes.
>
> **Mollusks** (including, snails, slugs, clams, octopuses, and squids) can have a hard, external shell or a very muscular, flexible body.
>
> **Echinoderms**—such as sea stars—have a hard, bumpy endoskeleton. *Endo-* means "inside," so an *endoskeleton* is a skeleton inside the body. Unlike the skeleton of a vertebrate, the echinoderm skeleton is not very flexible and cannot support much weight.
>
> There are several kinds of worms. All are invertebrates. The earthworms you dig up in the garden are **segmented worms**. Segmented worms are the most complex kind of worm. Each segment has its own muscles. The muscular segments allow the worm to keep its shape on land.
>
> Other worms, such as **roundworms** and **flatworms**, are usually very small compared to segmented worms. Because they are small, roundworms and flatworms do not need special adaptations to maintain their shape.
>
> **Arthropods**, including insects, spiders, and crabs, are some of the most successful and varied animals on Earth. Arthropods have an armored shell, called an **exoskeleton**. *Exo-* means "outside," so an *exoskeleton* is a skeleton on the outside of the body. An arthropod's exoskeleton is a lot like a knight's suit of armor, with joints that can bend and allow movement.

1. Octopuses and squids are    **mollusks** .

2. **Round**worms and    **flatworms**    are often very small.

3. Sea stars have an endoskeleton. They are a kind of    **echino**derm .

4. **Invert**ebrates    are animals without a backbone.

5. A **segmented**    worm is made up of many units, each of which has its own muscles.

6. Jellyfishes are    **cnidarians** .

7. Insects are **arthropods**    . They keep their shape by having an armored shell, called an    **exo**skeleton .

148   BIODIGEST 8   BIOLOGY: The Dynamics of Life    CONTENT MASTERY

CONTENT MASTERY

---

Name _____ Date _____ Class _____

### Chapter
## 30   Fishes and Amphibians

#### Get the Big Picture

Study the diagrams. Then answer the questions that follow.

Dorsal hollow nerve cord
Notochord
Mouth
Gill slits
Muscle blocks
Anus
Tail

Fins
Backbone
Nerve cord
Gills
Scales
Mouth
Tail
Muscle blocks
Anus
Intestine
Stomach
Liver
Heart

1. What structures do fishes share with invertebrate chordates?
**Both have gill slits, a nerve cord, muscle blocks, a mouth, a tail, and an anus.**

2. What structures do fishes have that invertebrate chordates don't have?
**Fishes have a backbone, fins, a heart, and scales.**

Read the paragraph in the box. Then answer the question that follows.

**Tadpoles** are young amphibians. They share many characteristics with fishes. Like fishes, tadpoles have a two-chambered heart, gill slits, and fins. As tadpoles grow, they develop features they need to live on land. These features include legs, lungs, a three-chambered heart, and moist skin.

3. Name four characteristics that adapt amphibians for living on land.
**legs, lungs, a three-chambered heart, and moist skin**

CONTENT MASTERY

CHAPTER 30   BIOLOGY: The Dynamics of Life   **149**

---

Name _____ Date _____ Class _____

### Chapter
## 30   Fishes and Amphibians, *continued*

**Section 30.1  Fishes**

#### Study the Diagram

Study the diagram. Then answer the questions that follow.

As fishes developed jaws, they were able to grasp and crush their prey. This made fishes better predators.

Gill arch

Jawless, filter-feeding fish.

Gill arch
Gill slit

Jaws began to evolve from the gill arches.

Skull
Jaw
Gill slit

Fish with jaws. Teeth evolved from skin.

1. From what structure did the jaws of fishes evolve?
**the gill arches**

2. How did the evolution of jaws help fishes survive?
**Jaws enabled fishes to grasp and crush their prey, making fishes better predators.**

**150**   CHAPTER 30   BIOLOGY: The Dynamics of Life   CONTENT MASTERY

Name _____ Date _____ Class _____

**Content Mastery**

Chapter **30** **Fishes and Amphibians,** *continued*

*Section 30.2 Amphibians*

## Study the Idea Maps

Use the idea maps to answer the questions.

**Fishes**

| Gills | Two-Chambered Heart | Scales | Reproduction |
|---|---|---|---|
| | | | Fishes reproduce and spend their entire lives in water. |

**Amphibians**

| Gills | Two-Chambered Heart | Moist, Smooth Skin | Life Stages | Legs |
|---|---|---|---|---|
| Young amphibians have them. Most adults develop lungs. | Young amphibians have this. Adult amphibians have a three-chambered heart. | Adult amphibians rely on their skin for respiration more than their lungs. | Most young amphibians live in water. Adults live in water and on land. Most adults lay their eggs in water. | Most adult amphibians use legs to move on land. |

1. Name two characteristics that young amphibians share with fishes.

**Answers may include any two of the following: They live in water. They have gills. They have a two-chambered heart.**

2. Name four characteristics that adult amphibians have that fishes don't have.

**Answers may include any four of the following: Adult amphibians have a three-chambered heart and skin without scales. Most have legs and lungs. Some live on land.**

---

Name _____ Date _____ Class _____

**Content Mastery**

Chapter **30** **Fishes and Amphibians,** *continued*

## Review the Vocabulary

| cartilage | ectotherm |
|---|---|
| fin | lateral line system |
| scale | spawning |
| swim bladder | vocal cords |

Use three of the Chapter 30 vocabulary words listed above to fill in the blanks in the statements.

1. The ___lateral line system___ is a line of canals along the side of a fish that help it detect movements and find its way in the dark.

2. A(n) ___swim bladder___ is a gas-filled sac in bony fishes that helps them control their depth.

3. ___Vocal cords___ are bands of tissue in the throats of frogs and mammals. These bands enable animals to make sounds.

Use the rest of the vocabulary words to fill in the puzzle.

**Across**

6. tough, flexible material that forms the skeleton in some fishes

7. animal whose body temperature is controlled by the environment

8. fan-shaped membrane used by fishes for balance

**Down**

4. kind of breeding in fish and some other animals

5. one of many thin, bony plates that cover the skin of a fish

**Content Mastery**

## Chapter 31 Reptiles and Birds

### Get the Big Picture

Read the paragraph in the box. Then answer the questions that follow.

> Unlike amphibians, most reptiles spend their entire life on land. Instead of smooth, moist skin, reptiles have a thick skin covered with scales. The thick skin protects them and helps them adjust to life on land. Like amphibians, most reptiles have a three-chambered heart. Large reptiles such as crocodiles need a greater oxygen supply than smaller reptiles and have a four-chambered heart. The legs of reptiles are set farther under their bodies than are the legs of amphibians. This difference in leg position helps reptiles move on land. Reptiles reproduce by laying eggs with shells on land.

1. Circle the letter of the sentence that states the main idea of the paragraph.
   a. Reptiles have scales, three-chambered hearts, and legs.
   b. Reptiles reproduce by laying eggs on land.
   c. Reptiles have a variety of structures that adapt them to life on land.
   d. Reptiles have thick skin that adapts them to climate changes.

2. Large reptiles need more oxygen than small reptiles. How are the hearts of large reptiles different from the hearts of small reptiles?
   **Large reptiles have a four-chambered heart, whereas small reptiles have a three-chambered heart.**

Read the paragraph in the box. Then answer the questions.

> Birds and reptiles share some characteristics. Many birds have claws and scaly feet. Like reptiles, birds reproduce by laying eggs. Unlike reptiles, birds evolved feathers and wings that adapted them for flight. Because they can fly, birds can find food in many different places. Life in the air also helps birds avoid land predators.

3. What is the main difference between birds and reptiles?
   **Birds can fly.**

4. Name one way that flying helps birds survive.
   **Answers may include one of the following: Birds can find food in many different places. Birds can avoid land predators.**

---

**Content Mastery**

## Chapter 31 Reptiles and Birds, *continued*

*Section 31.1 Reptiles*

### Study the Idea Map

Use the idea map to answer the questions that follow.

| Amphibians | Reptiles |
|---|---|
| Their legs stick out from the sides of their bodies. | Their legs are under their bodies. This helps reptiles move better on land. |
| They have moist, smooth skin. | They have thick skin with scales. Tough skin protects reptiles and helps them conserve body moisture on land. |
| They have a three-chambered heart. | Some reptiles also have a three-chambered heart. Large reptiles such as crocodiles have a four-chambered heart. |
| Amphibian eggs do not have a shell. Most amphibians need to lay their eggs in water. | Reptiles lay amniotic eggs. These eggs have shells and are filled with fluid. They don't need to be in water. Reptiles lay their eggs on land. |

1. Choose two reptile adaptations. How did these adaptations help reptiles to live on land?
   **Answers may include any of the explanations given in the *Reptiles* side of the idea map.**

2. Why are amniotic eggs important to reptiles?
   **Reptiles can lay them on land, so reptiles can live far from water.**

---

**CONTENT MASTERY**

Name _____ Date _____ Class _____

**Content Mastery**

## Chapter 31  Reptiles and Birds, *continued*

**Section 31.2 Birds**

### Study the Idea Map

Use the idea map to answer the questions.

**Reptiles**

**Body Covering**
Reptiles have thick skin with scales.

**Limb Type**
Most reptiles have legs.

**Ectotherms**
Reptiles cannot control their body temperature by producing heat internally.

**Reproduction**
Reptiles lay amniotic eggs on land.

**Birds**

**Body Covering**
Birds have feathers and scaly skin on their legs and feet.

**Limb Type**
Birds have legs and wings. Wings help birds find food. Wings also help birds escape land predators.

**Endotherms**
Birds can control their body temperature by producing heat internally. They can live in different climates.

**Reproduction**
Birds lay amniotic eggs on land.

1. What characteristics do birds share with reptiles?
**Both have scaly skin on their legs and feet. Both lay amniotic eggs on land. Birds**
**and most reptiles have legs.**

2. Birds are endotherms. How does this help them survive?
**Because they are endotherms, birds can live in different climates.**

CONTENT MASTERY

CHAPTER 31  BIOLOGY: The Dynamics of Life    155

---

Name _____ Date _____ Class _____

**Content Mastery**

## Chapter 31  Reptiles and Birds, *continued*

### Review the Vocabulary

| endotherm | amniotic egg (am nee YAH tihk) |
| feather | Jacobson's organ |
| sternum | |

Use the Chapter 31 vocabulary words listed above to fill in the puzzle.

<sup>1</sup>a m n i o t h e r m

<sup>2</sup>f
e
J<sup>3</sup> a c o b s o n ' <sup>4</sup>s t e r n u m
t
h
e
r

**Across**

3. Reptiles use their _____ organ to detect chemicals in the air.
5. animal that maintains a constant body temperature even if the temperature of its environment changes

**Down**

1. kind of egg that has a shell and fluid to protect the embryo
2. lightweight, modified scale that provides insulation for birds and allows them to fly
4. breastbone

156    CHAPTER 31  BIOLOGY: The Dynamics of Life    CONTENT MASTERY

---

**Content Mastery**

# Chapter 32 Mammals

## Get the Big Picture

Read the paragraphs in the boxes. Then answer the questions that follow.

What do a polar bear and a dolphin have in common? They are both mammals. Mammals, like birds, are **endotherms**. This means that they can maintain a constant body temperature. For example, when dolphins swim in cold water, their bodies stay warm. Most mammals also have hair or fur to help keep them warm and to protect them. The white fur of polar bears keeps them warm in very cold climates. It also helps them blend in with their snowy surroundings. In this way, they are not easily seen by their prey.

1. Name two characteristics of mammals that help keep them warm.
**Mammals are endotherms (can maintain their body temperature). Most mammals have hair or fur.**

Mammals have a sheet of muscle under their chest cavity. This muscle sheet is called a **diaphragm**. When the diaphragm contracts, the chest cavity expands. When the diaphragm relaxes, the cavity gets smaller. The diaphragm helps mammals take in the large amount of oxygen they need to support their active lifestyles.

2. What does the diaphragm help mammals do?
**It helps them take in the large amount of oxygen they need to support their active lifestyles.**

Mammals help their young survive by feeding them milk from their mammary glands. Mammals also teach their young survival skills.

3. How do mammals help their young survive?
**Mammals feed milk to their young and teach them survival skills.**

4. Review the paragraphs in the three boxes above. Then list three characteristics of mammals.
**Answers may include any three of the following: Mammals are endotherms; most have hair or fur; they have a diaphragm; they feed their young milk from mammary glands; they teach their young survival skills.**

---

**Content Mastery**

# Chapter 32 Mammals, *continued*

**Section 32.1 Mammal Characteristics**

## Study the Diagrams

Read the paragraph in the box and study the diagrams. Then answer the questions that follow.

Mammals have distinct types of teeth. Mammal teeth are adapted to eating various foods. Scientists can tell what type of food a mammal eats by looking at its teeth.

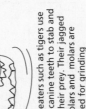

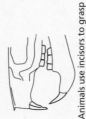

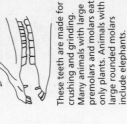

Animals use incisors to grasp and hold prey. Chisel-like incisors help beavers gnaw wood.

Meat-eaters such as tigers use sharp canine teeth to stab and hold their prey. Their jagged premolars and molars are adapted for grinding bones and chewing meat.

These teeth are made for crushing and grinding. Many animals with large premolars and molars eat only plants. Animals with large rounded molars include elephants.

1. Circle the letter of the word that best completes the following sentence. Animals with large, rounded molars are likely to eat _____ .
   a. wood
   b. meat
   **c. plants** ⟵(circled)

2. Circle the letter of the kind of teeth you would expect a meat-eating wolf to have.
   a. large, rounded molars
   **b. sharp canine teeth and jagged premolars and molars** ⟵(circled)
   Explain your choice.
   **A wolf needs sharp canine teeth for stabbing and holding its prey. Wolves use their jagged premolars and molars for grinding bones and chewing meat.**

3. What can scientists learn about extinct mammals by studying fossils of their teeth?
   **Scientists can learn what type of food extinct mammals ate by studying fossil teeth.**

---

**CONTENT MASTERY**

Name _____ Date _____ Class _____

**Content Mastery**

## Chapter 32 Mammals, *continued*

### Section 32.2 Diversity of Mammals

### Study the Idea Maps

Use the idea maps to answer the questions.

**Monotremes**
- lay eggs
- Only three species exist today.

**Examples**
Duck-billed platypus
Spiny anteater

**Where They Live**
Only in Australia, Tasmania, and New Guinea

**Marsupials**
- carry partly developed young in pouches

**Examples**
Kangaroo
Wombat
Tasmanian devil

**Where They Live**
Mostly in Australia and surrounding islands

**Placental Mammals**
- carry their young inside their bodies until development is nearly complete

**Examples**
Bats, rats, dolphins, elephants, monkeys, horses, hippopotamuses

**Where They Live**
Throughout the world in the sea, on land, and in the air

1. What are three ways that mammals reproduce?
**Some mammals lay eggs, some carry their partly developed young in pouches, and some carry their young inside their bodies until development is nearly complete.**

2. Which group of mammals live in environments all over the world?
**placental mammals**

3. How many species of living mammals lay eggs to reproduce?
**three**

---

Name _____ Date _____ Class _____

**Content Mastery**

## Chapter 32 Mammals, *continued*

### Review the Vocabulary

Use the Chapter 32 vocabulary words in the box to fill in the blanks below.

> gestation (jes TAY shun)    mammary gland
> marsupial                   placenta
> placental mammal            uterus (YEW tuh rus)

1. Muscular, hollow organ in which offspring develop ___ u t erus

2. Type of mammal that carries its young inside the uterus until development is nearly complete ___ pl a cental mam m al

3. Time during which young mammals develop in the uterus ___ ge s tation

4. Organ that develops during pregnancy, provides food and oxygen to the embryo, and removes wastes ___ p l ac e nta

5. Gland in female mammals that produces milk for the young ___ ma m m a ry

6. A kangaroo is a ___ m a rs u pial

Draw a line to match each vocabulary word in the box with its definition.

7. Egg-laying mammal
8. Mammal-like reptile ancestor of all mammals
9. Sheet of muscle under the chest cavity that helps mammals breathe
10. Group of cells that secrete substances needed by an animal

a. diaphragm (DI uh fram)
b. gland
c. monotreme (MAH nuh treem)
d. therapsid (thuh RAP sud)

---

**Content Mastery**

# Chapter 33 Animal Behavior

## Get the Big Picture

Read the paragraph in the box and look at the pictures. Then answer the questions that follow.

> Every animal has behaviors that help it survive. For example, vultures have social behaviors. They eat dead animals while in groups. Other animals, such as coyotes, prefer to live on their own. Some animal behaviors are innate. This means that an animal inherits genes that control certain behaviors. The genetic makeup of mallard ducks causes them to fly south for the winter. Other behaviors are learned. Learned behaviors result from practice or experience. Young birds learn to build nests by watching other birds and by using trial-and-error learning. Innate and learned behaviors help animals adapt and survive.

1. How are innate and learned behaviors different?
   **Innate behaviors result from an animal's genetic makeup. Learned behaviors result**
   **from practice or experience.**

2. Circle the letter of the sentence that states the main idea of the paragraph.
   a. Each animal has a certain way of behaving.
   b. Some animal behaviors are innate.
   c. Young birds learn to build better nests through trial-and-error learning.
   **d.** Innate and learned behaviors help animals adapt and survive.

---

**Content Mastery**

# Chapter 33 Animal Behavior, continued

Section 33.1 Innate Behavior

## Read the Words

Read the paragraphs in the boxes. Then answer the questions that follow.

> A **reflex** is the simplest form of innate behavior. A reflex is a quick, automatic response that happens without thought. Many reflexes can happen in less than a second. For example, you blink quickly when something passes in front of your eyes. A clam withdraws into its shell when something touches it. This reflex helps to protect the clam from predators.

> An **instinct** is a complex pattern of innate behavior. Unlike a reflex, an instinctive behavior may take hours or even weeks to complete. Instinctive behavior begins when an animal recognizes a stimulus. A **stimulus** is a condition in the environment that makes an animal change its behavior. When greylag geese recognize eggs that roll out of their nest, the stimulus is the presence of an object outside the nest. Instinctive behaviors end when an animal completes all parts of the behavior. Greylag geese retrieve the eggs one by one until they are all back in the nest. Instincts help animals survive.

1. What is the difference between a reflex and an instinct?
   **A reflex is a simple, innate behavior that happens quickly. An instinct is a complex**
   **pattern of innate behavior that takes longer to complete.**

2. Label each behavior as an instinct or a reflex.
   a. Geese retrieve eggs that have rolled out of their nests.          **instinct**
   b. You blink when something passes in front of your eyes.            **reflex**
   c. A clam withdraws into its shell when something touches it.        **reflex**

---

Name _____ Date _____ Class _____

**Content Mastery**

## Chapter 33 Animal Behavior, *continued*

Section 33.2 **Learned Behavior**

### Study the Diagram

Study the pictures. Then answer the questions.

**A.** Pavlov noted that dogs drool when they smell food. This response to food is a reflex.

**B.** Pavlov rang a bell whenever the dogs smelled food. After a while, the dogs connected the sound of the bell with the smell of food.

**C.** Later, the dogs drooled at the sound of the bell alone. The dogs were conditioned to respond to a stimulus they did not usually connect with food.

1. What reflex did Pavlov's dogs have before the experiment? **The dogs drooled when they smelled food.**

2. How did Pavlov condition the dogs to drool when they heard a bell? **Pavlov rang the bell whenever the dogs smelled food. The dogs connected the sound of the bell with food. They learned to drool when they heard the bell even if they did not smell food.**

---

Name _____ Date _____ Class _____

**Content Mastery**

## Chapter 33 Animal Behavior, *continued*

### Review the Vocabulary

Review the definitions of the Chapter 33 vocabulary words in bold type in the statements below. If the statement is true, write <u>true</u>. If the statement is false, write <u>false</u>.

| | |
|---|---|
| false | 1. An **instinct** is anything an animal does in response to a stimulus in the environment. |
| true | 2. **Innate behavior** is inherited behavior. |
| true | 3. **Courtship behavior** takes place before male and female animals mate. |
| false | 4. **Aggressive behavior** is not threatening to other animals. |
| true | 5. A **territory** is a physical space where animals breed, feed, or get shelter. |
| true | 6. The **fight-or-flight response** prepares the body for greater activity. |
| false | 7. Animals that live in very cold climates experience **estivation** (es tuh VAY shun). |
| true | 8. A 24-hour cycle of behavior is called a **circadian** (sur KAY dee un) **rhythm**. |
| false | 9. During **hibernation**, animals have a great need for oxygen and energy. |
| true | 10. A **dominance hierarchy** is a social order with several levels. |

Draw a line to match each word in the box with its definition.

**11.** Internal need that causes an animal to act

**12.** Occurs when an animal is given a stimulus without punishment or reward

**13.** Attachment to an object during a certain time in an animal's life

**14.** Kind of learning in which an animal is rewarded for a particular response

**15.** kind of learning in which an animal uses its experience to respond to something new

**16.** kind of learning in which an animal connects a new stimulus to a certain behavior

**17.** Using symbols to represent ideas

**18.** Sharing of information that results in a change of behavior

**a.** communication
**b.** conditioning
**c.** habituation (huh bih chuh WAY shun)
**d.** imprinting
**e.** insight
**f.** language
**g.** motivation
**h.** trial-and-error learning

## Page 165 (left)

Name _____ Date _____ Class _____

**Content Mastery**

**BioDigest 9**

# Vertebrates

## Get the Big Picture

**Read the paragraphs in the box. Then answer the questions that follow.**

> A vertebrate is an animal with a backbone. Some vertebrates, such as fishes, live in water. Others, such as reptiles and birds, live mostly on land. In these land animals, lungs and legs evolved. Birds also evolved wings. Wings provided birds with the adaptation for flight.
>
> When vertebrates moved from the water to the land and air, there was a change in the way they reproduced. In reptiles and birds, eggs evolved with shells that hold fluid inside. These eggs protect the growing embryos. Vertebrates that lay shelled eggs can reproduce on land instead of in water. In some female vertebrates, a uterus evolved. Animals with a uterus can carry their young inside their body until development is nearly complete.

1. What is a vertebrate?
   **an animal with a backbone**

2. Name three places a vertebrate might live.
   **in water, on land, and in the air**

3. Name two kinds of vertebrates. How did the bodies of these vertebrates change to allow the animals to live in new environments?
   **Sample answer: Birds and reptiles; lungs and legs evolved. These changes allowed**
   **these animals to live on land.**

BIODIGEST 9   BIOLOGY: The Dynamics of Life   **165**

## Page 166 (right)

Name _____ Date _____ Class _____

**Content Mastery**

**BioDigest 9**

# Vertebrates, *continued*

## Study the Table

**Read the following definitions and study the table. Then answer the questions that follow.**

**Endothermy:** Endothermic animals use their own energy to heat their bodies. Birds and mammals are the only endothermic vertebrates.

**Ectothermy:** Ectothermic animals use an external source of heat, like a warm rock, to heat their bodies.

**Amniotic Egg:** This egg has a thick shell and contains fluid, yolk for food, and the developing embryo. Amniotic eggs can be laid on land instead of in the water.

| Class | Example | Description |
|---|---|---|
| Reptile | Green sea turtle | • spends most of its life in water<br>• must surface to breathe with its lungs<br>• Females lay eggs on the beach. |
| Bird | Kentucky warbler | • migrates long distances across the Gulf of Mexico<br>• has feathers and hollow bones<br>• Females lay eggs in a nest. |
| Mammal | Arctic fox | • lives in northern Canada and Alaska<br>• has thick fur and short ears |
| Amphibian | Dusky salamander | • lives along streams and near springs<br>• breathes through its skin<br>• Females lay eggs in the water. |
| Fish | Pacific salmon | • lives in the ocean<br>• gets oxygen from the water with its gills<br>• Females lay eggs in freshwater streams. |

1. What adaptations does the arctic fox have to keep it from losing heat?
   **thick fur and short ears**

**166**   BIODIGEST 9   BIOLOGY: The Dynamics of Life

Name _____ Date _____ Class _____

**Content Mastery**

BioDigest
**9** **Vertebrates,** *continued*

**Study the Diagram**

Read the paragraphs in the box and study the diagram. Then answer the questions that follow.

Although fishes, amphibians, reptiles, birds, and mammals are all vertebrates—animals with a backbone—they are different in many ways. One important difference is the way in which they keep their body temperature. Birds and mammals can keep their temperature constant throughout the day and the seasons. Because of this ability, they are called **endotherms.** Animals that have a body temperature that changes with the outside temperature are called **ectotherms.**

Because you are a mammal, you are an endotherm—you can keep your body temperature constant. Even on a hot day, your body temperature is usually the same as it is on a cold day. You have an internal "thermostat" that cools you when the outside temperature gets too high and warms you when it gets too low. Endotherms can cool themselves by sweating and panting, and they can warm themselves by shivering. Some endotherms also use fur or feathers to keep themselves warm.

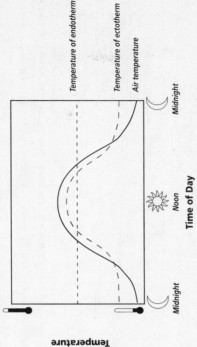

Temperature of endotherm

Temperature of ectotherm

Air temperature

Midnight    Noon    Midnight

**Time of Day**

Temperature (vertical axis)

Read each description below. Decide whether it describes an endotherm or an ectotherm. Then circle the correct word inside the brackets.

**1.** An animal wakes up on a cold winter morning and is hungry. It sits on a rock in the sun until it warms up enough to go hunting. [endotherm / (ectotherm)]

**2.** An animal is moving around on a very warm day. It begins to sweat, and the sweat cools it down so that it feels comfortable. [(endotherm) / ectotherm]

**3.** On a cold day, an animal keeps warm by using a layer of feathers to keep the cold wind out. [(endotherm) / ectotherm]

**168** BIODIGEST 9   BIOLOGY: The Dynamics of Life

CONTENT MASTERY

---

Name _____ Date _____ Class _____

**Content Mastery**

BioDigest
**9** **Vertebrates,** *continued*

**2.** A green sea turtle will sometimes bask at the surface of the water. Its body temperature rises as it does this. Is the turtle endothermic or ectothermic? What is its source of heat?

**ectothermic; the sun**
_____

**3.** Which animals in the table lay amniotic eggs?

**green sea turtle and Kentucky warbler**
_____

**4.** The vertebrates in the table get oxygen—breathe—in different ways. List three ways, and give an example of an animal that uses each way.

**a.** **with lungs—green sea turtle, arctic fox, or Kentucky warbler**
_____

**b.** **through skin—dusky salamander**
_____

**c.** **with gills—Pacific salmon**
_____

**5.** Kentucky warblers make long migrations in the spring and fall. What are some of the adaptations these warblers have that help them fly?

**feathers and hollow bones**
_____
_____
_____

CONTENT MASTERY

BIODIGEST 9   BIOLOGY: The Dynamics of Life   **167**

---

CONTENT MASTERY

ANSWER KEY   BIOLOGY: The Dynamics of Life   **T281**

**Content Mastery**

## Chapter 34 Protection, Support, and Locomotion

### Get the Big Picture

Read the paragraph in the box. Then answer the questions.

> Vertebrates have bones, muscles, and skin to give their bodies support, movement, and protection. Bones form a skeleton that supports body tissues. The skeleton also helps protect organs such as the heart, lungs, and brain. Muscles help to move the skeleton. Muscles are protein fibers attached to bones. Muscles help to move the skeleton and muscles. Skin surrounds and protects the skeleton and muscles. Skin also helps keep the body in a balanced internal state called **homeostasis**. For example, sweat glands and sweat help to prevent the body from overheating.

1. What are the two functions of the skeleton?
   **The skeleton supports body tissues and protects organs.**

2. What do muscles do?
   **Muscles help move the skeleton.**

3. What are two functions of skin?
   **Skin protects muscles and bone. Skin also helps the body keep a balanced internal**
   **state.**

4. What is the purpose or function of sweat glands in the body?
   **When the body starts to overheat, the sweat glands produce sweat to help**
   **maintain the internal state.**

5. Other than support for body tissues, what else do the bones provide?
   **The bones also provide protection for organs such as the heart, lungs, and brain.**

---

**Content Mastery**

## Chapter 34 Protection, Support, and Locomotion, *continued*

Section 34.1  *Skin: The Body's Protection*
Section 34.2  *Bones: The Body's Support*
Section 34.3  *Muscles for Locomotion*

### Study the Idea Maps

Study the idea maps. Then answer the questions.

**Epidermis** Thin, outer layer of skin
- Dead cells
  - Protect live cells
  - Elasticity
- Live cells
  - Contain pigment or melanin to protect skin from sun damage

1. What are the two kinds of cells that make up the epidermis? What does each kind of cell do?
   **Dead cells and live cells make up the epidermis. Dead cells protect the live cells and**
   **make the skin more elastic. Live cells contain melanin and protect the skin from sun**
   **damage.**

**Dermis** Thick, inner layer of skin
- Fat tissue cushions the body
- Blood vessels constrict and expand to help control body temperature
- Hair follicles grow hair
- Sweat glands produce sweat to cool the body
- Oil glands produce oil to keep hair and skin from drying out

2. a. What is the dermis?
   **the thick, inner layer of skin**

   b. Name one kind of gland found in the dermis. What does it do?
   **Answers may include one of the following: Sweat glands produce sweat to cool**
   **the body. Oil glands produce oil to keep hair and skin from drying out.**

Name _____ Date _____ Class _____

**Content Mastery**

## Chapter 34  Protection, Support, and Locomotion, *continued*

**Skeletal System Functions**

- Provides a framework for body tissues and organs
- Protects organs such as the heart, lungs, and brain
- Helps the body move
- Produces blood cells
- Stores minerals that the body needs to grow

3. What are the five functions of the skeleton?

(1) provides a framework for body tissues and organs  (2) protects organs

(3) helps the body move  (4) produces blood cells  (5) stores minerals

_____

**Muscle Types**

- **Smooth Muscle**
  - Found in organs and blood vessels
  - The most common function is to squeeze and put pressure on the space inside vessels, organs, or tracts

- **Cardiac Muscle**
  - Found only in the heart
  - Conducts electrical impulses to pump the heart with rhythm

- **Skeletal Muscle**
  - Found on the skeleton, this muscle is attached to bones
  - Provides the force needed to move the body

4. Fill in the table to give the location and the function of each muscle type.

| Muscle Type | Location | Function |
|---|---|---|
| Smooth | organs and blood vessels | squeezes and puts pressure on vessels, organs, and tracts |
| Cardiac | heart | conducts electrical impulses to make the heart pump |
| Skeletal | on the skeleton or attached to bones | provides the force to move the body |

CHAPTER 34   BIOLOGY: The Dynamics of Life   171

---

Name _____ Date _____ Class _____

**Content Mastery**

## Chapter 34  Protection, Support, and Locomotion, *continued*

**Review the Vocabulary**

Use the Chapter 34 vocabulary words in the box to complete the spelling of the word defined to the left. You will not use all the words.

> dermis (DUR mus)  epidermis  hair follicle
> keratin (KAYR uh tun)  melanin (MEL uh nun)  myosin (MI uh sun)

1. thin, outer layer of skin  **epi** d **ermis**

2. protein in dead epidermal cells  **ker** at **in**

3. cell pigment that colors the skin and protects it from sun damage  **m** el **anin**

4. thick, inner layer of skin  **derm** is

5. small cavity in the dermis that grows hair  h **air** f **ollicle**

Review the definitions of the underlined vocabulary words in the statements below. If the statement is true, write *true*. If the statement is false, replace the underlined word with another vocabulary word that will make the statement true.

6. The <u>axial</u> skeleton includes the bones of the arms and legs.  **appendicular skeleton**

7. A knee is an example of a <u>joint</u>.  **true**

8. A <u>ligament</u> is a thick band of tissue that attaches muscles to bone.  **tendon**

9. <u>Bursae</u> (BUR sigh) are fluid-filled sacs in joints.  **true**

10. A potential bone cell is called an <u>osteoblast</u> (AH stee uh blast).  **true**

11. Compact bone has many holes and spaces.  **spongy bone**

12. <u>Marrow</u> is the soft tissue inside of bones.  **true**

13. <u>Smooth muscle</u> is found in the heart.  **cardiac muscle**

14. <u>Skeletal</u> muscle is attached to bones and moves the skeleton.  **true**

15. <u>Involuntary</u> muscle contracts when you try to contract it.  **voluntary muscle**

16. A small fiber that makes up larger muscle fibers is called a <u>myofibril</u> (mi yuh FI brul).  **true**

17. Thick filaments in myofibrils are made of the protein <u>actin</u>.  **myosin**

18. Each section of a myofibril is called a <u>sarcomere</u> (SAR koh meer).  **true**

19. The <u>sliding filament theory</u> states that actin filaments slide together during muscle contraction.  **true**

172   CHAPTER 34   BIOLOGY: The Dynamics of Life

---

**Chapter 35** The Digestive and Endocrine Systems

## Get the Big Picture

Read the paragraphs in the box. Then use the pictures to answer the questions that follow.

> Your body breaks down the food you eat into sugars, proteins, vitamins, and minerals that it can use. This breaking down process is called digestion. As you eat, the food moves through your digestive system. Along the way, important tissues and organs help in the process of digestion.
>
> The food you eat helps your body stay healthy by providing it with the nutrients it needs to function, including carbohydrates for energy and vitamins and minerals for body maintenance. If your digestive system is not working properly, your body cannot get the nutrients it needs, and serious health problems may occur.

Explain the roles that the following items play in digestion or nutrition.

**1.** Mouth

**The mouth is responsible for initiating the digestion of ingested food. Teeth mechanically grind the food, while enzymes such as amylase attack it chemically.**

**2.** Wheat bread and apple

**Wheat bread provides both carbohydrates for energy and fiber for eliminating wastes. Apples also provide fiber and carbohydrates, as well as important vitamins.**

**3.** Diet soft drink and candy

**Diet soft drinks do not provide any nutrition for the body. While candy does supply carbohydrates, they are in a highly processed form that can damage teeth. Also, they only provide energy for a short period of time.**

**4.** Liver

**The liver produces chemicals used in the process of digestion. It also stores glucose in the form of glycogen.**

**5.** Water

**While water supplies no nutrients to the body, it is needed to perform all cellular functions and so must be consumed several times per day.**

CONTENT MASTERY         CHAPTER 35   BIOLOGY: The Dynamics of Life    **173**

---

**Chapter 35** The Digestive and Endocrine Systems, *continued*

Section 35.1 *Following Digestion of a Meal*
Section 35.2 *Nutrition*
Section 35.3 *The Endocrine System*

## Study the Diagrams

Study the diagram. Then answer the questions that follow.

**How Long Is Your Digestive System?**

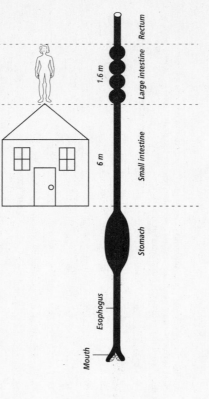

**1.** What part of the digestive system is the shortest? Explain your answer.
**The mouth; it can only hold small bites of food.**

**2.** What part of the digestive system is the longest? Explain your answer.
**The small intestine; it is about 6 m long.**

**3.** The entire digestive system is about 9 m long. How tall are you? How can your digestive system fit inside your body?
**Student heights will vary. The small and large intestines fold over and over themselves inside the body.**

**174**   CHAPTER 35   BIOLOGY: The Dynamics of Life         CONTENT MASTERY

Name _____ Date _____ Class _____

**Content Mastery**

Read the paragraph in the box. Then answer the questions that follow.

> The human body works actively to maintain a balance within itself. This balance is affected by both the hormones of the endocrine system and by the food we eat. If we eat too much of one thing and not enough of another, the body falls out of balance. Similarly, if an endocrine gland produces too much or too little of a certain hormone, the body can also lose its balanced inner state.

**4.** Is eating very little food good for your body? Explain.
**No. Your body needs a minimum intake of a variety of nutrients every day. Without**

**enough food, your body cannot function properly.**

_____

**5.** Do sugary foods give you a lot of long-term energy? Explain.
**No. Sugary foods provide short-term energy by raising blood glucose levels a lot in**

**a short period of time. Complex carbohydrates such as starches provide more long-**

**term energy.**

_____

**6.** What kind of control mechanism does the endocrine system use to maintain balance within the body? How does it work?
**A negative feedback system; a hormone released by an endocrine gland, or the**

**effect of the hormone, is fed back to the gland to inhibit the original signal. In this**

**way, the gland does not produce too much of the hormone and throw the body**

**out of balance.**

_____

_____

---

Name _____ Date _____ Class _____

**Content Mastery**

**Review the Vocabulary**

> amylase (AM uh lays)
> bile
> pituitary
> endocrine
> gallbladder
> negative feedback
>
> pancreas (PANG kree us)
> peristalsis (payr uh STAWL sus)
> small intestine
> stomach
> villus (VIH lus)
> vitamin (VI tuh mun)

Use the Chapter 35 vocabulary words in the box to fill in the blanks in the sentences.

**1.** The pouchlike, muscular organ that secretes acids and digestive enzymes is the _____ **stomach** _____.

**2.** _____ **Bile** _____ is a chemical produced by the liver that helps break down fats.

**3.** The endocrine system is regulated by a _____ **negative feedback** _____ system.

**4.** _____ **Amylase** _____ is a digestive enzyme that breaks starches into sugars.

**5.** The _____ **pituitary** _____ gland controls many other glands of the endocrine system.

**6.** _____ **Peristalsis** _____ is a wave of muscular contractions that moves food through the digestive system.

**7.** The organ that stores bile is the _____ **gallbladder** _____.

**8.** A _____ **villus** _____ is a fingerlike projection in the lining of the small intestine.

**9.** The gland that produces both hormones and digestive enzymes is the _____ **pancreas** _____.

**10.** Digestion is completed in the organ called the _____ **small intestine** _____.

**11.** A _____ **vitamin** _____ is an organic substance that regulates body processes.

**12.** _____ **Endocrine** _____ glands release hormones directly into the bloodstream.

**Content Mastery**

# Chapter 36 The Nervous System

## Get the Big Picture

Read the paragraphs in the boxes and look at the diagram. Then answer the questions that follow.

The **nervous system** gives directions to all the other systems in your body. It also gets information from your senses and keeps track of how well the different parts of your body are working together. The nervous system is made up of two parts: the **central nervous system** (CNS), and the **peripheral nervous system** (PNS). Peripheral means "not central." Your brain and spinal cord make up your CNS and send and receive messages through your PNS.

Your senses allow you to perceive the world by seeing, hearing, feeling, tasting, and smelling. Your sense organs collect information about the world and send it to your brain. The brain decodes the signals and makes them meaningful.

Many drugs act to disrupt the normal functioning of the nervous system. Drugs can change your brain's ability to think and to control the rest of your body.

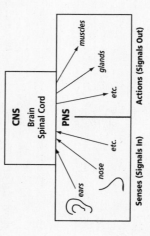

**CNS**
Brain
Spinal Cord

**PNS**
ears
nose
etc.

muscles
glands
etc.

Senses (Signals In)          Actions (Signals Out)

1. How does your central nervous system receive information? **from the PNS, including the senses**

2. Which part of the nervous system do the nerves in your skin belong to? **peripheral nervous system (PNS)**

3. You may not think that caffeine is a drug, but it is. When you drink a soft drink that contains caffeine, you may feel jittery. Why do you think this is so? **Caffeine affects the nervous system. It is a stimulant.**

---

**Content Mastery**

# Chapter 36 The Nervous System, *continued*

Section 36.1  *The Nervous System*

## Study the Diagram

Read the paragraph in the box and study the diagram. Then answer the questions that follow.

Electrical signals travel throughout your nervous system, carrying information from one place to another. The nervous system is made up of nerve cells, or **neurons**. The neurons have gaps between them, called **synaptic spaces**, which an electrical signal has to jump across in order to continue. In some electrical machinery, electrical signals jump across a tiny gap as a spark. In your body, an electrical impulse is passed by a chemical signal called a **neurotransmitter**.

*Direction of impulse*

Neuron

Neuron

Neuron

*Synaptic space with neurotransmitters*

1. What would happen to your nervous system if the neurotransmitters in your body were suddenly blocked from passing into the synaptic spaces? **The nervous system, including the brain, would stop functioning. The neurotransmitters pass electrical impulses from one neuron to the next across the synaptic space.**

2. What do you think would happen if a lot of neurotransmitters were suddenly released throughout your nervous system? **All of your nerve cells would fire at once, and normal communication between neurons would be disrupted or distorted.**

---

**CONTENT MASTERY**

Name _____ Date _____ Class _____

**Content Mastery**

## Study the Diagram

**Read the paragraphs in the boxes and study the diagram. Then answer the questions that follow.**

> Your senses give you all of your information about the world. We receive three kinds of information through our senses: information about chemicals, information about light, and information about mechanical stimulation.

> Our senses of smell and taste tell us about chemicals in the air or in our food. Smell and taste are very similar, both in the way they work and in the way we perceive them. A lot of the time things we think we are tasting we are actually smelling.

> Our senses of touch, hearing, and balance are very closely related. The sense of touch comes from pressure directly on the skin. Pressure receptors in the ears sense changes in sound waves and allow us to hear. Organs in the ears called semicircular canals maintain our balance by detecting the movement of fluid that occurs when we move our head.

> Our sight is based on the light information received by our eyes. Our eyes have cells adapted for seeing different kinds of light. Rods allow us to see in dim light; cones work best at seeing color, as well as sharp images in bright light.

1. Which sense do you think an acrobat uses the most when walking blindfolded on a tightrope? Which organ is responsible for this sense?
**sense of balance; semicircular canals in the ears**

2. Why is it hard to taste food when you have a stuffed-up nose?
**A stuffed-up nose diminishes the sense of smell. Smell and taste are closely related.**

3. Cats have many rods and few cones in their eyes. Do you think cats see well in the dark? How well do you think they see colors?
**Rods are responsible for vision in dim light, and cones are important for color vision. Cats probably see quite well in the dark but do not see colors well.**

CONTENT MASTERY

---

Name _____ Date _____ Class _____

**Content Mastery**

## Review the Vocabulary

| | | |
|---|---|---|
| addiction | nervous system | cerebellum |
| cerebrum | cochlea | retina |
| neuron (NEW rahn) | reflex | taste bud |
| rods | withdrawal | synapse (SIH naps) |

Use the Chapter 36 vocabulary words listed above to complete the puzzle. First, write the correct word on the line after each definition. Then find the same word in the letter grid and circle it. Words may be written on horizontal, vertical, or diagonal lines.

```
f r a x e d h l u c e n   e
c e r e b e l l u m t   r
e w i t h d r a w a l   v
r n l d j h e d m l c v   o
e e f f i o f d r k o u   s
b r u i e e c t q i   s y
u o e m n n e x r o d   a s
m n s h d a s i a j e   e
r g s y h e b n s d   s
t a s t e b u d f a e   e
w f s a s y n a p s e   m
a d e b n l g i w n e   q
```

1. Psychological or physiological drug dependence ___**addiction**___

2. Layer of the eye containing rods and cones ___**retina**___

3. Body's control center ___**nervous system**___

4. Taste receptor on tongue ___**taste bud**___

5. Portion of brain that maintains balance and muscle coordination ___**cerebellum**___

6. Psychological or physiological illness resulting from cessation of drug use ___**withdrawal**___

7. Largest portion of the brain ___**cerebrum**___

8. Place where neurons meet ___**synapse**___

9. Fluid-filled structure of the ear in which sound vibrations are converted into nerve impulses ___**cochlea**___

10. Light receptors in the retina responsible for vision in low light ___**rods**___

11. Basic structural and functional unit in the nervous system ___**neuron**___

12. Rapid, automatic response to a stimulus ___**reflex**___

---

CONTENT MASTERY                    ANSWER KEY   BIOLOGY: The Dynamics of Life   **T287**

## Content Mastery

### Chapter 37 Respiration, Circulation, and Excretion

**Get the Big Picture**

Read the paragraphs in the boxes. Then answer the questions that follow.

> The **respiratory system**, the **circulatory system**, and the **urinary system** are very important for maintaining homeostasis—your body's constant internal environment.

> The **respiratory system** breathes in oxygen and takes it into the body. It also breathes out waste carbon dioxide.

> The **circulatory system** delivers oxygen from the respiratory system and nutrients from digestion to your body's tissues. It also picks up waste products from tissues and delivers them to the urinary and respiratory systems for removal from the body. Carbon dioxide goes out through the respiratory system. Other wastes exit through the urinary system.

> Finally, the **urinary system** removes waste products from your blood through the kidneys—two small, but powerful, filters.

1. Which two systems are involved in the removal of carbon dioxide from the body?
   **circulatory and respiratory systems**

2. Which two systems carry waste products out of the body?
   **respiratory and urinary systems**

3. Which two gases does your respiratory system breathe in and breathe out?
   **oxygen and carbon dioxide**

4. Which system delivers nutrients throughout your body?
   **circulatory system**

5. What do the circulatory, respiratory, and urinary systems of your body maintain?
   **homeostasis**

---

## Content Mastery

### Chapter 37 Respiration, Circulation, and Excretion, *continued*

Section 37.1 *The Respiratory System*
Section 37.3 *The Urinary System*

**Study the Diagram**

Read the paragraphs in the boxes and study the diagram. Then answer the questions that follow.

> The **respiratory system** controls the balance between oxygen entering the body and waste carbon dioxide leaving the body. Our cells need oxygen to make energy. We inhale oxygen through our nose and mouth. This oxygen travels to the lungs and crosses into the bloodstream through thin-walled sacs called alveoli (singular: alveolus). At the same time, waste carbon dioxide passes from the blood back through the alveoli into the lungs. We then breathe it out of the body. The diaphragm—a powerful sheet of muscle below the lungs—helps pull air in and push air out of the lungs.

> The **urinary system** collects other kinds of cell waste products from the blood and stores them until they are passed out of the body in urine. The kidneys are the most important organs in the urinary system. Kidneys act like complex filters. When blood goes through the kidneys, materials that the body needs stay in the blood. Toxic waste products are removed from the blood and stored in the bladder as urine.

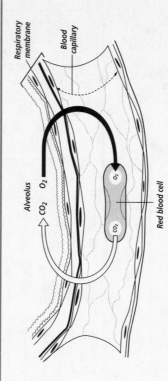

Respiratory membrane
Blood capillary
Alveolus
CO$_2$   O$_2$
O$_2$
CO$_2$
Red blood cell

1. Does the white arrow show the transport of oxygen or of carbon dioxide?
   **carbon dioxide**

2. Does the black arrow show the transport of oxygen or of carbon dioxide?
   **oxygen**

3. Why do you think damage to the kidneys is so dangerous?
   **If the body's filters are damaged, toxins build up in the blood and poison the body.**

---

---

Copyright © Glencoe/McGraw-Hill, a division of The McGraw-Hill Companies, Inc.

Name _____ Date _____ Class _____

**Chapter 37** **Content Mastery**

## Respiration, Circulation, and Excretion, *continued*

**Section 37.2 The Circulatory System**

### Study the Diagram

Read the paragraphs in the boxes and study the diagram. Then answer the questions that follow.

> Your **circulatory system** supplies all the different parts of your body with nutrients and oxygen. It also carries carbon dioxide and other cellular waste products away from the cells. The **heart** is the most important organ in the circulatory system. It pumps blood through your body all the time, all during your life. The blood is carried through vessels that are like a highway system. This system has freeways that carry large numbers of fast-moving blood, smaller roads that carry a steady stream of blood cells, and tiny vessels called **capillaries** that are like neighborhood streets. Some capillaries are so small that only one cell can pass through them at a time. Vessels called **arteries** carry blood away from the heart and lungs. Vessels called **veins** carry the blood from the body back to the heart.

> Blood is a tissue because it is made up of several different cell types. **Red blood cells** are the most common and are like delivery trucks, carrying oxygen to body cells. **White blood cells** are less common but cruise your network of blood vessels ready to identify and destroy enemy invaders. **Platelets** are sticky fragments that patch damaged vessels by forming clots.

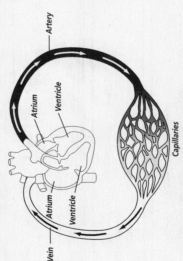

Artery

Atrium

Ventricle

Vein

Atrium

Ventricle

Capillaries

The heart constantly pumps blood to all parts of the body through a network of blood vessels.

1. Think about the jobs that red blood cells and white blood cells do. When you get a cold, do you think your body will make more red blood cells or more white blood cells? __white blood cells__

2. Which blood vessels carry blood away from the heart? __arteries__

3. Which blood vessels carry blood toward the heart? __veins__

CHAPTER 37   BIOLOGY: The Dynamics of Life   **183**

---

Name _____ Date _____ Class _____

**Chapter 37** **Content Mastery**

## Respiration, Circulation, and Excretion, *continued*

### Review the Vocabulary

| | |
|---|---|
| alveoli (al VEE uh li) | nephron (NE frawn) |
| aorta | plasma |
| artery | pulse |
| atrium | ureter (YUR uh tur) |
| hemoglobin (HEE muh gloh bun) | vein |
| kidneys | |

Crossword puzzle:

```
¹n e p h r o n
²a l v e o l i   ³h e m o g l o b i n
              ⁴u r e t e r
              ⁵a o r t a
        ⁶p u l s e
        ⁷a t r i u m
        ⁸a r t e r y
⁹p l a s m a
   ¹⁰v e i n
¹¹k i d n e y s
```

Review the definitions of the Chapter 37 vocabulary words listed above. Then use the clues to complete the puzzle. The letters in the dark boxes will make up a word that means the process by which the body balances nutrients and other things it needs for life.

1. filtering unit of the kidney
2. tiny, thin-walled sacs in the lungs
3. iron-containing molecule of red blood cells
4. tube that transports urine from each kidney to the urinary bladder
5. largest blood vessel in the human body
6. rhythmic surge of blood through an artery
7. thin-walled upper chambers of the heart
8. thick-walled blood vessel that transports blood away from the heart
9. fluid portion of the blood
10. large blood vessel that returns blood from the tissues back to the heart
11. pair of organs that filter waste from blood

**184**   CHAPTER 37   BIOLOGY: The Dynamics of Life

---

## Left Page

**Content Mastery**

### Chapter 38   Reproduction and Development

#### Get the Big Picture

Read what is in the boxes. Then use the pictures to answer the questions that follow.

> Our bodies are adapted for reproduction.

> **In a man, this means that:**
> 1. sperm is produced.
> 2. sperm passes to the female body where it can fertilize an egg.

> **In a woman, this means that:**
> 1. eggs are produced in her ovaries.
> 2. eggs are fertilized in her oviducts.
> 3. the fertilized egg is protected and nourished while it develops into a fetus.
> 4. the reproductive process delivers a fully developed baby.

> Hormones, including testosterone and estrogen, are the messengers that tell the different parts of the body what to do. In addition to controlling many body functions, they play a large role in reproduction.

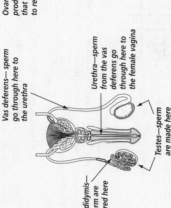

Bladder
Urethra
Testis
1

Oviduct
Ovary
Uterus
2

1. Which picture shows the male reproductive system?   **picture 1**

2. Write S on the picture where sperm are made.
 **S should be written on the testes in picture 1.**

3. Write E on the picture where the eggs are made.
 **E should be written on the ovaries in picture 2.**

4. Write F on the picture where fertilization takes place.
 **F should be written on the oviducts in picture 2.**

5. Write B on the picture where the fertilized egg develops into a fetus.
 **B should be written on the uterus in picture 2.**

CONTENT MASTERY     CHAPTER 38   BIOLOGY: The Dynamics of Life    **185**

## Right Page

**Content Mastery**

### Chapter 38   Reproduction and Development, *continued*

Section 38.1 Human
Reproductive Systems

#### Study the Diagram

Study the diagram. Then fill in the blanks in the statements that follow.

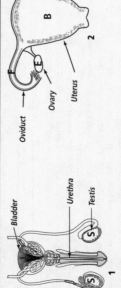

Vas deferens— sperm go through here to the urethra

Urethra—sperm from the vas deferens go through here to the female vagina

Testes—sperm are made here

Epididymis—sperm are stored here

Oviduct—the egg travels through here on the way to the uterus

Ovary—releases egg and produces progesterone that keeps the uterus ready to receive the egg

Egg

Uterus

Vagina

1. The egg travels down the _____**oviduct**_____ to the uterus.

2. Sperm are made in the testes and stored in the _____**epididymis**_____.

3. Sperm are deposited in the vagina. To get to the vagina from the epididymis, the sperm first go through the _____**vas deferens**_____ and then through the _____**urethra**_____.

4. The ovary produces the hormone progesterone. Progesterone keeps the _____**uterus**_____ ready to receive a fertilized egg.

186   CHAPTER 38   BIOLOGY: The Dynamics of Life     CONTENT MASTERY

Name _____ Date _____ Class _____

**Content Mastery**

## Chapter 38 Reproduction and Development, *continued*

Section 38.2 *Development Before Birth*
Section 38.3 *Birth, Growth, and Aging*

### Match the Pictures

Some of the steps of the human reproductive and developmental cycles are given in the box. Write the number of the step on the line under the picture that illustrates it.

1. When a sperm penetrates the egg, a zygote is formed.
2. The umbilical cord attaches the embryo to the placenta.
3. Through the placenta, nutrients from the mother's blood pass to the fetus.
4. Body systems, like the circulatory system, develop during the first few months of pregnancy.
5. At birth, the cervix opens so that the baby can be pushed out.
6. People continue growing until they are adults.

*Mother's blood vessels*
*Baby's blood vessels*

A. _____ 3

B. _____ 1

*Umbilical cord* *Placenta* *Uterus*

E. _____ 2

D. _____ 5

C. _____ 6

F. _____ 4

---

Name _____ Date _____ Class _____

**Content Mastery**

## Chapter 38 Reproduction and Development, *continued*

### Review the Vocabulary

a. first trimester
b. cervix
c. epididymis (ep uh DIHD uh mus)
d. follicle (FAH lih kul)
e. implantation
f. labor
g. ovulation
h. puberty
i. scrotum
j. seminal vesicles
k. vas deferens (vas • DEF uh runtz)

Write the letter of the Chapter 38 vocabulary words in the box in front of their definitions.

__d__ 1. Group of epithelial cells that surround a developing egg in the ovary

__a__ 2. First part of pregnancy when all the organ systems of the embryo begin to form

__i__ 3. Testes-containing sac of males

__b__ 4. Lower end of the uterus that opens into the vagina

__h__ 5. Growth stage that occurs in both males and females, characterized by the development of secondary sex characteristics

__c__ 6. Single-coiled tube in which sperm complete maturation

__k__ 7. Duct through which sperm move from the epididymis toward the urethra

__g__ 8. Process in which the follicle ruptures to release the egg from the ovary

__e__ 9. Attachment of the fertilized egg to the uterine lining

__f__ 10. Physical and psychological changes that the mother experiences during birth

__j__ 11. Paired glands at the base of the urinary bladder that produce fluid to nourish sperm

**Content Mastery**

## Chapter 39   Immunity from Disease

### Get the Big Picture

Find the red and blue headings in Chapter 39 of your textbook. Use the blue headings to fill in the ovals in the idea map. The rectangles and some of the ovals have been filled in for you.

**39.1 The Nature of Disease**      **39.2 Defense Against Infectious Diseases**

(A)
- The Spread of Infectious Diseases (B)
- Innate Immunity (C)
- Acquired Immunity (D)

*Determining What Causes a Disease*

First pathogen identified

*A procedure to establish the cause of a disease*

Reservoirs of pathogens

Exceptions to Koch's postulates

*Transmission of disease*

Skin and body secretions

Inflammation of body tissues

Phagocytosis of pathogens

*Protective Proteins*

The lymphatic system

Glands of the lymphatic system

Each statement below goes with one of the headings in the rectangles above. Write the letter of each heading on the line in front of the statement it goes with.

**B**   Infectious diseases may be spread by direct contact or through the air.

**C**   The skin is the body's first line of defense.

**A**   A German doctor named Robert Koch first identified that pathogens can cause diseases.

**D**   The body can become immune to an infectious disease.

---

**Content Mastery**

## Chapter 39   Immunity from Disease, *continued*

*Section 39.1 The Nature of Disease*

### Complete the Idea Map

Read the paragraphs in the boxes. Then use the terms in bold type in the paragraphs to complete the idea map.

Do you remember the last time you had a cold? A cold is one example of an **infectious disease**. Infectious diseases can be caused by viruses, bacteria, and other microbes.

Disease-causing microbes such as viruses and bacteria are known as **pathogens**. Pathogens enter the body in many ways. They can enter through **direct contact** with someone who carries a disease, through the air, or through **contaminated food or water**. After the pathogens enter your body, you may have **symptoms** of an infectious disease. A stuffy nose and sore throat are examples of symptoms caused by a cold.

**Antibiotics** are drugs used to treat some diseases caused by bacteria. Antibiotics have no effect on diseases caused by viruses.

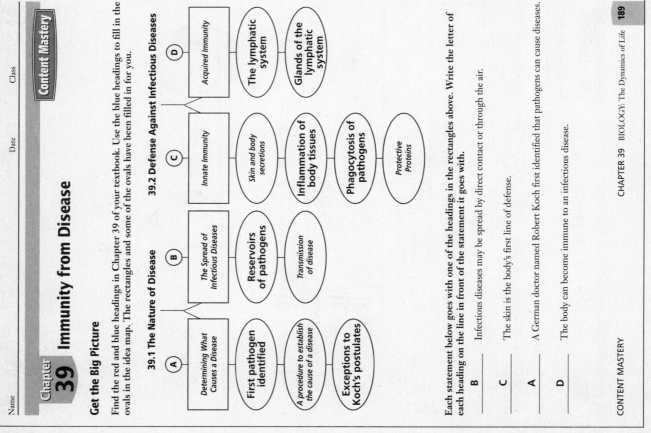

Pathogens enter the body through **direct contact**
- the air
- **contaminated food or water**

Viruses and bacteria that cause infectious diseases are called _pathogens_

**A cold is an example of an infectious disease**

**Antibiotics** _____ can treat _____ diseases caused by bacteria.

You know you have an infectious disease when you have **symptoms** such as a sore throat.

---

Name _____ Date _____ Class _____

**Content Mastery**

## Chapter 39 Immunity from Disease, continued

*Section 39.2 Defense Against Infectious Diseases*

### Complete the Idea Map

Read the paragraphs in the boxes. Then use the terms in bold type in the paragraphs to complete the idea map.

Remember that infectious diseases are caused by pathogens. Pathogens may come in the form of viruses, bacteria, or other agents. Our bodies have two types of defenses against pathogens: (1) innate (nonspecific) defenses that are immediately ready to fight all pathogens, and (2) acquired (specific) defenses that gear up to fight against particular pathogens.

Our **skin** is one nonspecific defense. It acts like the walls of a castle to keep all foreign intruders out of our body. Our body fluids also serve as nonspecific defenses. Body fluids such as **mucus, sweat, tears, saliva,** and **stomach acid** trap or destroy pathogens. Pathogens that get past our skin and body fluids are attacked by the nonspecific defenders found in the bloodstream. These defenders are certain types of **white blood cells** and **proteins**.

While the nonspecific defenses fight pathogens, the specific defenses prepare to join the battle. After several days, the body will begin to **recognize** the pathogens as intruders. The body then adapts by acquiring specific defenses, including **antibodies** and **T cells,** that identify and destroy particular pathogens.

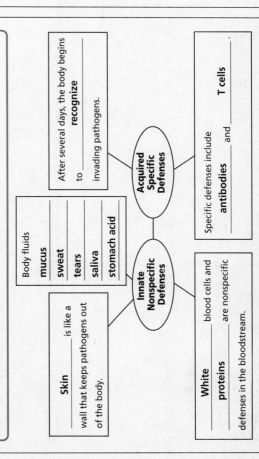

**Skin** is like a _____ wall that keeps pathogens out of the body.

Body fluids
**mucus**
**sweat**
**tears**
**saliva**
**stomach acid**

**Innate Nonspecific Defenses**

**Acquired Specific Defenses**

After several days, the body begins to **recognize** _____ invading pathogens.

**White** _____ blood cells and **proteins** _____ are nonspecific defenses in the bloodstream.

Specific defenses include **antibodies** and **T cells** _____.

CHAPTER 39 BIOLOGY: The Dynamics of Life **191**

CONTENT MASTERY

---

Name _____ Date _____ Class _____

**Content Mastery**

## Chapter 39 Immunity from Disease, continued

### Review the Vocabulary

| | |
|---|---|
| antibiotic | Koch's postulates |
| B cell | (KAHKS • PAHS chuh lutz) |
| interferon | lymph (LIHMF) |
| endemic disease | lymph node |
| epidemic | lymphocyte |
| immunity | (LIHMF uh site) |
| (ihm YEW nut ee) | macrophage |
| infectious disease | (MAK ruh fayj) |

pathogen (PATH uh jun)
phagocyte (FAG uh site)
pus
T cell
tissue fluid
vaccine (vak SEEN)
virus

For each statement below, circle the Chapter 39 vocabulary word inside the brackets that best completes the statement. You will not use every word.

1. Diseases are caused by the presence of [oxygen / antibiotics / (a pathogen) / alleles] in the body.

2. During a(n) [antibiotic / (epidemic) / genetic disorder / abnormality], many people have the same disease at the same time.

3. Penicillin is an example of a(n) [(antibiotic) / pathogen / endemic disease / lymphocyte].

4. The fluid in the lymphatic system is called [pus / blood / salt water / (lymph)].

5. A [lymphocyte / (virus) / phagocyte / macrophage] is *not* a white blood cell that protects the body against foreign substances.

6. The [(B cell) / C cell / D cell / F cell] is a type of lymphocyte.

7. [Pus / Skin / Mucus / (A vaccine)] can cause immunity to a disease.

8. Chicken pox, tetanus, tuberculosis, and AIDS are all [reproductive disorders / genetic disorders / (infectious diseases) / environmental diseases].

9. A disease that is continually present in the population is called a(n) [(endemic disease) / epidemic / plague / abnormality].

10. Lymph is filtered in the [(lymph nodes) / heart / brain / stomach].

11. When [calcium / carbon dioxide / blood / (tissue fluid)] enters the lymphatic vessels, it is called lymph.

12. The collection of dead white blood cells and different body fluids that are found around an infected area is called [an antibiotic / (pus) / complement / a vaccine].

**192** CHAPTER 39 BIOLOGY: The Dynamics of Life

CONTENT MASTERY

---

**Name** _____ **Date** _____ **Class** _____

**BioDigest**
**10** **The Human Body**

## Get the Big Picture

Read the paragraphs in the boxes. Then complete the idea map. Part of the map has been filled in for you.

All organisms are made of **cells**. In humans, most cells function in groups called **tissues**. The four basic tissues of the human body are epithelial tissue, muscle tissue, connective tissue, and nervous tissue. When a group of tissues works together for a single purpose, it makes up an **organ**. Organs usually receive help from other organs to accomplish a large job for the body. When organs work together, they are called an **organ system**.

The **digestive system** is one organ system. In the digestive system, the food you eat is broken down into smaller and smaller pieces until the vitamins, proteins, minerals, and other important substances in the food are small enough to be delivered to the cells of the body. The digestive system is made up of the mouth, esophagus, stomach, small intestine, large intestine, and rectum. Other major organ systems include the skeletal system, the muscular system, the respiratory system, the circulatory system, the urinary system, the nervous system, and the reproductive system.

**Cells**

*are organized into*

**Tissues**

**Four types**
1. epithelial
2. muscle
3. connective
4. nervous

*which work together in groups that make up*

**Organs**

**Major systems**
1. skeletal
2. muscular
3. digestive
4. respiratory
5. circulatory
6. urinary
7. nervous
8. reproductive

*which work together in groups that make up*

**Organ Systems**

**Examples**
1. mouth
2. esophagus
3. stomach
4. small intestine
5. large intestine
6. rectum

BIODIGEST 10   BIOLOGY: The Dynamics of Life   **193**

---

**Name** _____ **Date** _____ **Class** _____

**BioDigest**
**10** **The Human Body,** *continued*

## Study the Diagram

Read the paragraph in the box. Then study the diagram and answer the questions on the next page.

The digestive system is a major organ system of the human body. The numbers in the diagram below show you the order in which food travels through the digestive system.

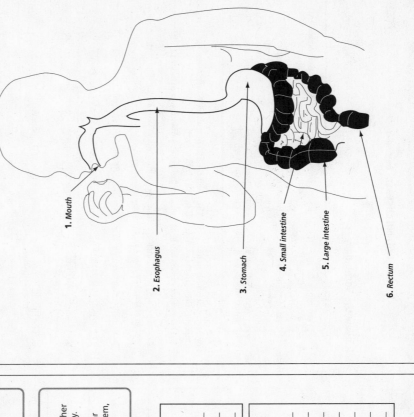

1. *Mouth*

2. *Esophagus*

3. *Stomach*

4. *Small intestine*

5. *Large intestine*

6. *Rectum*

**194**   BIODIGEST 10   BIOLOGY: The Dynamics of Life

Name _____ Date _____ Class _____

**Content Mastery**

1. Where does food enter the digestive system?
**in the mouth**

2. When food travels from the mouth to the stomach, what organ does it go through?
**the esophagus**

3. Where is the small intestine?
**between the stomach and the large intestine**

4. Some food materials are not absorbed or digested. These materials travel through the entire digestive system. Where do they leave the digestive system?
**through the rectum**

5. True or false? Most of the lower portion of the human body is filled with digestive organs.
**true**

6. True or false? Digestion occurs only in the stomach.
**false**

7. True or false? The mouth is considered part of the digestive system.
**true**

---

Name _____ Date _____ Class _____

**Content Mastery**

### Fill in the Organ System

| | |
|---|---|
| muscular system | skeletal system |
| respiratory system | digestive system |
| nervous system | circulatory system |
| endocrine system | reproductive system |
| urinary system | lymphatic system |

**Review the descriptions of the major human organ systems listed above. Then fill in the blanks in the sentences with the correct organ system from the list. You will not use all the systems.**

1. The cells in your body get their oxygen and nutrients from blood. Your blood is pumped through your body through the **circulatory** system.

2. Waste products are removed from your blood by the **urinary** system. This system also regulates the balance of water in your blood.

3. Your brain, spinal cord, nerves, and sensory organs make up your **nervous** system.

4. The blood in your body receives oxygen, and carbon dioxide is removed, through your **respiratory** system.

5. If a foreign substance enters your bloodstream, the cells that fight infection are part of the **lymphatic** system.

6. Your **digestive** system is responsible for breaking down the food you eat and converting it to forms that your body can use for energy.

7. The supporting framework of your body is the **skeletal** system. This system also acts as a storehouse for calcium and phosphorus.

8. The movements you make with your arms are possible because of your **muscular** system.

9. The **endocrine** system controls the metabolic activities of your other body systems. It operates by secreting hormones that affect different tissues.